JOURNAL OF PEDIATRIC PSYCHOLOGY

Contents

Systematic Review

Systematic Review: Bullying Involvement of Children With and Without Chronic Physical Illness and/or Physical/Sensory Disability—a Meta-Analytic Comparison With Healthy/Nondisabled Peers
Martin Pinquart 245

Regular Article with Commentary

Early Childhood Sleep Patterns and Cognitive Development at Age 6 Years: The Generation R Study
Desana Kocevska, Jolien Rijlaarsdam, Akhgar Ghassabian, Vincent W. Jaddoe, Oscar H. Franco, Frank C. Verhulst, and Henning Tiemeier 260

Commentary: Longitudinal Observational Research Informs Child Health Research
Robert D. Annett 269

Regular Articles

Peer Victimization in Adolescents With Severe Obesity: The Roles of Self-Worth and Social Support in Associations With Psychosocial Adjustment
Jennifer Reiter-Purtill, Marissa A. Gowey, Heather Austin, Kevin C. Smith, Dana L. Rofey, Todd M. Jenkins, Beth H. Garland and Meg H. Zeller for the TeenView Study Group and in cooperation with Teen-LABS Consortium 272

Group-Based Trajectory Modeling of Distress and Well-Being Among Caregivers of Children Undergoing Hematopoetic Stem Cell Transplant
Stephen A. Sands, Laura Mee, Abraham Bartell, Sharon Manne, Katie A. Devine, Mirko Savone, and Deborah A. Kashy 283

Evaluating Parents' Self-Efficacy for Diabetes Management in Pediatric Type 1 Diabetes
Amy E. Noser, Susana R. Patton, Jason Van Allen, Michael B. Nelson, and Mark A. Clements 296

Maternal and Paternal Distress and Coping Over Time Following Pediatric Traumatic Brain Injury
Megan E. Narad, Keith O. Yeates, H. Gerry Taylor, Terry Stancin, and Shari L. Wade 304

Bidirectional Associations Between Disordered Eating and Health-Related Quality of Life in Elementary School-Age Youth
Tarrah B. Mitchell and Ric G. Steele 315

Empirically Derived Patterns of Pain, Stooling, and Incontinence and Their Relations to Health-Related Quality of Life Among Youth With Chronic Constipation
Kimberly L. Klages, Kristoffer S. Berlin, Alan H. Silverman, Suzanne Mugie, Carlo Di Lorenzo, Samuel Nurko, Ananthasekar Ponnambalam, Rina Sanghavi, and Manu R. Sood 325

Daily Pain, Physical Activity, and Home Fluid Intake in Pediatric Sickle Cell Disease
Cynthia W. Karlson, Anna M. Baker, Maggie H. Bromberg, Thomas David Elkin, Suvankar Majumdar, and Tonya M. Palermo 335

Cognitive Functioning and Academic Achievement in Children Aged 6–8 Years, Born at Term After Intrauterine Growth Restriction and Fetal Cerebral Redistribution
Mercedes Bellido-González, Miguel Ángel Díaz-López, Setefilla López-Criado, and José Maldonado-Lozano 345

Journal of Pediatric Psychology (ISSN 0146-8693) is published ten times a year by Oxford University Press for the Society of Pediatric Psychology, P.O. Box 170231, Atlanta, GA 30317. The journal is a scientific publication of the Society of Pediatric Psychology (SSP), Division 54 of the American Psychological Association. As such, the journal publishes articles related to theory, research, and professional practice in pediatric psychology. Pediatric psychology is an interdisciplinary field addressing physical, cognitive, social, and emotional functioning and development as they relate to health and illness issues in children, adolescents, and families. The journal publishes papers on a wide variety of topics exploring the interrelationship between psychological and physical well-being of children, adolescents, and families including: psychosocial and developmental factors contributing to the etiology, course, treatment and outcome of pediatric conditions; assessment and treatment of behavioral and emotional concomitants of disease, illness, and developmental disorders; the role of psychology in healthcare settings; behavioral aspects of pediatric medicine; the promotions of health and health-related behaviors; the prevention of illness and injury among children and youth; and issues related to the training of pediatric psychologists.

Membership in Society of Pediatric Psychology

Individuals interested in becoming a member of the Society of Pediatric Psychology should contact Society of Pediatric Psychology, P.O. Box 170231, Atlanta, GA 30317. Tel/fax: 404-373-8251.

Subscriptions

A subscription to the *Journal of Pediatric Psychology* comprises 10 issues. Prices include postage; for subscribers outside the Americas, issues are sent air freight. Airmail rates are available on request.

Annual Subscription Rate (Volume 42, 10 issues, 2017)
Institutional
Print edition and site-wide online access: US$1,393/£926/€1,393
Print edition only: US$1,282/£853/€1,282
Site-wide online access only: US$1,115/£742/€1,115
Personal
Print edition and individual online access: US$307/£204/€307

Please note: US$ rate applies to US & Canada, Euros applies to Europe, UK£ applies to UK and Rest of World.

There are other subscription rates available; for a complete listing, please visit https://academic.oup.com/jpepsy.

Full prepayment in the correct currency is required for all orders. Orders are regarded as firm, and payments are not refundable. Subscriptions are accepted and entered on a complete volume basis. Claims cannot be considered more than four months after publication or date of order, whichever is later. All subscriptions in Canada are subject to GST. Subscriptions in the EU may be subject to European VAT. If registered, please supply details to avoid unnecessary charges. For subscriptions that include online versions, a proportion of the subscription price may be subject to UK VAT. Personal rates are applicable only when a subscription is for individual use and are not available if delivery is made to a corporate address.

The current year and two previous years' issues are available from Oxford Journals. Previous volumes can be obtained from the Periodicals Service Company at http://www.periodicals.com/oxford.html or from the Periodicals Service Company, 11 Main Street, Germantown, NY 12526, USA. E-mail: psc@periodicals.com. Tel: (518) 537-4700. Fax: (518) 537-5899.

Contact Information: Journals Customer Service Department, Oxford University Press, Great Clarendon Street, Oxford OX2 6DP, UK. E-mail: jnls.cust.serv@oup.com. Tel: +44 (0)1865 353907. Fax: +44(0)1865 353485. **In the Americas, please contact:** Journals Customer Service Department, Oxford University Press, 2001 Evans Road, Cary, NC 27513, USA. E-mail: jnlorders@oup.com. Tel: (800) 852-7323 (toll-free in USA/Canada) or (919) 677-0977. Fax: (919) 677-1714. **In Japan, please contact:** Journals Customer Service Department, Oxford University Press, 4-5-10-8F Shiba, Minato-ku, Tokyo, 108-8386, Japan. E-mail: custserv.jp@oup.com. Tel: +81 3 5444 5858. Fax: +81 3 3454 2929.

Methods of payment: (i) Check (payable to Oxford University Press, to Oxford University Press, Cashiers Office, Great Clarendon Street, Oxford OX2 6DP, UK) in GB£ Sterling (drawn on a UK bank), US$ Dollars (drawn on a US bank), or EU€ Euros. (ii) Bank transfer to Barclays Bank Plc, Oxford Group Office, Oxford (bank sort code 20-65-18) (UK), overseas only Swift code BARC GB 22 (GB£ Sterling to account no. 70299332, IBAN GB89BARC20651870299332; US$ Dollars to account no. 66014600, IBAN GB27BARC20651866014600; EU€ Euros to account no. 78923655, IBAN GB16BARC20651878923655). (iii) Credit card (Mastercard, Visa, Switch or American Express).

Oxford Journals Environmental and Ethical Policies

Oxford Journals is committed to working with the global community to bring the highest quality research to the widest possible audience. Oxford Journals will protect the environment by implementing environmentally friendly policies and practices wherever possible. Please see https://academic.oup.com/journals/pages/authors/ethics for further information on Oxford Journals' environmental and ethical policies.

Postal Information

Journal of Pediatric Psychology (ISSN 0146-8693) is published ten times a year, in Jan./Feb., Mar., Apr., May, June, July, Aug., Sept., Oct., and Nov./Dec., by Oxford University Press, 2001 Evans Road, Cary, NC 27513-2009. Periodical Postage Paid at Cary, NC and additional mailing offices. Postmaster: send address changes to *Journal of Pediatric Psychology*, Journals Customer Service Department, Oxford University Press, 2001 Evans Road, Cary, NC 27513-2009.

Supplements, Reprints, and Corporate Sales

For requests from industry and companies regarding supplements, bulk article reprints, sponsored subscriptions, translation opportunities for previously published material, and corporate online opportunities, please e-mail special.sales@oup.com, fax +44 (0) 1865 353774, or visit www.oxfordjournals.org/jnls/sales.

Digital Object Identifiers

For information on dois and to resolve them, please visit www.doi.org.

Permissions

For information on how to request permissions to reproduce articles or information from this journal, please visit https://academic.oup.com/journals/pages/access_purchase/rights_and_permissions.

Advertising

Advertising, inserts, and artwork enquiries should be addressed to Advertising and Special Sales, Oxford Journals, Oxford University Press, Great Clarendon Street, Oxford, OX2 6DP, UK. Tel: +44 (0)1865 354767; Fax: +44 (0)1865 353774; E-mail: jnlsadvertising@oup.com.

Indexing and Abstracting

Journal of Pediatric Psychology is abstracted or indexed in *Beck Medical Information, Behavioral Medicine Abstracts, Biological Abstracts, Child and Youth Services, Child Development Abstracts and Bibliography, Cumulative Index to Nursing and Allied Health Literature, Current Contents, Exceptional Child Education Resources, Excerpta Medics, Family Resources Database, Health Instrument File, Index Medicus, Mental Health Abstracts, Psychological Abstracts, Referativnyi Zhurnal, Sage Family Studies Abstracts, Science Citation Index, Selected List of Tables of Contents of Psychiatric Periodicals, Social Work Research & Abstracts, Sociological Abstracts, Special Educational Needs Abstracts, The Psychological Reader's Guide,* and *Zeitschrift fur Kinder- und Jugendpsychiatrie*.

Journal of Pediatric Psychology is printed on acid-free paper that meets the minimum requirements of ANSI Standard Z39.48-1984 (Permanence of Paper), beginning with Volume 23, Number 1.

Disclaimer

Statements of fact and opinion in the articles in the *Journal of Pediatric Psychology* are those of the respective authors and contributors and not of the Society of Pediatric Psychology or Oxford University Press. Neither Oxford University Press nor the Editors, Editorial Board, or Society of Pediatric Psychology make any representation, express or implied, in respect of the accuracy of the material in this journal and cannot accept any legal responsibility or liability for any errors or omissions that may be made. The reader should make her or his own evaluation as to the appropriateness or otherwise of any experimental technique described.

Copyright © 2017 Society of Pediatric Psychology

All rights reserved; no part of this publication may be reproduced, stored in a retrieval system, or transmitted in any form or by any means, electronic, mechanical photocopying, recording or otherwise without prior written permission of the publisher or a license permitting restricted copying issued in the UK by the Copyright Licensing Agency Ltd, 90 Tottenham Court Road, London W1P 9HE.

Oxford University Press is a department of the University of Oxford. It furthers the University's objective of excellence in research, scholarship, and education by publishing worldwide.

Systematic Review: Bullying Involvement of Children With and Without Chronic Physical Illness and/or Physical/Sensory Disability—a Meta-Analytic Comparison With Healthy/Nondisabled Peers

Martin Pinquart, PHD

Department of Psychology, Philipps University

All correspondence concerning this article should be addressed to M Pinquart, Department of Psychology, Philipps University, Gutenbergstr. 18, D-35032 Marburg, Germany. E-mail: pinquart@staff.uni-marburg.de

Received April 13, 2016; revisions received August 24, 2016; accepted August 28, 2016

Abstract

Objective To compare levels of victimization and perpetration associated with bullying among children and adolescents with and without chronic physical illnesses and/or physical or sensory disabilities. **Methods** In total, 107 studies were identified using a systematic search in electronic databases and cross-referencing. A random-effects meta-analysis was computed. **Results** Children and adolescents with chronic physical illness or disability were more likely to be victims of bullying in general (odds ratio [OR] = 1.65), particularly physical bullying (OR = 1.47), relational bullying (OR = 1.47), verbal bullying (OR = 1.67), cyberbullying (OR = 1.39), and illness-specific teasing (OR = 5.29). They were also more likely to be bullies in general (OR = 1.28), as well physical (OR = 1.38) and relational bullies (OR = 1.13). The effect sizes varied across different illnesses and disabilities and, in part, by visibility of the disease, school type, and year of assessment. **Conclusions** Although most between-group differences tend to be small, some form of intervention is needed to reduce bullying among children and adolescents with chronic physical illnesses and/or physical or sensory disabilities, and illness-specific weight- and appearance-related teasing in particular.

Key words: bullying; chronic illness; disability; peer victimization; teasing.

Bullying or peer victimization can be defined as an aggressive behavior repeated over time with the intention to harm the victim. It is characterized by an imbalance of power between the bully and the victim, with the bullied person being the weaker of the two (e.g., Juvonen & Graham, 2014). Different forms of bullying have been distinguished (e.g., Faith, Reed, Heppner, Hamill, Tarkenton, & Donewar, 2015; Scheithauer, Hayer, Petermann, & Jugert, 2006): Physical bullying is characterized by observable behaviors including hitting, pushing, and insulting. Relational forms of bullying or aggression refer to more subtle, indirect forms of behavior such as spreading untrue rumors and socially excluding the victim. Verbal bullying involves teasing, taunting, spreading rumors, and threatening. Finally, cyberbullying refers to victimization by means of electronic media. About 15–18% of 11- to 15-year-old students report being bullied, although the rates vary depending on the measures and cutoff scores which are used (Due et al., 2005). Peer victimization has been found to increase the risk for mental health problems, such as anxiety or depression (Reijntjes, Kamphuis, Prinzie, & Telch, 2010), and also leads to poor academic outcomes

(Schwartz, Gorman, Nakamoto, & Toblin, 2005). In children with chronic illnesses, peer victimization has also been linked to poorer treatment adherence (Janicke, Gray, Kahhan, Junger, Marciel, Storch, & Jolley, 2009; Storch, Heidgerken, Geffken, Lewin, Ohleyer, Freddo, & Silverstein, 2006).

It has been suggested that children and adolescents with chronic health conditions have an increased risk of being bullied (Faith et al., 2015). First, a child who is physically different is an easy target for victimization (Dawkins, 1996). Symptoms of the disease or treatment regimens may cause peers to perceive them as being different. For example, children with facial disfigurement may not meet the beauty standards of their peer group. In addition, children with chronic illnesses may be perceived as physically weaker, and are therefore vulnerable to peer victimization (Nadeau & Tessier, 2006; Twyman et al., 2010). Next, young people with chronic illnesses are at increased risk for showing reduced social functioning (social and communication skills) and academic performance, which could provoke negative reactions from their peers (Pinquart & Teubert, 2012). In addition, psychological vulnerabilities, such as reduced self-esteem (Pinquart, 2013a) or a negative body image, of these children may increase the risk of being bullied (Fox & Farrow, 2009; Pinquart, 2013b). Finally, some authors have suggested that negative attitudes expressed by peers toward an illness, or even peer prejudices about children with disabilities, may increase the risk of being bullied (e.g., Storch et al., 2004a).

No attempts have been made to integrate the results of available studies on bullying involvement of children with chronic physical illness or physical/sensory disability into a meta-analysis, with the exception of obesity. Based on 16 articles, van Geel, Vedder, and Tanilon (2014) observed that the odds of being bullied increased for obese young people by 51%. Unfortunately, this meta-analysis did not compare different forms of bullying. For example, obese children may be more likely to become victims of weight-related teasing than of physical bullying because they may be perceived as physically able to defend themselves when being physically attacked.

As victims of bullying are also often perpetrators (e.g., Ilola, Lempinen, Huttunen, Ristkari, & Sourander, 2016), it would also be relevant to know whether young people with chronic physical illnesses and/or physical or sensory disabilities are more likely to bully other students. However, the argument that children with physical illnesses or disabilities may, at least in part, be weaker than their peers (Nadeau & Tessier, 2006; Twyman et al., 2010) would suggest that the opposite would be true, at least with regard to physical bullying.

In sum, the first research question of the present meta-analysis asks whether young people with chronic physical illnesses and/or physical or sensory disabilities are at an increased risk for being bullied in general, and for being the victims of physical, relational, verbal, cyberbullying, and particularly appearance- and weight-related bullying. The second research question asks whether young people with chronic physical illnesses and/or physical or sensory disabilities are more likely to bully other children rather than healthy and nondisabled children, and whether this is true for the different forms of bullying.

Moderator Effects of Kind of Illness and Other Study Characteristics

Results of individual studies are inconsistent when it comes to whether children with chronic illnesses and/or physical or sensory disabilities have an increased risk of being bullied or of bullying other children. For example, Hamiwka, Yu, Hamiwka, Sherman, Anderson, and Wirrell (2009) observed that children with epilepsy were more likely to be bullied than their healthy peers, whereas children with chronic kidney disease were not. Similarly, some studies found elevated levels of perpetration among children with chronic physical illnesses and/or physical or sensory disabilities (e.g., Hamiwka et al., 2009), while the opposite was found in other studies (Percy-Smith, Caye-Thomasen, Gudman, Jensen, & Thomsen, 2008). Possible reasons for the heterogeneity of the results of the individual studies were analyzed in the next step of the meta-analysis (Lipsey & Wilson, 2001). We limited the search for moderator variables to studies on victimization and perpetration in general rather than to the different forms of bullying because larger numbers of studies were available on general measures, thus increasing the chances for identifying moderating effects (Lipsey & Wilson, 2001). The following moderator variables were considered:

Type of illness. Few studies have compared levels of bullying within different kinds of physical illnesses or disabilities. Nordhagen, Nielsen, Stigum, and Köhler (2005) found higher levels of bullying among children with epilepsy and obesity than in those with visual impairments and asthma. As already reported, Hamiwka et al. (2009) identified higher levels of bullying among children with epilepsy than among those with chronic kidney disease. The present meta-analysis explores whether these results can be generalized to other studies.

Visibility. Because being physically different has been identified as a risk factor for being bullied (Dawkins, 1996; Storch et al., 2004a), children with visible diseases and disabilities were expected to be more likely to be bullied than their peers with invisible chronic conditions.

School type. If students with chronic illnesses and disabilities are mainly bullied by their healthy peers, then attending special schools for students with chronic illnesses or disabilities should reduce their risk for being bullied. Nonetheless, school-type differences may be smaller than expected because students from special schools may be bullied by class mates with disabilities or by healthy/nondisabled students from outside their school. In a study not specific to chronic physical illness, school-type differences in levels of bullying were inconsistent (Rose, Stormont, Wang, Simpson, Preast, & Green, 2015). Thus, school-type differences were analyzed in an exploratory analysis.

Information source for bullying. Children with more internalizing behavior problems or poor self-esteem might be more likely to perceive mild teasing as victimization, which could contribute to elevated reports of peer victimization of children with chronic physical illness. Thus, it was tested whether stronger elevations of peer victimization would be found if child self-reports were used, rather than reports by parents, peers, or teachers.

Sampling. As clinical samples may be more likely to include children with severe chronic illnesses than community-based (school-based) samples, it was tested whether between-group differences in bullying are higher in clinical samples than in community-based samples.

Age. Appearance-related teasing increases during adolescence (Helfert & Warschburger, 2013). Thus, it was tested whether the risk of being bullied or bullying increases with age among children with chronic illnesses.

Gender. Boys report bullying other children or being bullied in general more often than girls (Scheithauer, 2003). In addition, they also report being both perpetrators and victims of physical aggression in particular more frequently than girls (e.g., Scheithauer et al., 2006). The present meta-analysis tests whether a chronic physical illness increases or decreases these gender differences.

Year of publication. In many countries, the prevalence of bullying tends to be lower in more recent cohorts, possibly because of increased prevention and intervention efforts (Molcho, Craig, Due, Pickett, Harel-Fisch, & Overpeck, 2009). The present meta-analysis tests whether the differences between bullying involvement of children with and without chronic physical illnesses and/or disabilities also declines in recent studies.

Study quality. We assessed three variables as indicators of study quality: whether children with and without chronic illness and/or disability did not differ in third variables (e.g., age, gender), whether a validated bullying measure was used, and whether the study has been published. While the first two variables may cause nonsystematic errors and were considered for exploratory analysis, publication status may lead to a systematic error: Nonsignificant effects may be less likely to be published than significant effects (e.g., Lipsey & Wilson, 2001). The focus was, therefore, whether larger between-group differences would be found in published as compared with unpublished studies.

Moderating effects of study design (cross-sectional vs. longitudinal studies) could not be tested, as only two longitudinal studies were available.

Methods

Studies were selected through electronic databases (MEDLINE, PSNYDEX, PSYCINFO, Google Scholar) by using specific search terms ([teasing, bullying, or peer victimization] and [chronic illness of disability]) and search for additional studies that were cited in the identified papers. Criteria for the inclusion of studies in the present meta-analysis were as follows:

1. The studies were published or presented before August 2016.
2. They compared the levels of bullying experienced by children with chronic physical illnesses and/or physical or sensory disabilities with their healthy peers.
3. They provided sufficient information for computing effect sizes.
4. The mean age of participants was <20 years.

In regard to the question whether an illness is defined as chronic, we followed the suggestion by Thompson and Gustafson (1996), stating that a chronic illness can be defined as a condition that is associated with functional impairment and lasts for a considerable period, has a sequela that persists for a substantial period, persists for >3 months in a year, and/or necessitates a period of continuous hospitalization for >1 month. As obesity is associated with functional impairments, orthopedic and other physical complications, and reduced life expectancy, and shows a considerable persistence over time, we included studies on obesity (Price & Proietto, 2015; Sokol, 2000). Documentation of physician diagnosis was not a requirement because some broad-based survey studies do not have access to medical documentation. Identified, unpublished studies were also included.

We identified 410 studies. After exclusion of 303 papers that did not meet the inclusion criteria or that were not available (Figure 1), the meta-analysis included 107 studies that provided results from 180 samples. Seven unpublished studies were included. Selected study characteristics are provided in Supplementary Appendix I.

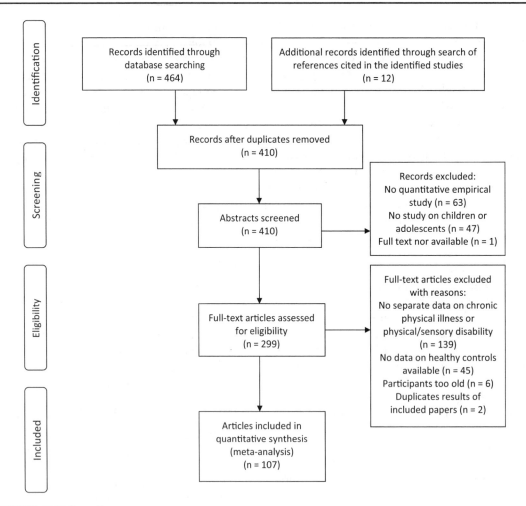

Figure 1 PRISMA 2009 flow diagram.

All studies were coded by the author. To proof the interrater reliability for these codes, the author and a graduate student trained in pediatric psychology and research methods coded 20% of the selected studies independently. All variables were checked for interrater reliability. Differences were resolved by discussion.

The following variables were coded: the number of patients (interrater agreement: intraclass correlation coefficient [ICC] = 0.99) and control group members (ICC = 0.97), mean age (ICC = 1.0), percentage of girls (ICC = 1.0), year of publication (ICC = 1.0), type of illness (interrater agreement 93%), the sampling procedure (1 = community- or school-based sample, 2 = clinical sample; interrater agreement 95%), school type (1 = regular school, 2 = special school, 3 = information not available, mixed schools; interrater agreement 95%), equivalence of patient and control group with regard to third variables (1 = yes, 2 = not tested/no; ICC = 0.90), publication status (1 = published, 2 = unpublished; ICC = 1.0), the quality of the measure of bullying (ICC = 0.86), the rater of bullying (1 = child, 2 = parents, 3 = peers, 4 = teachers; interrater agreement 95%), the odds ratios (ORs) for sum measures of bullying, and different forms of bullying (physical, relational, verbal, cyber, illness-specific teasing; ICC = 0.92). The information on most of these variables was directly provided in the publication. The extent to which the illness or disability was visible was coded as high if it affected the appearance of the child and was clearly visible to others (e.g., cerebral palsy, cleft lip, obesity, short stature; 1 = yes, 2 = no). Regarding the equivalence of patient and control group in third variables (e.g., age, gender), the papers were checked whether they provided this information. If not, the coders tested the equivalence as long as descriptive information was provided for the patient group and control group. With regard to the quality of the bullying measure, we checked whether the paper or related studies provided support for the validity of the measure, such as meaningful correlations with other bullying scales (1 = yes, 0 = no).

If between-group differences were reported for several subgroups within the same publication (e.g., for different illnesses or for boys vs. girls), they were entered separately in the analysis.

Eight studies provided results for more than one disease. Their effect sizes are therefore statistically dependent because of the use of the same control condition. In principle, three strategies could be applied for carrying out analyses of dependent effect size data (Hedges, Tipton, & Johnson, 2010). First, the correlations among the effect size estimates could be explicitly modeled using multivariate methods. This strategy could not be used in the present meta-analysis because knowledge of the covariance structure of the effect size estimation errors was lacking. Hedges et al. (2010) suggested a statistical procedure if the covariance structure of the dependent estimates is not known. However, this approach could not be used because >20 studies with more than one effect size per study would be needed for a reliable estimation. Second, a mean effect size of these studies could be computed across diseases. However, as we were interested in a comparison of chronic diseases, this would lead to a loss of relevant information. A third strategy is to ignore the dependence of some effect sizes. According to Hedges et al. (2010), this strategy is not too misleading if few studies report more than one effect size. This is the case in the present meta-analysis.

Statistical Integration of the Findings

A random-effects meta-analysis was computed in four steps, as outlined by Lipsey and Wilson (2001). In random effects models, it is assumed that the identified studies are a random sample of a theoretical universe of all possible studies on a given research question, and that these studies vary in the size of their effects. Random-effects models are preferred when effect sizes vary significantly between studies and not all possible reasons for heterogeneity can be identified (Lipsey & Wilson, 2001).

First, ORs were extracted or calculated for the individual studies. The odds are the ratio of the probability that the event of being bullied or bullying others, respectively, occurs in a defined group to the probability that it does not. The OR is then computed as a quotient of the odds of children with and without illness/disability. An OR that is >1 indicates an elevated level of bullying in children with chronic physical illnesses and/or physical or sensory disabilities. Logged ORs were computed because they were normally distributed.

Next, logged ORs were weighted by the inverse of the squared standard error of the mean and combined to compute an overall weighted mean effect size. The weighting procedure takes into account differences in sample sizes. The significance of the mean was tested by dividing the weighted mean effect size by the estimated standard error of the mean. Then, confidence intervals (CIs) that included 95% of the effects were computed for each effect size. The weighted effect sizes and the 95% CIs were later converted back to ORs by taking the antilogarithms. Fail-safe $\underline{N}$s were computed based on Rosenberg (2005).

Then, the homogeneity of the effect sizes was tested by use of the homogeneity statistic Q. Finally, an analog to the analysis of variance was applied to test whether the effect sizes differed by categorical moderator variables, such as visibility of the illness or disability. A significant Q score indicates that the size of the effects differs significantly between studies. If more than two conditions are compared, differences between individual conditions were interpreted as significant when the 95% CIs did not overlap (Lipsey & Wilson, 2001, p. 114). Effects of continuous moderator variables were tested with weighted regression analyses.

Results

In total, 62,855 children and adolescents with chronic physical illnesses and/or sensory or physical disabilities were included. The largest subgroups were obesity ($N = 29,570$), asthma ($N = 14,390$), chronic skin diseases ($N = 3,118$), and visual impairments ($N = 1,312$). The respondents had a mean age of 13.8 years ($SD = 2.6$); 49% were girls and 45% were members of ethnic minorities.

Bullying was most often assessed with the revised Olweus Bully/Victim Questionnaire (Olweus, 1996; 8 studies), the Social Experience Questionnaire (Crick and Grotpeter, 1996; 6 studies), the bullying items from the Health Behavior in School-Aged Children studies (Olweus, 1992, 6 studies), peer nominations (6 studies), and other related instruments (73 studies). In total, 76 studies provided data on sum measures of victimization, 23 on physical victimization, 19 on relational victimization, 16 on verbal victimization, 7 on victimization by cyberbullying, and 15 on illness-specific teasing. In addition, 24 studies used sum measures of perpetration, 9 studies assessed physical perpetration, 8 assessed relational perpetration, 3 studies assessed being a cyberbully, and 2 verbal perpetrations. No study examined being a perpetrator of illness-specific weight- or appearance-related teasing.

Comparison of Bullying in Children With and Without Chronic Illness

Most studies reported only total scores of victimization and/or perpetration that do not take account individual forms of bullying (e.g., physical, verbal, relational), for example, by using a global question or by summing-up different kinds of bullying experiences. Weighted percentages of reports of total victimization indicate that 34.6% of children with a chronic physical illness or disability were victimized by peers, as were 25.8% of children without a chronic illness or disability (Table 1). Note that some studies provided only summary statistics such as ORs, without information on the percentages of bullied children.

Table I. Odds Ratio of Bullying Victimization and Perpetration of Children With and Without Chronic Illness

Kind of bullying	k	%Pat	%CG	OR	95% CI		Z	Q	Fail-safe N
Victim									
Total score	131	34.6	25.8	1.65	1.51	1.80	11.41***	128.05	7517
Physical bullying	39	27.2	20.7	1.47	1.31	1.65	6.60***	39.75	293
Relational bullying	32	36.5	23.5	1.47	1.29	1.64	5.91***	34.43	243
Verbal bullying	27	47.9	26.8	1.67	1.36	2.04	4.94***	30.29	51
Cyberbullying	8	17.1	12.7	1.38	1.29	1.48	9.12***	14.77*	12
Illness-specific teasing	19	60.6	21.9	5.29	3.60	7.76	8.51***	23.11	12
Perpetrator									
Total score	39	27.7	22.0	1.28	1.17	1.39	5.40***	47.84	108
Physical bullying	18	16.8	11.5	1.38	1.25	1.51	6.62***	101.40***	7
Relational bullying	17	16.9	14.5	1.13	1.03	1.23	2.60**	13.05	1
Verbal bullying	3	14.5	10.3	1.31	.96	1.79	1.70	.78	
Cyberbullying	3	3.9	1.1	1.39	.73	2.67	.99	4.58	
Illness-specific teasing	0								

Note: OR > 0 indicate larger odds in children with chronic illness/disability than in their healthy peers. k = number of effect sizes included; %Pat/%CG = weighted percentage of patients/control group members reporting victimization/perpetration; OR = effect size (weighted mean odds ratio); Z = test for significance of r. 95% CI = lower and upper limits of 95% confidence interval; Q = test for homogeneity of effect sizes.
*p < .05,
**p < .01,
***p < .001.

Compared with their healthy and nondisabled peers, young people with chronic illnesses and/or physical or sensory disabilities were more likely to be bullied in general (OR = 1.65) as well as to be a victim of physical bullying (OR = 1.47), relational bullying (OR = 1.47), verbal bullying (OR = 1.67), cyberbullying (OR = 1.38), and illness-specific weight- or appearance-related teasing (OR = 5.29). With the exception of cyberbullying, the effect sizes were homogenous. The fail-safe N indicates that between 7,517 (total bullying) and 12 (cyberbullying, disease-specific bullying) additional studies reporting null results would be needed to reduce the cumulated effect size to the point of nonsignificance.

The nonoverlap of the 95% CIs indicates significantly stronger between-group differences for illness-specific teasing than for all other indicators of being bullied (Table 1). Thus, children with chronic conditions most often reported to be bullied because their illness changed their appearance (e.g., in the case of craniofacial conditions) or weight (in the case of obesity).

Young people with chronic physical illnesses and/or physical or sensory disabilities were also more likely to bully other children in general (OR = 1.28), and to be a perpetrator of physical (OR = 1.38) and relational bullying (OR = 1.13) in particular. According to the fail-safe N, 108 additional studies with null results would be needed to reduce the cumulated effect size of total perpetration to nonsignificance. However, only seven (physical bullying) and one (relational bullying) additional studies with null results would be needed to reduce these effect sizes on a nonsignificant level. No between-group differences were observed for being a perpetrator of teasing and cyberbullying. With the exception of physical bullying, the effect sizes were, again, homogeneous (Table 1).

Influence of Moderator Variables
Type of Illness

The ORs of the total scores of bullying and perpetration varied according to type of illness or disability (Table 2). Young people with chronic headaches (OR = 1.80), craniofacial conditions (such as cleft lip or palate, OR = 5.50), epilepsy (OR = 1.82), hearing impairments (OR = 1.58), obesity (OR = 1.78), skin diseases (OR = 1.39), visual impairments (OR = 1.80), or other/multiple diseases (OR = 1.52) were more likely to be bullied than their peers without these illnesses and disabilities. No such difference was observed for children with asthma or spina bifida. The nonoverlap of the 95% CIs indicates that children with craniofacial conditions showed a higher OR of being bullied than the other illness groups. In addition, young people with obesity were more likely to be bullied than children with spina bifida or cerebral palsy.

Furthermore, children with epilepsy (OR = 3.34), obesity (OR = 1.34), spina bifida/cerebral palsy (OR = 2.39), and those with other/multiple diseases (OR = 1.27) were more likely to bully other children than young people without these illnesses or disabilities. No such patterns were observed in young people with hearing or visual impairments. The nonoverlap of the 95% CIs indicates a stronger elevation of the OR in children with epilepsy, obesity, and cerebral palsy/spina bifida than in their peers with visual impairments (Table 2).

Table II. Influences of Categorical Moderator Variables on the Odds Ratio of Bullying and Perpetration (Total Scores)

Moderators	Victimization					Perpetration				
	k	OR	95% CI	Z	Q	k	OR	95% CI	Z	Q
Illness/disability					29.82**					19.10**
Asthma	7	1.20	0.91 1.59	1.29	1.41	0				
Chronic headache/migraine	5	1.80	1.22 2.65	2.96**	4.49	0				
Craniofacial conditions	3	5.50	3.01 10.03	5.55***	1.55					
Epilepsy	6	1.82	1.27 2.61	3.25**	9.00	2	3.34	1.48 7.51	2.91**	5.89**
Hearing impairment	4	1.58	1.04 2.42	2.12*	0.68	1	1.16	0.75 1.78	0.66	0.00
Obesity	44	1.78	1.55 2.03	8.38***	39.85	21	1.34	1.20 1.51	4.98**	25.91
Skin diseases	8	1.39	1.01 1.90	2.04*	3.07	0				
Spina bifida/cerebral palsy	4	1.02	0.68 1.55	0.11	10.89*	1	2.39	1.20 4.75	2.49*	0.00
Visual impairment	15	1.80	1.44 2.27	5.05***	6.86*	5	0.86	0.67 1.11	−1.14	7.55
Other diseases	35	1.52	1.30 1.79	5.11***	25.59	9	1.27	1.05 1.53	2.52*	9.61
Visibility					5.73*					0.36
High	85	1.81	1.62 2.02	10.52***	85.52	32	1.27	1.11 1.46	3.56***	34.90
Moderate/low	46	1.44	1.25 1.66	5.11***	35.16	7	1.43	1.01 2.03	2.00*	13.66*
School					0.20					4.51*
Regular school	109	1.65	1.50 1.82	10.06***	91.29	32	1.36	1.20 1.54	4.90***	36.55
Special school	6	1.79	1.23 2.61	2.84**	3.75	3	0.99	0.69 1.42	−0.04	0.95
Mixed schools	12	1.61	1.28 2.01	3.94***	26.63*					
Information source for bullying					7.07					5.39
Child	101	1.58	1.44 1.74	9.34***	83.51	31	1.33	1.16 1.51	4.24***	36.18
Parents	20	1.69	1.38 2.07	5.11***	30.26*	3	0.78	0.50 1.24	−1.05	5.93
Peers	2	3.36	1.74 6.48	3.62***	3.36	1	1.65	0.75 3.65	1.23	0.00
Teachers	7	2.33	1.51 3.60	3.84***	3.62	4	1.47	0.90 2.40	1.54	3.65
Sampling					0.02					3.48
Random (community or school based)	102	1.65	1.49 1.82	9.85***	81.27	29	1.23	1.08 1.40	3.07**	33.24
Clinical sample	30	1.67	1.38 2.03	5.27***	40.89*a	10	1.65	1.24 2.20	3.45***	14.83
Equivalence of the samples					1.84					1.08
Yes	31	1.47	1.21 1.78	3.91***	26.60	13	1.18	0.96 1.45	1.61	35.94***
No/not tested	100	1.72	1.55 1.90	10.49***	91.61	26	1.35	1.17 1.55	4.19***	16.52
Quality of bullying measure					1.40					0.65
Low	97	1.60	1.44 1.77	8.85***	77.04	28	1.25	1.08 1.45	3.04**	32.79
High	33	1.84	1.55 2.18	6.92***	42.83	11	1.41	1.10 1.82	2.72**	14.87
Publication status					0.77					0.73
Unpublished	4	2.18	1.17 4.07	2.45***	0.90	2	0.85	0.32 2.24	−0.33	0.15
Published	127	1.65	1.51 1.80	11.04***	120.33	37	1.30	1.15 1.47	4.16***	49.26

Note: OR > 0 indicates larger odds in children with chronic illness/disability than in their healthy peers. k = number of effect sizes included; OR = effect size (weighted mean odds ratio); Z = test for significance of OR. 95% CI = lower and upper limits of 95% confidence interval; Q = test for homogeneity of effect sizes.
*$p < .05$,
**$p < .01$,
***$p < .001$.

Visibility

Young people with visible conditions are more likely to be bullied than their peers with diseases that are less visible. However, visibility of the disease did not affect the odds of being a bully.

School Type

While ORs of being bullied did not vary between regular and special schools, the odd of being a bully was only elevated in children with chronic illnesses or disabilities from regular schools. However, studies in special schools mainly focused on students with sensory impairments.

Source of Information

The source of information regarding victimization and perpetration did not affect the size of between-group differences. Bullying involvement also did not vary between school-based samples and clinical samples.

Age and Gender

Similarly, the results did not vary according to participants' age or gender (Table 3).

Year of Publication

We identified a moderating effect of year of the studies' publication, with between-group differences in

Table III. Influences of Continuous Moderator Variables on the Odds Ratio of Bullying and Perpetration (Total Scores)

Independent variable	Victimization				Perpetration			
	k	B	β	t	k	B	β	t
Age	108	.005	.03	.31	32	.003	.02	−.11
% female children	126	−.000	−.02	−.22	39	.002	.13	.93
Year of publication/presentation	120	.017	.18	−2.02*	38	.005	.05	−.34

Note: k = number of studies; B/β non-/standardized regression coefficient, t = test for significance. *$p < .05$.

victimization being smaller in more recent studies (Table 3).

Study Quality
The three indicators of study quality (sociodemographic equivalence of the samples, quality of bullying measure, and publication status) were not significant moderators (Table 2).

Additional Analyses
Because studies with healthy children show gender differences in physical bullying (e.g., Scheithauer et al., 2006), possible moderating effects of gender on the ORs of being a victim and perpetrator of physically bullying were also examined. Again, no significant moderating effects were observed (β = .16, t = 0.96, p < .34 and β = .17, t = 0.75, p < .47).

As about 47% of the included children with chronic diseases had obesity and there is some controversy whether obesity is a chronic illness (Price & Proietto, 2015), we also tested whether the results would change if the studies on obesity are excluded. Although the ORs slightly decreased, we still found that young people with chronic illnesses and/or physical or sensory disabilities were more likely to be bullied in general as well as to be a victim of all assessed forms of bullying. They were also still more likely to bully others in general and to show relational bullying in particular. However, the odds of being a perpetrator of physical bullying was no longer elevated (see Supplementary Table S1). In contrast, obese young people showed higher levels of physical perpetration than their healthy peers (k = 14, OR = 1.58, Z = 5.32, p < .001). The moderator effect of visibility was only marginally significant in the reduced sample, probably because of lower statistical power. A new moderator effect was detected: Between-group differences in total victimization were larger if peer reports rather than self-reports were used. However, this effect has to be interpreted with caution, as only one study used peer reports (see Supplementary Table S2). Results on continuous moderator variables did not change after exclusion of studies on obesity (see Supplementary Table S3).

Discussion
The present meta-analysis is the first to compare levels of different forms of bullying involvement in young people with and without a chronic physical illness and/or a physical or sensory disability. Children and adolescents with these illnesses and disabilities were more likely to be victims of bullying in general, particularly physical bullying, relational bullying, verbal bullying, cyberbullying, and illness-specific teasing. They were also more likely to be a bully, particularly that of a relational or physical nature. However, the latter effect was limited to children with obesity. The effect sizes varied across different illnesses and disabilities and, in part, by visibility of the disease, school type, and year of publication.

Although the ORs of young people with chronic illnesses and/or physical or sensory disabilities were elevated for all assessed aspects of bullying, the present meta-analysis indicates that most between-group differences tend to be small, as average victimization rates were only elevated by about 7%. The only exception was illness-specific weight- or appearance-related teasing where almost a 30% difference was found. However, the latter studies mainly referred to craniofacial conditions and obesity, which are easily visible to others. This study's results indicate that in the case of visible diseases, bullying most often focuses on appearance-related characteristics of the illness.

Children with a chronic illness or disability were more likely to bully other children than their healthy peers, but these differences tended to be smaller than differences in victimization. Elevated levels of perpetration may, in part, be a reaction to being bullied. Unfortunately, no longitudinal studies that analyzed the temporal order of victimization and perpetration were found. Because rates of perpetration were lower than the victimization rates, one could gather that some children with chronic illnesses or disabilities may be less likely to become a bully because of being weaker (Nadeau & Tessier, 2006; Twyman et al., 2010) or more socially withdrawn than their peers (Pinquart & Shen, 2011). Elevated levels of physical perpetration were observed in young people with obesity rather than other diseases probably because their high body weight may give them more physical power.

The highest risk of total victimization was observed in children with craniofacial conditions, epilepsy, chronic headache, visual impairment, and obesity. In contrast, children with spina bifida/cerebral palsy or asthma were not more often bullied than their healthy peers. The high prevalence of total victimization in children with craniofacial conditions may, first, be based on the fact that these conditions are highly visible. However, visibility of the disease is not a sufficient explanation for the high risk of victimization of children with craniofacial conditions, as spina bifida and cerebral palsy are also visible conditions that were not associated with elevated levels of victimization. A second and better explanation of the high levels of victimization of children with craniofacial conditions refers to not meeting the beauty standards of their peer because facial appearance exerts a strong impact on social interactions (Masnari et al., 2012).

Other factors probably explain the observed above-average risk of victimization in young people with epilepsy and chronic headache, such as elevated levels of behavior problems and reduced social functioning (e.g., lower social competence; Cook, Williams, Guerra, Kim, & Sadek, 2010; Pinquart & Shen, 2011; Pinquart & Teubert, 2012). Psychological vulnerabilities, such as low self-esteem and body dissatisfaction, have been identified as potential mediators of the association between weight status and peer victimization (Fox & Farrow, 2009). Thus, some risk factors may be associated with some chronic diseases (e.g., Fox & Farrow, 2009; Masnari et al., 2012), but not with others.

The high risk of perpetration of children with epilepsy can be easily explained. Neuroimaging studies have identified frontal lobe brain abnormalities in patients with epilepsy (Herrman et al., 2002), which are associated with executive function deficits that impair the inhibition of aggressive behavior toward others.

The present meta-analysis did not find lower total scores of peer victimization in special schools than in regular schools. Although children from special schools for students with disabilities or chronic illnesses cannot be bullied by healthy or nondisabled classmates, they are probably bullied by classmates with disabilities or chronic illnesses, or by children outside their schools. Students with chronic illnesses from regular schools showed higher levels of perpetration. This difference should be interpreted with caution, as school type and the type of illness/disability were confounded (most students from special schools had sensory disabilities, and students with these disabilities did not show higher levels of perpetration). Therefore, studies from special schools on students with other physical illnesses are needed before further conclusions can be drawn.

Interestingly, between-group differences in total victimization were smaller in more recent studies. This might be the result of the increasing dissemination of antibullying programs (Molcho et al., 2009; Nicholas et al., 2012).

Results did not vary according to how the bullying was reported. Thus, between-group differences in bullying involvement are unlikely to be based on, for example, children with chronic illnesses overreporting bullying events, or perceiving mild teasing as victimization.

No moderating effects were found in regard to sampling procedure, quality of the bullying measure, publication status, age, and gender. Thus, the results were robust in regard to these study characteristics.

Limitations and Conclusions

Some limitations of the present meta-analysis have to be mentioned. First, separate analyses of victimization could only be computed for nine illness groups. Perpetration could only be analyzed in five illness groups. More studies on bullying involvement are needed for other diseases, such as cancer and diabetes. Next, only a limited number of studies are available on the involvement of children with chronic physical illnesses and/or physical or sensory disabilities in cyberbullying and illness-specific teasing. Additionally, only concurrent associations between chronic illnesses and bullying involvement were analyzed. Although it was hypothesized that having a chronic illness or disability increases the risk of being bullied, victimization could also affect the risk for developing some chronic diseases, such as migraine or obesity (e.g., Gray, Kahhan, & Janicke, 2009). Finally, given this study's quantitative approach, young people's phenomenological experiences of bullying could not be examined.

As a first conclusion, children and adolescents with chronic physical illnesses or disabilities are more likely to be bullied than their healthy, nondisabled peers, but differences between these groups tend to be small. Most adolescents with chronic physical illnesses or disabilities do not report being victims of bullying in general, although illness-related teasing about appearance or weight is common among young people with craniofacial conditions and obesity. Between-group differences in general measures of peer victimization tend to be small because healthy children may be bullied for other reasons, such as sexual orientation, ethnicity, or academic problems.

Second, the results indicate that action is needed to prevent and reduce illness-specific forms of bullying. Although average effects of general school-based antibullying programs tend to be small to very small (Jiménez-Barbero, Ruiz-Hernández, Llor-Zaragoza,

Pérez-García, & Llor-Esteban, 2016), the establishment of a school policy on bullying, training of emotional control, and promotion of supportive peer relations lead to above-average reduction of bullying (Lee, Kim, & Kim, 2015). Coping with bullying is a part of some psychosocial interventions for children with chronic illnesses (e.g., Nicholas et al., 2012), but more information is needed about their effects on bullying-related events.

Finally, given the fact that bullying involvement varies between chronic illnesses, more research is needed to help us understand the differences and factors that may play a role. Thus, further studies are needed that assess bullying involvement of children with different chronic physical diseases as well as potential risk factors, such as visibility of the disease, physical strength/weakness, attractiveness, social competence, and psychological health. Identifying the factors that explain elevated levels of bullying in children with chronic physical illnesses and/or disabilities would also help with designing interventions aimed at preventing and reducing bullying in these groups.

Supplementary Data

Supplementary data can be found at: http://www.jpepsy.oxfordjournals.org/.

Conflicts of interest: None declared.

References

References marked with an asterisk indicate studies included in the meta-analysis.

*Araújo, P., Carvalho, M. G. N., Weelden, M., Lourenco, B., Queiroz, L. B., & Silva, C. A. (2016). Uso indevido de drogas e funcão sexualem adolescentes com doencas crônicas [Substance misuse and sexual function in adolescents with chronic diseases]. *Revista Paulista De Pediatria*, 34, 323–329.

*Arruda, M. A., Arruda, R., Guidetti, V., & Bigal, M. E. (2015). Psychosocial adjustment of children with migraine and tension-type headache—A nationwide study. *Headache*, 55, 39–50.

*Azeredo, C. M., Levy, R. B., Araya, R., & Menezes, P. R. (2015). Individual and contextual factors associated with verbal bullying among Brazilian adolescents. *BMC Pediatrics*, 15, 49.

*Bacchini, D., Licenziati, M. R., Garrasi, A., Corciulo, N., Driul, D., Tanas, R., & Valerio, G. (2015). Bullying and victimization in overweight and obese outpatient children and adolescents: An Italian multicentric study. *PLoS One*, 10, e0142715.

*Bauman, S., & Pero, H. (2010). Bullying and cyberbullying among deaf students and their hearing peers: An exploratory study. *Journal of Deaf Studies and Deaf Education*, 16, 236–253.

*Bear, G. G., Mantz, L. S., Glutting, J. J., Yang, C., & Boyer, D. E. (2015). Differences in bullying victimization between students with and without disabilities. *School Psychology Review*, 44, 98–116.

*Bell, L. M., Curran, J. A., Byrne, S., Roby, H., Suriano, K., Jones, T. W., & Davis, E. A. (2011). High incidence of obesity co-morbidities in young children: A cross-sectional study. *Journal of Paediatrics & Child Health*, 47, 911–917.

*Berg, I. M., Simonsson, B., & Ringqvist, I. (2005). Social background, aspects of lifestyle, body image, relations, school situation, and somatic and psychological symptoms in obese and overweight 15-year-old boys in a county in Sweden. *Scandinavian Journal of Primary Health Care*, 23, 95–101.

*Bergsiek, L. (2015). Bullyingerfahrungen, psychisches Wohlbefinden und die Rolle des Attributionsstils bei Jugendlichen mit und ohne Hörschädigung [Bullying victimization, psychological well-being, and the role of attributional style in adolescents with and without hearing impairment]. Unpublished Diploma thesis, University of Marburg, Germany.

*Blackman, J. A., & Gurka, M. J. (2007). Developmental and behavioral comorbidities of asthma in children. *Journal of Developmental and Behavioral Pediatrics*, 28, 92–99.

*Bookhout, M. K. (2015). *The role of peer victimization in the relations between obesity, negative body cognitions, andnegative psychosocial outcomes*. Unpublished Master thesis, University of Delaware, Delaware.

*Brixval, C. S., Rayce, S. L. B., Rasmussen, M., Holstein, B. E., & Due, P. (2011). Overweight, body image and bullying – an epidemiological study of 11- to 15-years-olds. *European Journal of Public Health*, 22, 126–130.

*Broder, H. L., Smith, F. B., & Strauss, R. P. (2001). Developing a behavior rating scale for comparing teachers' ratings of children with and without craniofacial anomalies. *Cleft Palate-Craniofacial Journal*, 28, 560–565.

*Brunnberg, E., Boström, M. L., & Berglund, M. (2008). Self-rated mental health, school adjustment, and substance use in hard-of-hearing adolescents. *Journal of Deaf Studies and Deaf Education*, 13, 24–35.

*Bucchianeri, M. M., Gower, A. L., McMorris, B. J., & Eisenberg, M. E. (2016). Youth experiences with multiple types of prejudice-based harassment. *Journal of Adolescence*, 51, 68–75.

*Carne, S. H. (2008). *Aspects of adolescent obesity in New Zealand: Quality of life, psychosocial factors and psychological theory*. Unpublished dissertation, University of Auckland, Auckland, New Zealand.

*Carroll, P., & Shute, R. (2005). School peer victimization of young people with craniofacial conditions: A comparative study. *Psychology, Health & Medicine*, 10, 291–305.

*Case, K. R., Pérez, A., Saxton, D. L., Hoelscher, D. M., & Springer, A. E. (2016). Bullied status and physical activity in Texas adolescents. *Health Education and Behavior*, 43, 313–320.

Cook, C. R., Williams, K. R., Guerra, N. G., Kim, T. E., & Sadek, S. (2010). Predictors of bullying and victimization in childhood and adolescence: A meta-analytic investigation. *School Psychology Quarterly*, 25, 65–83.

Crick, N. R., & Grotpeter, J. K. (1996). Children's treatment by peers: Victims of relational and overt aggression. *Development and Psychopathology*, 8, 367–380.

*Curtis, C. E., & Luby, J. L. (2008). Depression and social functioning in preschool children with chronic medical conditions. *Journal of Pediatrics*, 153, 408–413.

Dawkins, J. (1996). Bullying, physical disability and the paediatric patient. *Developmental Medicine and Child Neurology*, 38, 603–612.

*Demir, T., Karacetin, G., Baghaki, S., & Aydin, Y. (2011). Psychiatric assessment of children with nonsyndromic cleft lip and palate. *Hospital Psychiatry*, 33, 584–603.

*Dertlioglu, D. B., Cicek, D., Balci, D. D., & Halisdemir, D. (2013). Dermatology life quality index scores in children with vitiligo: Comparison with atopic dermatitis and healthy control subjects. *International Journal of Dermatology*, 52, 96–101.

*DeSmet, A., Deforche, B., Hublet, A., Tanghe, A., Strenersch, E., & De Bourdeaudhuij, I. (2014). Traditional and cyberbullying victimization as correlates of psychosocial distress and barriers to a healthy lifestyle among severely obese adolescents—A matched case–control study on prevalence and results from a cross-sectional study. *BMC Public Health*, 14, 224.

*Devine, K. A., Storch, E. A., Geffken, G. R., Freddo, M., Humphrey, J. L., & Silverstein, J. H. (2008). Prospective study of peer victimization and social-psychological adjustment in children with endocrine disorders. *Journal of Child Health Care*, 12, 76–86.

*Devine, K. A., Holmbeck, G. N., Gayes, L., & Purnell, J. Q. (2012). Friendships of children and adolescents with spina bifida: Social adjustment, social performance, and social skills. *Journal of Pediatric Psychology*, 37, 220–231.

Due, P., Holsten, B. E., Lynn, J., Diderichsen, F., Gabhain, S. N., Scheidt, P., & Currie, C. (2005). Bullying and symptoms among school-aged children: International comparative cross sectional study in 28 countries. *European Journal of Public Health*, 15, 128–132.

*Eaton, J. (1999). *Adjustment in adolescents with cleft lip and palate: A preliminary investigation into experiences of shame and bullying.* Unpublished dissertation, University of Leicester, Leicester.

*Eisenberg, M. E., Gower, A. L., McMorris, B. J., & Bucchianeri, M. M. (2015). Vulnerable bullies: Perpetration of peer harassment among youths across sexual orientation, weight, and disability status. *American Journal of Public Health*, 105, 1784–1791.

*Elgar, F. J., Roberts, C., Moore, L., & Tudor-Smith, C. (2005). Sedentary behaviour, physical activity and weight problems in adolescents in Wales. *Public Health*, 119, 518–524.

*Ejerskov, C., Lasgaard, M., & Østergaar, J. R. (2015). Teenagers and young adults with neurofibromatosis type 1 are more likely to experience loneliness than siblings without the illness. *Acta Pædiatrica*, 104, 604–609.

Faith, M. A., Reed, G., Heppner, C. E., Hamill, L. C., Tarkenton, T. R., & Donewar, C. W. (2015). Bullying in medically fragile youth: A review of risks, protective factors, and recommendations for medical providers. *Journal of Developmental and Behavioral Pediatrics*, 36, 285–301.

*Farhat, T., Iannotti, R. J., & Simons-Morton, B. G. (2010). Overweight, obesity, youth, and health-risk behaviors. *American Journal of Preventive Medicine*, 38, 258–267.

*Farrant, B., Utter, J., Ameratunga, S., Clark, T., Fleming, T., & Denny, S. (2013). Prevalence of severe obesity among New Zealand adolescents and associations with health risk behaviors and emotional well-being. *Journal of Pediatrics*, 163, 143–149.

Fox, C. L., & Farrow, C. V. (2009). Global and physical self-esteem and body dissatisfaction as mediators of the relationship between weight status and being a victim of bullying. *Journal of Adolescence*, 32, 1287–1301.

*García-Continente, X., Pérez-Giménez, A., Espelt, A., & Adell, M. N. (2013). Bullying among schoolchildren: Differences between victims and aggressors. *Gaceta Sanitaria*, 27, 350–354.

*Gibson, L. Y., Byrne, S. M., Blair, E., Davis, E. A., Jacoby, P., & Zubrick, S. R. (2008). Clustering of psychosocial symptoms in overweight children. *Australian and New Zealand Journal of Psychiatry*, 42, 118–125.

*Gibson-Young, L., Martinasek, M. P., Clutter, M., & Forrest, J. (2014). Are students with asthma at increased risk for being a victim of bullying in school or cyberspace? Findings from the 2011 Florida Youth Risk Behavior Survey. *Journal of School Health*, 84, 429–434.

*Gray, W. N., Janicke, D. M., & Dumont-Driscoll, M. (2014). Peer victimization, caregiver restriction of food intake, and degree of overweight in youth. *Journal of Developmental and Behavioral Pediatrics*, 35, 411–418.

Gray, W. N., Kahhan, N. A., & Janicke, D. M. (2009). Peer victimization and pediatric obesity: A review of the literature. *Psychology in the Schools*, 46, 720–727.

*Griffiths, L. J., Wolke, D., Page, A. S., & Horwood, J. P. (2006). Obesity and bullying: Different effects for boys and girls. *Archives of Diseases in Childhood*, 91, 121–125.

*Guo, Q. Z., Ma, W. J., Nie, S. P., Xu, Y. J., Xu, H. F., & Zhang, Y. R. (2010). Relationships between weight status and bullying victimization among school-aged adolescents in Guangdong Province of China. *Biomedical and Environmental Sciences*, 23, 108–112.

*Haavet, O. R., Straand, J., Saugstad, O. D., & Grünfeld, B. (2004). Illness and exposure to negative life experiences in adolescence: Two sides of the same coin? A study of 15-year-olds in Oslo, Norway. *Acta Paediatrica*, 93, 405–411.

*Halvorsen, J. A., Lien, L., Dalgard, F., Bjertness, E., & Stern, R. S. (2014). Suicidal ideation, mental health problems, and social function in adolescents with eczema: A population-based study. *Journal of Investigative Dermatology*, 134, 1847–1854.

*Halvorsen, J. A., Stern, R. S., Dalgard, F., Thoresen, M., Bjertness, E., & Lien, L. (2011). Suicidal ideation, mental health problems, and social impairment are increased in adolescents with acne: A population-based study. *Journal of Investigative Dermatology*, 131, 363–370.

*Hamiwka, L. D., Yu, C. G., Hamiwka, L. A., Sherman, E. M., Anderson, B., & Wirrell, E. (2009). Are children with epilepsy at greater risk for bullying than their peers? *Epilepsy and Behavior*, 15, 500–505.

*Harrist, A. W., Swindle, T. M., Hubbs-Tait, L., Topham, G. L., Shriver, L. H., & Page, M. C. (2016). The social and emotional lives of overweight, obese, and severely obese children. *Child Development*, in press.

*Hayden-Wade, H. A., Stein, R. I., Ghaderi, A., Saelens, B. E., Zabinski, M. F., & Wilfley, D. E. (2005). Prevalence, characteristics, and correlates of teasing experiences among obese vs. non-obese peers. *Obesity Research*, *13*, 1381–1392.

Hedges, L. V., Tipton, E., & Johnson, M. C. (2010). Robust variance estimation in meta-regression with dependent effect size estimates. *Research Synthesis Methods*, *1*, 39–65.

Helfert, S., & Warschburger, P. (2013). The face of appearance-related social pressure: Gender, age and body mass variations in peer and parental pressure during adolescence. *Child and Adolescent Psychiatry and Mental Health*, *7*, 16.

Herrman, B., Seidenberg, M., Bell, B., Rutecki, P., Sheth, R., Ruggles, K. . . . , & Magnotta, V. (2002). The neurodevelopmental impact of childhood-onset temporal lobe epilepsy on brain structure and function. *Epilepsia*, *43*, 1062–1071.

*Horwood, J., Waylen, A., Herrick, D., Williams, C., & Wolke, D. (2005). Common visual defects and peer victimization in children. *Investigative Ophthalmology and Visual Science*, *46*, 1177–1181.

*Hunt, O., Burden, D., Hepper, P., Stevenson, M., & Johnston, C. (2006). Self-reports of psychosocial functioning among children and young adults with cleft lip and palate. *Cleft Palate-. Craniofacial Journal*, *43*, 598–605.

*Hunt, O., Burden, D., Hepper, P., Stevenson, M., & Johnston, C. (2007). Parent reports of the psychosocial functioning of children with cleft lip and/or palate. *Cleft Palate-. Craniofacial Journal*, *44*, 304–311.

*Ilola, A. M., Lempinen, L., Huttunen, J., Ristkari, T., & Sourander, A. (2016). Bullying and victimisation are common in four-year-old children and are associated with somatic symptoms and conduct and peer problems. *Acta Pædiatrica*, *105*, 522–528.

Janicke, D. M., Gray, W. N., Kahhan, N. A., Junger, K. W., Marciel, K. M., Storch, E. A., & Jolley, C. D. (2009). The association between peer victimization, prosocial support, and treatment adherence in children and adolescents with inflammatory bowel disease. *Journal of Pediatric Psychology*, *34*, 769–773.

*Jansen, P. W., Verlinden, M., Dommisse-van Berkel, A., Mieloo, C. L., Raat, H., Hofman, A., & Tiemeier, H. (2014). Teacher and peer reports of overweight and bullying among young primary school children. *Pediatrics*, *134*, 473–480.

*Janssen, I., Craig, W. M., Boyce, W. F., & Pickett, W. (2004). Associations between overweight and obesity with bullying behaviors in school-aged children. *Pediatrics*, *113*, 1187–1194.

*Jeong, S., Davis, J., & Rodriguez, J. (2016). What makes them more vulnerable than others? Obesity, negative emotions, and peer bullying victimization. *International Journal of Offender Therapy and Comparative Criminology*, *60*, 1690–1705.

Jiménez-Barbero, J. A., Ruiz-Hernández, J. A., Llor-Zaragoza, L., Pérez-García, M., & Llor-Esteban, B. (2016). Effectiveness of anti-bullying school programs: A meta-analysis. *Children and Youth Services Review*, *61*, 165–175.

*Jones, J. E. (1983). *Self-concept and parental evaluations of peer relationships in cleft lip and palate children*. Unpublished Master thesis, Indiana University, Bloomington.

Juvonen, J., & Graham, S. (2014). Bullying in schools: The power of bullies and the plight of victims. *Annual Review of Psychology*, *65*, 159–185.

*Kalar, M., Faizi, T. Q., Jawed, M., Khalil, S., Hussain, S. M., Fatima, M., & Naqvi, T. (2015). Bullying, overweight and physical activity in school children of Karachi. *International Archives of Medicine*, *8*, 1–9.

*Kent, B. A. (2003). Identity issues for hard of hearing adolescents aged 11, 13, and 15 in mainstream settings. *Journal of Deaf Studies and Deaf Education*, *8*, 315–324.

*Kim, S. G., Yun, I., & Kim, J. H. (2016). Associations between body weight and bullying among South Korean adolescents. *Journal of Early Adolescence*, *36*, 551–574.

*Kouwenberg, M., Rieffe, C., Theunissen, S. C., & de Rooij, M. (2012). Peer victimization experienced by children and adolescents who are deaf or hard of hearing. *PLoS One*, *7*, e52174.

*Kukaswadia, A., Craig, W., Janssen, I., & Pickett, W. (2011). Obesity as a determinant of two forms of bullying in Ontario youth: A short report. *Obesity Facts*, *4*, 469–472.

*Kukaswadia, A., Craig, W., Janssen, I., & Pickett, W. (2012). Bullying as a mediator of relationships between adiposity status and weapon carrying. *International Journal of Public Health*, *57*, 505–512.

*Kvist, B., Kvist, M., & Rajantie, J. (1990). School absences, school achievements and personality traits of the haemophilic child. *Scandinavian Journal of Social Medicine*, *18*, 125–132.

*Lähteenmäki, P. M., Huostila, J., Hinkka, S., & Salmi, T. T. (2002). Childhood cancer patients at school. *European Journal of Cancer*, *38*, 1227–1240.

*Layte, R., & McCrory, C. (2013). Paediatric chronic illness and educational failure: The role of emotional and behavioural problems. *Social Psychiatry & Psychiatric Epidemiology*, *48*, 1307–1316.

*Lee, S., Kim, C. J., & Kim, D. H. (2015). A meta-analysis of the effect of school-based anti-bullying programs. *Journal of Child Health Care*, *19*, 136–153.

*Lembeck, P. T. (2015). Adolescent bullying: Do weight, body size, and body size dissatisfaction influence victimization? Unpublished dissertation, University of Nebraska.

*Lipsey, M. W., & Wilson, D. B. (2001). *Practical meta-analysis*. Thousand Oaks, CA: Sage.

*Liu, X., Chen, G., Yan, J., & Luo, J. (2016). Weight status and bullying behaviors among Chinese school-aged children. *Child Abuse & Neglect*, *52*, 11–19.

*Locker, D., Jokovic, A., & Tompso, B. (2005). Health-related quality of life of children aged 11 to 14 years with orofacial conditions. *Cleft Palate-Craniofacial Journal*, *42*, 260–266.

*Lumeng, J. C., Forrest, P., Appugliese, D. P., Kaciroti, N., Corwyn, R. F., & Bradley, R. H. (2010). Weight status as a predictor of being bullied in third through sixth grades. *Pediatrics*, *125*, e1301–e1307.

*Luukkonen, A. H., Räsänen, P., Hakko, H., & Riala, K. (2010). Bullying behavior in relation to psychiatric disorders and physical health among adolescents: A clinical cohort of 508 underage inpatient adolescents in Northern Finland. *Psychiatry Research, 178,* 166–170.

*Maggio, A. B., Martin, X. E., Gasser, C. S., Gal-Duding, C., Beghetti, M., Farpour-Lambert, N. J., & Chamay-Weber, C. (2014). Medical and non-medical complications among children and adolescents with excessive body weight. *BMC Pediatrics, 14,* 232.

*Masnari, O., Landoldt, M. A., Roessler, J., Weingaertner, S. K., Neuhaus, K., Meuli, M., & Schiestl, C. (2012). Self- and parent-perceived stigmatisation in children and adolescents with congenital or acquired facial differences. *Journal of Plastic, Reconstructive & Aesthetic Surgery, 65,* 1664–1670.

*Merrill, R. M., & Hanson, C. L. (2016). Risk and protective factors associated with being bullied on school property compared with cyberbullied. *BMC Public Health, 16,* 145.

*Metsähonkala, L., Sillanpää, M., & Tuominen, J. (1998). Social environment and headache in 8- to 9-year-old children: A follow-up study. *Headache, 38,* 222–228.

*Mezgebe, M., Akhtar-Danesh, G. G., Streiner, D. L., Fayed, N., Rosenbaum, P. L., & Ronen, G. M. (2015). Quality of life in children with epilepsy: How does it compare with the quality of life in typical children and children with cerebral palsy? *Epilepsy & Behavior, 52,* 239–243.

Molcho, M., Craig, W., Due, P., Pickett, W., Harel-Fisch, Y., & Overpeck, M. (2009). Cross-national time trends in bullying behaviour 1994-2006: Findings from Europe and North America. *International Journal of Public Health, 54,* s1–s10.

*Muraro, A., Polloni, L., Lazzarotto, F., Toniolo, A., Baldi, I., Bonaguro, R., & Massiello, M. (2014). Comparison of bullying of food allergic versus healthy schoolchildren in Italy. *Journal of Allergy and Clinical Immunology, 134,* 749–751.

*Musaiger, A. O., bin Zaal, A. A., & D'souza, R. (2012). Body weight perception among adolescents in Dubai, United Arab Emirates. *Nutricion Hospitalaria, 27,* 1966–1972.

*Nadeau, L., & Tessier, R. (2006). Social adjustment of children with cerebral palsy in mainstream classes: Peer perception. *Developmental Medicine & Child Neurology, 48,* 331–336.

*Nadeau, L., & Tessier, R. (2009). Social adjustment at school: Are children with cerebral palsy perceived more negatively by their peers than other at-risk children? *Disability and Rehabilitation, 31,* 302–308.

*Neumark-Sztainer, D., Falkner, N., Story, M., Perry, C., & Hannan, P. J. (2002). Weight-teasing among adolescents: Correlations with weight status and disordered eating behaviors. *International Journal of Obesity & Related Metabolic Disorders, 26,* 123–131.

Nicholas, D. B., Fellner, K. D., Frank, M., Small, M., Hetherington, R., Slater, R., & Daneman, D. (2012). Evaluation of an online education and support intervention for adolescents with diabetes. *Social Work in Health Care, 51,* 815–827.

*Nordhagen, R., Nielsen, A., Stigum, H., & Köhler, L. (2005). Parental reported bullying among Nordic children: A population-based study. *Child: Health, Care and Development, 31,* 693–701.

Olweus, D. (1992). Bullying among schoolchildren: Intervention and prevention. In R. D. Peters, R. J. McMahon, & V. L. Quinsey (Eds.), *Aggression and Violence Throughout the Life Span* (pp. 100–125). Newbury Park: Sage.

Olweus, D. (1996). *The revised Olweus bully/victim questionnaire.* University of Bergen, Research Center for Health Promotion.

*Pearce, M. J., Boergers, J., & Prinstein, M. J. (2002). Adolescent obesity, overt and relational peer victimization, and romantic relationships. *Obesity Research, 10,* 386–393.

*Pengpid, S., & Peltzer, K. (2015). Overweight and obesity and associated Factors among school-aged adolescents in six Pacific Island countries in Oceania. *International Journal of Environmental Research and Public Health, 12,* 14505–14518.

*Percy-Smith, L., Caye-Thomasen, P., Gudman, M., Jensen, J. H., & Thomsen, J. (2008). Self-esteem and social well-being of children with cochlear implant compared to normal-hearing children. *International Journal of Pediatric Otorhinolaryngology, 72,* 1113–1120.

Pinquart, M. (2013a). Self-esteem of children and adolescents with chronic illness: A meta-analysis. *Child: Care, Health and Development, 39,* 153–161.

Pinquart, M. (2013b). Body image of children and adolescents with chronic illness: A meta-analytic comparison with healthy peers. *Body Image, 10,* 141–148.

*Pinquart, M., & Pfeiffer, J. (2011). Bullying in German adolescents attending special schools for students with visual impairment. *British Journal of Visual Impairment, 29,* 163–176.

*Pinquart, M., & Pfeiffer, J. P. (2015). Bullying in students with and without hearing loss. *Deafness & Education International, 17,* 101–110.

Pinquart, M., & Shen, Y. (2011). Behavior problems in children and adolescents with a chronic physical illness: A meta-analysis. *Journal of Pediatric Psychology, 36,* 1003–1016.

Pinquart, M., & Teubert, D. (2012). Academic, physical, and social functioning of children and adolescents with chronic physical illness: A meta-analysis. *Journal of Pediatric Psychology, 37,* 376–389.

Price, S., & Proietto, J. (2015). Is obesity a chronic disease? In G. Blashki, & N. Sykes (Eds.), *Dancing in the rain: Living with noncommunicable diseases* (pp. 69–82). Albert Park: Future Leaders.

*Puhl, R. M., & Luedicke, J. (2012). Weight-based victimization among adolescents in the school setting: Emotional reactions and coping behaviors. *Journal of Youth & Adolescence, 41,* 27–40.

*Rao, P. C. S., & Kishore, M. T. (2013). Effect of obesity in self-esteem, peer victimization and behavior problems in adolescents. *Indian Journal of Clinical Psychology, 40,* 137–141.

*Rastogi, R., Rastogi, D., & Silver, E. J. (2014). Quality of life among urban children with obesity and asthma. *Journal of Health Care for the Poor and Underserved, 25,* 683–693.

Reijntjes, A., Kamphuis, J. H., Prinzie, P., & Telch, M. J. (2010). Peer victimization and internalizing problems in children: A meta-analysis of longitudinal studies. *Child Abuse & Neglect*, *34*, 244–252.

*Reulbach, U., Ladewig, E. L., Nixon, E., O'moore, M., Williams, J., & O'dowd, T. (2013). Weight, body image and bullying in 9-year-old children. *Journal of Paediatrics and Child Health*, *49*, 288–293.

*Rojo-Moreno, L., Rubio, T., Plumed, J., Barberá, M., Serrano, M., Gimeno, N. ..., & Livianos, L. (2013). Teasing and disordered eating behaviors in Spanish adolescents. *Eating Disorders*, *21*, 53–69.

Rose, C. A., Stormont, M., Wang, Z., Simpson, C. G., Preast, J. L., & Green, A. L. (2015). Bullying and students with disabilities: Examination of disability status and educational placement. *School Psychology Review*, *44*, 425–444.

Rosenberg, M. S. (2005). The file-drawer problem revisited: A general weighted method for calculating fail-safe numbers in meta-analysis. *Evolution*, *59*, 464–468.

Scheithauer, H. (2003). *Aggressives Verhalten von Jungen und Mädchen [Aggressive behavior of boys and girls]*. Göttingen: Hogrefe.

Scheithauer, H., Hayer, R., Petermann, F., & Jugert, G. (2006). Physical, verbal, and relational forms of bullying among German students: Age trends, gender differences, and correlates. *Aggressive Behavior*, *21*, 261–275.

Schwartz, D., Gorman, A.H., Nakamoto, J., & Toblin, R.L. (2005). Victimization in the peer group and children's academic functioning. *Journal of Educational Psychology*, *97*, 425–435.

Sokol, R. J. (2000). The chronic disease of childhood obesity: The sleeping giant has awakened. *The Journal of Pediatrics*, *136*, 711–713.

Storch, E. A., Heidgerken, A., Geffken, G., Lewin, A., Ohleyer, V., Freddo, M., & Silverstein, J. H. (2006). Bullying, regimen self-management, and metabolic control in youth with type 1 diabetes. *Journal of Pediatrics*, *148*, 784–787.

*Storch, E. A., Lewin, A., Silverstein, J. H., Heldgerken, A. D., Strawser, M. S., Baumeister, A., & Geffken, G. R. (2004a). Peer victimization and psychosocial adjustment in children with type 1 diabetes. *Clinical Pediatrics*, *43*, 467–471.

*Storch, E. A., Lewin, A. B., Silverstein, J. H., Heidgerken, A. D., Strawser, M. S., Baumeister, A., & Geffken, G. (2004b). Social-psychological correlates of peer victimization in children with endocrine disorders. *Journal of Pediatrics*, *145*, 784–789.

*Sweeting, H., & West, P. (2001). Being different: Correlates of the experience of teasing and bullying at age 11. *Research Papers in Education*, *16*, 225–246.

*Sweeting, H., Wright, C., & Minnis, H. (2005). Psychosocial correlates of adolescent obesity, 'slimming down' and 'becoming obese'. *Journal of Adolescent Health*, *37*, 409.e9–409.e17.

*Teyhan, A., Galobardes, B., & Henderson, J. (2015). Child allergic symptoms and well-being at school: Findings from ALSPAC, a UK Cohort Study. *PLoS One*, *10*, e0135271.

*Thompson, R. J., & Gustafson, K. E. (1996). *Adaptation to chronic childhood illness*. Washington, DC: American Psychological Association.

*Timmons-Mitchell, J. (n.d.). Bullying prevention in youth with chronic illness and psychiatric diagnosis. Retrieved from http://begun.case.edu/wp-content/uploads/2015/03/Jane-Timmons-Mitchell-AACAPpresentation_10_22_13_jtmFINAL_edited.pdf. Rrtrieved 2016-03-16.

*Turner, H. A., Vanderminden, J., Finkelhor, D., Hamby, S., & Shattuck, A. (2011). Disability and victimization in a national sample of children and youth. *Child Maltreatment*, *16*, 275–286.

*Twyman, K. A., Saylor, S. F., Saia, D., Macias, M. M., Taylor, L. A., & Spratt, E. (2010). Bullying and ostracism experiences in children with special health care needs. *Journal of Developmental and Behavioral Pediatrics*, *31*, 1–8.

van Geel, M., Vedder, P., & Tanilon, J. (2014). Are overweight and obese youths more often bullied by their peers? A meta-analysis on the correlation between weight status and bullying. *International Journal of Obesity*, *38*, 1263–1267.

*van Weelden, M., Queiroz, L. B., Louren, D. M., Kozu, K., Loureno, B., & Silva, C. A. (2016a). Alcohol, smoking and illicit drug use in pediatric systemic lupus erythematosus patients. *Revista Brasileira De Rheumatologia*, *56*, 228–243.

*van Weelden, M., Queiroz, L. B., Louren, D. M., Kozu, K., Loureno, B., & Silva, C. A. (2016b). Uso de substâncias e função sexual na artrite idiopática juvenile [Substance use and sexual function in juvenile idiopathic arthritis]. *Revista Brasileira De Rheumatologia*, *56*, 323–329.

*Verzeletti, C., Santinello, M., & Vieno, A. (2010). Frequenza e tipologia degli episodi di vittimizzazione in adolescenza: che ruolo gioca l'indice di massa corporea?. *Psicoterapia Cognitiva E Comportamentale*, *16*, 39–51.

*Voss, L. D., & Mulligan, J. (2000). Bullying in school: Are short pupils at risk? Questionnaire study in a cohort. *British Medical Journal*, *320*, 612–613.

*Wang, J., Iannotti, R. J., & Luk, J. W. (2010). Bullying victimization among underweight and overweight U.S. youth: Differential associations for boys and girls. *Journal of Adolescent Health*, *47*, 99–101.

*Wauters, L. N., & Knoors, H. E. T. (2008). Social integration of deaf children in inclusive settings. *Journal of Deaf Studies & Deaf Education*, *13*, 21–36.

*Wei, H. S., Hwa, H. L., Shen, A. C. T., Feng, J. Y., Hsieh, Y. P., & Huang, S. C. Y. (2016). Physical conditions and special needs as risk factors of peer victimization among school children in Taiwan. *Journal of School Nursing*, in press.

*Weiner, M. T., Day, S. J., & Galvan, D. (2013). Deaf and hard of hearing students' perspectives on bullying and school climate. *American Annals of the Deaf*, *158*, 324–343.

*Westbom, L. (1992). Well-being of children with chronic illness. A population-based study in a Swedish primary care district. *Acta Paediatrica*, *81*, 625–629.

*Willard, V. W., Long, A., & Phipps, S. (2016). Life stress versus traumatic stress: The impact of life events on psychological functioning in children with and without serious illness. *Psychological Trauma: Theory, Research, Practice, and Policy*, *8*, 63–71.

*Williams, K., Chambers, M., Logan, S., & Robinson, D. (1996). Association of common health symptoms with bullying in primary school children. *British Medical Journal*, *313*, 17–19.

*Wilson, M. L., Viswanathan, B., Rousson, V., & Bovet, P. (2013). Weight status, body image and bullying among adolescents in the Seychelles. *International Journal of Environmental Research and Public Health*, *10*, 1763–1774.

*Yang, S. J., Stewart, R., Kim, J. M., Kim, S. W., Shin, I. S., Dewey, M. E. ... , ,& Yoon, J. S. (2013). Differences in predictors of traditional and cyber-bullying: A 2-year longitudinal study in Korean school children. *European Child and Adolescent Psychiatry*, *22*, 309–318.

*Yude, C., Goodman, R., & McConachie, H. (1998). Peer problems of children with hemiplegia in mainstream primary schools. *Journal of Child Psychology and Psychiatry*, *39*, 533–541.

// Early Childhood Sleep Patterns and Cognitive Development at Age 6 Years: The Generation R Study

Desana Kocevska,[1,3] MD, MSc, Jolien Rijlaarsdam,[1,3] MSc, PhD, Akhgar Ghassabian,[3] MD, PhD, Vincent W. Jaddoe,[1,2,4] MD, PhD, Oscar H. Franco,[2] MD, PhD, Frank C. Verhulst,[3] MD, PhD, and Henning Tiemeier,[2,3,5] MD, PhD

[1]Generation R Study Group, Erasmus University Medical Center, [2]Department of Epidemiology, [3]Department of Child and Adolescent Psychiatry, Erasmus Medical Center, [4]Department of Pediatrics, Sophia Children's Hospital, Erasmus Medical Center and [5]Department of Psychiatry, Erasmus Medical Center

All correspondence concerning this article should be addressed to Henning Tiemeier, MD, PhD, Department of Child and Adolescent Psychiatry, Erasmus University Medical Center, PO Box 2060, 3000 CB Rotterdam, The Netherlands. E-mail: h.tiemeier@erasmusmc.nl

Received June 26, 2015; revisions received November 29, 2015; accepted December 10, 2015

Abstract

Objective To explore the association of sleep duration and awakening frequency with cognitive outcomes in young children. **Methods** Mothers of 2,800 children from the Generation R cohort reported sleep duration and awakenings at children's age 24 months. At age 6 years, validated Dutch measures were used to assess children's nonverbal intelligence and language comprehension. **Results** We found a nonlinear association of total sleep time at 24 months with nonverbal intelligence ($p = 0.03$) and language comprehension ($p = 0.04$) at 6 years. Toddlers sleeping within the recommended 11–14 hr had more favorable cognitive development compared with both extremes. Frequent awakenings were negatively associated with nonverbal intelligence, but not with verbal comprehension. **Conclusion** Sleep duration in toddlerhood has an inverted-U-shaped relation with childhood cognitive measures. Frequent awakenings are associated with lower nonverbal intelligence. Given the marked decline in sleep duration and awakenings in toddlerhood, developmental changes of sleep patterns might be important for cognitive development.

Key words: awakenings; development; IQ; language; sleep duration.

Sufficient sleep has been defined as the amount necessary to permit optimal daytime performance, which primarily includes good behavioral and cognitive functions (Dahl, 1996). About 20–30% of children aged 1–3 years experience sleep problems; frequent night awakenings and insufficient sleep duration are most commonly reported (Sadeh, Mindell, Luedtke, & Wiegand, 2009). Pediatric sleep problems were shown to adversely influence children's health-related outcomes such as growth, body mass index, and blood pressure (Nixon et al., 2008), and are closely related to behavior (Jansen et al., 2011).

Interesting parallels between developmental patterns of sleep and cognition have been observed. A study in adolescents found relations between slow wave activity (SWA) of the sleep electroencephalogram and variety of indices of cortical maturation derived from magnetic resonance images (Buchmann et al., 2011). For example, both the quantity of SWA during sleep and synaptic density of the frontal cortex, which is most vulnerable to sleep deprivation, follow an inverted-U-shaped time course across development (Buchmann et al., 2011; Shaw et al., 2006). However, the empirical evidence relating childhood sleep duration with cognition is inconclusive. Children who sleep short were found to score both higher (Geiger, Achermann, & Jenni, 2010) and lower (Touchette et al., 2007) on intelligence quotient (IQ) tests than longer sleepers. Another study found no cross-sectional association between sleep duration and cognition in 7-year-old children (Nixon et al., 2008). These studies hypothesized linear associations. However, several large studies in elderly population have reported nonlinear associations of sleep duration with cognitive functioning (Auyeung et al., 2013) and memory impairment (Xu et al., 2011). Given that the steep developmental decline in sleep duration is coincided by maturation of complex cognitive functions of the frontal cortex (Buchmann et al., 2011), a curvilinear association between sleep duration and cognition in childhood seems plausible. Correspondingly, a population-based study in 1,724 adolescents aged 10–19 years reported both short and long sleep duration to be associated with lower academic performance scores (Eide & Showalter, 2012). The neural density of the frontal lobe starts to decline around the age of 7 years (Buchmann et al., 2011; Shaw et al., 2006), and thus, the potential impact of sleep on cortical maturation may be most obvious early in development (Touchette et al., 2007). Nevertheless, previous research on sleep and cognition has primarily focused on school-aged children and adolescents (Eide & Showalter, 2012; Geiger et al., 2010; Nixon et al., 2008).

In addition, lack of consolidated sleep (e.g., frequent awakenings)—a proxy for maturation of sleep patterns (Sadeh et al., 2009)—has been related to deficits in neurobehavioral tasks, like reaction time, sustained attention, and working memory. The association appeared to be stronger in young children (Sadeh, 2007). However, most of the current knowledge about the possible adverse effects of frequent awakenings is inferred from cross-sectional studies (O'Brien, 2009), whereas prospective findings might unravel cumulative effects.

Against this background, we examined the prospective associations of toddlerhood sleep duration and consolidation with nonverbal intelligence and language comprehension in school-aged children from the general population. We hypothesized that the relation between sleep duration and cognitive outcomes would follow an inverted-U-shaped pattern, meaning that sleep duration more or less than recommendations appropriate for age would be adversely associated with cognitive development. We also investigated the number of nighttime awakenings as a determinant for cognitive outcomes at 6 years, expecting a negative association.

Methods

Design and Participants

The present research was conducted within the Generation R Study, a population-based cohort based in Rotterdam, the Netherlands (Jaddoe et al., 2012). Briefly, all pregnant women living in Rotterdam with an expected delivery date between April 2002 and January 2006 were invited to participate. The Medical Ethics Committee of the Erasmus Medical Centre, Rotterdam, approved the study, and written informed consent was obtained from all participants.

Data on sleep duration and/or awakenings at 2 years was available for 5,362 children. We previously published significant differences in bed-sharing practices among the heterogeneous ethnic groups in the Generation R Study (Luijk et al., 2013), which influenced sleep habits and hygiene in this sample (Supplementary Table 1). To reduce the chance of information bias in the maternal reports of sleep, we restricted our analyses to 3,461 (64%) Dutch children. If both parents were born in the Netherlands, the child was considered "Dutch." Data on cognitive development at 6 years was available for 2,800 (81%) children of which 2,662 children had nonverbal intelligence assessment and 2,461 children had language comprehension assessment.

Sleep Assessment

Sleep variables were assessed by postal questionnaire at children's age 24 months (interquartile range [IQR]: 23.8–24.7). Parents reported about their child's sleep habits in the previous week. Nighttime sleep duration was assessed with an open question of the number of hours the child slept. For daytime sleep (napping) categorical approximation of <0.5 hr, 0.5–1 hr, 1–2 hr, and >2 hr, from which estimates of 0, 1, 2, and 2.5, respectively, were used to compute total sleep time (TST). First, sleep was analyzed continuously. Next, based on the American National Sleep Foundation's (National Sleep Foundation, 2015) age-appropriate recommendations, we defined three categories of sleep duration, namely, optimal (11–14 hr/24 hr), short (<11 hr/24 hr), and long (>14 hr/24 hr).

Sleep consolidation was assessed with a categorical question of the average number of awakenings per night: Never, 1–2 times, 3–4 times, and >5 times. In the categorical analyses, the latter two categories were collapsed to "≥3 times" (>5 times = 1.5%).

Nonverbal Intelligence

When the children were 6 years old ($SD = 0.35$), nonverbal intelligence was assessed using a validated

Dutch nonverbal intelligence test: Snijders-Oomen Niet-verbale intelligentie test–Revisie (2½–7) (Tellegen, Winkel, Wijnberg-Williams, & Laros, 2005). Owing to time constraints, two subsets were chosen: Mosaics, assessing spatial visualization abilities, and Categories, assessing abstract reasoning abilities. A scaled total score can be calculated for any combination of subtests with the same distribution characteristics as the IQ score. A correlation of $r = .86$ was found between the score derived from the Mosaics and Categories subsets, and the IQ scores derived from the complete test (Tellegen et al., 2005). Raw test scores were converted into nonverbal IQ scores using norms constructed as a continuous function of age, with a sample mean value of 105 and SD of 14.

Language Comprehension
During the same visit to the research center, children's language development at 6 years was assessed using an age-appropriate receptive subtest of a Dutch battery: Taaltest voor Kinderen (van Bon, 1982). To reduce burden to the children, 27 difficult items were selected from the full battery consisting of 40 items (Ghassabian et al., 2014). By choosing the correct alternative from two pictures that matches a given word, information about children's comprehension vocabulary skills was obtained. Correct answers were summed and divided by the number of items answered, yielding a correct percentage score (Ghassabian et al., 2014).

Covariates
The following characteristics were considered as potential confounders in the association of childhood sleep and cognition (Dionne et al., 2011; Jansen et al., 2011; Luijk et al., 2013).

Child Characteristics
Information on *gender* was obtained from midwives and hospital registries. *Gestational age* at birth was established using ultrasound examination during pregnancy. To assess history of *breastfeeding*, mothers were asked whether they breastfed their child (yes/no), by questionnaires at 2, 6, and 12 months after birth. For this study, we dichotomized the breastfeeding information from all questionnaires in "never breastfed" and "ever breastfed". To assess *behavioural problems*, we used the Child Behavior Checklist (1.5–5) questionnaire when children were 1.5 years old. This is a parent-reported questionnaire, with well-established psychometric properties, containing 99 items on problem behavior rated on a 3-point scale: 0 (*not true*), 1 (*somewhat or sometimes true*), and 2 (*very true or often true*) (Achenbach & Rescorla, 2000). A total problems weighted sum score was used. Mothers reported on child's general health status at six years ("How would you describe the general state of your child's health? Excellent/Very good/Good/Fair/Bad"). Information on wheezing (no/yes) was obtained by questionnaires, which were adapted from the International Study on Asthma and Allergy in Childhood (Asher et al., 1995) at the ages of 1, 2, 3, 4, and 6 years. To assess persistence of wheezing over time, three wheezing patterns were created: early-only wheezing (wheezing at ages 1, 2, and/or 3 years), late-only wheezing (wheezing at ages 4 and/or 6 years), and persistent wheezing (reported wheezing between 1 and 6 years) (Luijk et al., 2015).

Baseline Cognitive Function
Parent report of Children's Ability was used to provide a valid estimate of children's nonverbal cognitive functioning at 2.5 years (Ghassabian et al., 2014). It consists of two sections: a parent-administered part (22 items assessing three functions: matching-to-sample, block building, and imitation), and a parent-report part (26 questions on quantitative abilities, symbolic play, planning and organizing, adaptive behavior, and memory), which were combined in an overall sum score (Henrichs et al., 2010). *Early receptive language skills* were assessed by maternal report when children were 1.5 years old with the Dutch version of MacArthur Short Form Vocabulary Checklist, appropriate for measuring receptive vocabulary of children aged 16–30 months. The instrument contains a list of 112 words of which mothers checked the words they think their child understands, and the number of positive responses was summed to a score (details in Ghassabian et al., 2014).

Maternal, Socioeconomic, and Demographic Background Characteristics
Parity (previous pregnancies: 0 vs. ≥ 1), *maternal age*, *education*, and *marital status* (married and cohabiting vs. single) were assessed by questionnaires at enrolment. *Parental education* was defined by the highest completed education using the categories established by Netherlands Statistics (2006), and classified as "high" (higher vocational training or higher academic education), "intermediate" (more than 3 years general secondary school), and "low" (lower vocational training or 3 years general secondary school). *Maternal history of tobacco smoking* was obtained by postal questionnaire in early, mid-, and late pregnancy. On the basis of all three questionnaires, we defined the following categories: "never smoked," "stopped smoking when pregnancy was known," and "continued smoking during pregnancy." The depression and anxiety subscales from the Dutch version of the Brief Symptom Inventory

(De Beurs, 2004) were averaged to obtain an *affective symptoms scale*, as filled in by the mother 6 months postpartum. *Monthly household income* at enrolment was categorized into >2,000 Euros (more than modal income), 1,200–2,000 Euros, and <1,200 Euros (below social security level). *Maternal cognitive ability* was assessed during the visit to the research center at child's age 5–7 years, with a computerized version of the Ravens Advanced Progressive Matrices Test, set I (Prieler, 2003).

Statistical Analyses

The sample for analysis consists of 2,800 Dutch children with sleep assessment (duration and/or awakenings) at 2 years and nonverbal intelligence and/or verbal comprehension at 6 years. In this sample, the missing values on all covariates were below 20%, except for maternal affective symptoms 6 months postpartum (26%) and childhood wheezing patterns (21%). To impute the missing values of the covariates, we used Markov Chain Monte Carlo multiple imputation technique to create 10 complete data sets (Sterne et al., 2009). All statistical analyses were run in the 10 imputed data sets, and results were pooled. For the nonresponse analysis (Supplementary Material), we tested group differences in the sleep determinants and covariates between the children with and without cognitive assessments at 6 years (19%).

We used linear regression models to investigate the association of sleep duration and consolidation (awakenings) with cognitive development on a continuous scale. Two main outcomes were explored: nonverbal intelligence score and language comprehension percentage score. The skewed language variable was transformed using natural log to approximate a normal distribution. Sleep duration and awakenings were analyzed as continuous and categorical determinants. To test nonlinear association, squared term of sleep duration (h^2) was included into the regression models. In the same manner, nighttime sleep and napping were tested as determinants of cognitive outcomes. We progressively adjusted the regression models to show the associations explained by the covariates (Supplementary Tables 2a, b and 3a, b). The final model was adjusted for child's gender and age at outcome assessment, early childhood characteristics (gestational age, breastfeeding, problem behavior score at 1.5 years, baseline cognitive scores, longitudinal wheezing patterns and health status at 6 years), sociodemographic and maternal factors (household income, maternal age, education, IQ, parity, history of smoking during pregnancy, and affective symptoms 6 months postpartum). To test the dependence of the sleep measures we mutually adjusted sleep duration and number of awakenings in the final models.

Table I. Child and Parent Characteristics (n = 2,800)

Child characteristics	
Gender, % girls	50.1
Age at outcome assessment, years	6.02 ± 0.36
Gestational age at birth, weeks	40 (39–41)
Breastfed, % never	8.7
Problem behavior at 1.5 years, score	18.7 (19–29)
Language comprehension at 1.5 years, score	55.47 ± 23.87
Nonverbal intelligence at 2.5 years, score	46.94 ± 4.42
Wheezing patterns up to age 6 years	
Never, %	54.5
Early-only, %	28.9
Late-only, %	4.1
Persistent, %	12.5
Sleep at 24 months	
Total sleep time per day, hours	13.16 ± 0.96
<11 hr, %	3.8
11–14 hr, %	85.9
>14 hr, %	10.3
Awakenings per night, %	
Never	44.1
1–2 times	50.2
>3 times	5.7
Cognitive outcomes at 6 years	
Nonverbal Intelligence, score	105.24 ± 14.37
Language comprehension, % correct	0.88 (0.81–0.96)
Maternal characteristics	
Age, years	32.0 ± 4.2
IQ, score	101.3 ± 12.5
Marital status, % single	4.8
Parity, % multiparous	38.8
Education, %	
High	63.8
Middle	26.5
Low	9.7
Pregnancy smoking, %	
Never	77.9
Until pregnancy was known	10.4
Continued smoking	11.7
Affective symptom, score	0.08 (0.00–0.25)
Family Income, %	
>2,000 €	85.4
1,200–2,000 €	10.9
<1,200 €	3.7

Note. Numbers are means ± SD for continuous normally distributed variables or medians (interquartile range) for variables with skewed distributions.

Results

Characteristics of the children and their mothers are presented in Table I. The children slept on average 13 hr per day; nearly 86% slept within the recommended range of 11–14 hr. About 50% of the 2-year-old children awoke one or two times per night, and 5.7% awoke more than three times a night. Average nonverbal intelligence score was 105.2 ($\pm SD = 14.4$); median verbal comprehension percentage score was 0.88 (IQR: 0.81–0.96).

Sleep Duration as a Determinant of Cognitive Outcomes

Table II shows the associations of sleep duration with nonverbal intelligence and language comprehension. We found no evidence of a linear association; rather a

Table II. Association Between Sleep Duration at 2 Years and Cognitive Outcomes at 6 Years

Sleep duration	Nonverbal intelligence ($n = 2,662$)[a]			Language comprehension ($n = 2,461$)[a]		
	B	95% CI	p	B	95% CI	p
Linear model						
TST, hr	−0.18	−0.74, 0.38	.53	−0.01	−0.01, −0.002	.01
Quadratic model						
TST, hr^2	−0.32	−0.60, −0.04	.03	−0.002	−0.004, 0.00	.04
TST, hr	7.96	0.80, 15.12	.03	0.05	−0.004, 0.11	.07
National Sleep Foundation recommendations for TST						
<11 hr	−1.67	−4.50, 1.16	.25	−0.01	−0.03, 0.02	.60
11–14 hr		Reference			Reference	
>14 hr	−1.77	−3.53, −0.01	<.05	−0.02	−0.03, −0.01	<.01
Nighttime sleep						
Linear model						
Hours	−0.27	−0.92, 0.39	.42	−0.003	−0.01, 0.002	.29
Quadratic model						
Hours^2	−0.46	−0.81, −0.10	.01	−0.003	−0.01, 0.000	.06
Hours	9.63	1.81, 17.44	.02	0.06	−0.01, 0.12	.08
Napping, hr	−0.16	−1.00, 0.68	.70	−0.01	−0.02, −0.01	<.01
0–1 hr/day	−0.81	−2.82, 1.19	.43	0.02	0.01, 0.03	.01
1–2 hr/day		Reference			Reference	
>2 hr/day	−0.73	−1.93, 0.46	.23	−0.01	−0.02, −0.003	.01

Note. Linear regression analysis of child sleep duration and cognitive outcomes. Betas are averaged from 10 imputed data sets. TST denotes total sleep time in 24 hr.

[a]Models are adjusted for child's age and gender at cognitive testing, family income, maternal age, education and IQ, marital status, parity, smoking during pregnancy, affective symptoms 6 months postpartum, breastfeeding, child's gestational age at birth, behavioral problem score at 1.5 years, longitudinal wheezing patterns, and child's general health status at 6 years, and baseline cognitive scores (nonverbal intelligence score at 2.5 [IQ model] or language comprehension score at 1.5 years [language model]).

quadratic-U-shaped model adequately described the relation between sleep duration and cognitive outcomes (Table II, see Supplementary Figure 1a and b). The association of the quadratic term of TST and both cognitive outcomes attenuated, but remained significant when adjusted for the child, sociodemographic, and maternal characteristics (IQ points, B per h^2 = −0.32; 95% CI: −0.60 to −0.04, $p = .03$; language comprehension percentage score, B per h^2 = −0.002; 95% CI: −0.004 to −0.0001; $p = .04$). Children who slept longer at 2 years had 1.77 point (95% CI: −3.53 to −0.01, $p < .05$) lower IQ scores and 2% (95% CI: −0.03 to −0.01; $p < .01$) lower language comprehension scores at 6 years than those who slept within the recommended range of 11–14 hr. The group sleeping less than the recommended range did not reach statistically significant difference. Further analyses revealed a nonlinear association between nighttime sleep duration and both cognitive outcomes (see Supplementary Figure 2a and b), although estimates reached statistical significance only for nonverbal intelligence (IQ points, B per h^2 = −0.46; 95% CI: −0.81 to −0.10, $p = .01$). In contrast, napping was significantly related to language comprehension only; children sleeping more during the day had lower language comprehension scores (B = −0.01; 95% CI: −0.02 to −0.01; $p < .01$, Supplementary Figure 3).

Nighttime Awakening as a Determinant of Cognitive Outcomes

Table III demonstrates the association between number of awakenings at 2 years and nonverbal intelligence and language comprehension at 6 years. Children who awake frequently (>3 times) during the night scored 1.9 IQ (95% CI: −4.23 to 0.42) points lower than those waking up 1–2 times a night and 2.4 IQ (95% CI: −4.71 to −0.03) points lower than those reported to sleep through the night (Supplementary Figure 4). Mutual adjustment of sleep duration and number of awakenings in a single model did not attenuate the associations with cognitive outcomes (Supplementary Table 4).

Discussion

This large population-based study explored the prospective associations of sleep duration and nighttime awakenings in toddlers with cognitive outcomes at 6 years. We found evidence for a nonlinear relation of sleep duration with nonverbal intelligence and verbal comprehension. The nonlinear association of sleep duration was driven by nighttime sleep for both cognitive outcomes, whereas daytime napping was negatively related only to language comprehension. Frequent awakenings (>3 times per night) were independently associated with lower nonverbal intelligence, but not with verbal comprehension.

Table III. Association Between Nighttime Awakenings at 2 Years and Cognitive Outcomes at 6 Years

Sleep consolidation	Nonverbal intelligence (n = 2,662)[a]			Language comprehension (n = 2,461)[a]		
	B	95% CI	p	B	95% CI	p
Number of awakenings	−0.86	−1.7, −0.02	<.05	−0.000	−0.01, 0.01	.99
Never		Reference			Reference	
1–2 times	−0.53	−1.63, 0.56	.34	0.001	−0.01, 0.01	.83
>3 times	−2.44	−4.79, −0.09	.04	0.000	−0.02, 0.02	.99

Note. Linear regression analysis of child nighttime awakenings and cognitive outcomes. Betas are averaged from 10 imputed datasets.

[a]Models are adjusted for child's age and gender at cognitive testing, family income, maternal age, education and IQ, marital status, parity, smoking during pregnancy, affective symptoms 6 months postpartum, breastfeeding, child's gestational age at birth, behavioral problem score at 1.5 years, longitudinal wheezing patterns and child's general health status at 6 years, and baseline cognitive scores (nonverbal intelligence score at 2.5 [IQ model] or language comprehension score at 1.5 years [language model]).

Several previous studies found an association between sleep duration and cognition in early childhood. However, most of them reported linear associations (Geiger et al., 2010; Touchette et al., 2007). For example, Touchette et al. (2007) reported that children with persistently short sleep duration from the age of 2 years scored lower on vocabulary test at 5 years. Additionally, short sleepers who "improved" sleep duration in the third year still scored lower on the nonverbal intelligence test at 6 years. They interpreted this as residual effect of insufficient sleep early in cognitive development. In the study of Touchette et al. (2007), the long sleepers were the reference, hypothesizing a linear association between sleep duration and cognition, the more the better. In contrast, we tested a nonlinear association and took the children sleeping within the recommended range (11–14 hr per day [NSF]) as the reference group. Interestingly, Geiger et al. (2010) found a negative association between sleep duration and intelligence in a cross-sectional study of 7–11-year-old adolescents. The authors posited that results were consistent with an extension of the cognitive efficiency theory; "intelligence is not a function of how hard, rather how efficient the brain works" (Haier, Sigel, Tang, Abel, & Buchsbaum, 1992). However, our analyses were controlled for preexisting cognitive differences, which reduce the possibility that preexisting cognitive development influenced sleep (e.g., children with higher cognitive ability being more efficient in recovering neuronal synapses during sleep). In line with several large studies in elderly population (Auyeung et al., 2013; Xu et al., 2011) and one study in older children (Eide & Showalter, 2012), our data suggest that both short and long sleep duration in toddlers are risk factors for unfavorable cognitive outcomes at age 6 years. However, the short sleeping group in our sample may have been too small to detect statically significant differences. Consistent with previous evidence (Acebo et al., 2005), we found that the proportion of sleep consolidated during the night resembles cognitive development; the nonlinear relation between sleep duration and cognitive outcomes was driven by nighttime sleep. In agreement with findings of two studies in a twin sample of similar age, daytime napping was inversely related to language development. These studies reported higher ratio of daytime versus nighttime sleep to be associated with language delays (Dionne et al., 2011), and most the variance in consolidated nighttime sleep was shown to be genetically determined (Touchette et al., 2013).

In line with previous research reviewed by O'Brien (2009), our results showed that frequent awakenings are associated with lower nonverbal intelligence scores. However, in the present study, frequent awakenings appeared to be unrelated to verbal comprehension, which might be because we only measured receptive vocabulary. Lack of sleep consolidation might have more pronounced adverse effects on expressive verbal skills.

A common underlying factor affecting both the developmental changes of sleep patterns and cognitive development could explain why toddlers who sleep longer score lower on cognitive tests at 6 years. A recent meta-analysis showed a developmental declining trend in sleep duration and number of awakenings, which is steeper at younger ages (Galland, Taylor, Elder, & Herbison, 2012). Thus, children who sleep longer than expected and lack sleep consolidation at 2 years of age, might lag behind the usual developmental changes of sleep patterns (Acebo et al., 2005). Correspondingly, toddlers who slept more during the day had lower language comprehension scores at 6 years. However, if a factor contributed to both, sleeping patterns and cognitive delay, then adjustment for previous cognitive development could attenuate the observed association. Given that measures of cognition in early childhood are only moderately predictive of later cognitive outcomes (Ghassabian et al., 2014), our baseline cognitive measures might have been unsuccessful in fully capturing all underlying effects. Alternately, sleep efficiency might be underpinning the relation of sleep duration with cognition. Yet, mutual adjustment of sleep duration and consolidation did not attenuate the relation.

Lower cognitive performance following short or fragmented sleep in children has been previously reported (Beebe, 2011; Carskadon, 2011). Support for this association also comes from nonrespiratory sleep disorders research, although the pathology behind remains a puzzle (reviewed in Blunden & Beebe, 2006). In our study, we found no differences in cognitive performance between the short sleepers and the reference group, possibly owing to lack of power. However, in a semi-experimental study, Sadeh, Gruber, & Raviv (2003) showed that sleep restriction of only half an hour already affects daytime performance in children. Children of 1–3 years who awake during the night lose on average 1.5 hr of sleep (Touchette et al., 2013).

The inverted-U-shaped association between sleep and cognitive outcomes might represent a measure of general well-being of the child, affecting both sleep and cognitive development (Nixon et al., 2008). It was previously shown in children (Chaput et al., 2011; Spruyt, Molfese, & Gozal, 2011) and adults (Leng et al., 2015; van den Berg et al., 2008) that sleep duration at both extremes is associated with negative health-related outcomes. This means either sleeping less or more than the average affects children's cognitive development, possibly accounted for by impact on health or well-being. However, adjusting for mother reported health status did not explain the observed associations. Likewise, respiratory complaints might be a plausible explanation; however, childhood wheezing patterns also did not attenuate the association.

In terms of absolute difference in cognitive scores, effect estimates are modest. Children who awoke frequently or slept longer than current recommendations scored 2.4 points (15% of a SD) and 1.8 points lower (10% of a SD) on the IQ scale, respectively. Although a difference of this size might not be clinically relevant for a single child, on a population level, small effects often reflect large differences. Small changes on the natural log scale of language comprehension can be interpreted as percentage changes (Nau, 2014); thus, compared with the reference group, children who slept >14 hr per day scored on average 2% lower on the language test.

The main advantage of our study is the prospective design, which captures the long-term consequences of early childhood sleep disturbance on cognitive outcomes. Moreover, the study is population-based, and we were able to account for various confounding variables, including child cognitive development at baseline. Furthermore, we expect that by including the cognitive ability of the mother into our models, we corrected for a part of the heritability of cognitive traits. Another major strength of this study is the large sample of toddlers, an age-group for which paucity of sleep data has been pointed out (Galland et al., 2012). Finally, age-appropriate and validated batteries were used to obtain information on child cognition.

Our study also has several limitations. Because cognitive development and sleep practices are greatly influenced by the cultural context in which they occur, we restricted our sample to children of Dutch national origin; thus, our findings cannot be generalized to other ethnic groups. The nonresponse analysis indicated that children with behavioral problems at 18 months are less likely to participate at follow-up. Non-respondent mothers were younger, less educated, and were more likely to have continued smoking during pregnancy compared with those included in the analyses. A methodological limitation is that the measures used and the longitudinal timeframe were not designed specifically for this study. Repeated measures of sleep are needed to thoroughly understand the longitudinal relation between sleep and cognition. Although maternal reports give a fairly clear picture of toddlers' habitual sleep (Carskadon, 2011), this may have reduced the precision of our sleep estimates. Future studies should measure sleep objectively (e.g., actigraphy, a relatively cheap method suitable for large samples).

To conclude, sleep duration and nighttime awakenings in toddlerhood were associated with cognitive outcomes at age 6 after controlling for prior cognitive development, child, maternal, and demographic characteristics. Given the marked decline in sleep duration and awakenings in toddlerhood, developmental changes of sleep patterns might influence cognitive development. Rather than assuming that only short sleep has adverse effects on cognition, sleep duration at both extremes should be considered in future studies of cognitive development.

Supplementary Data

Supplementary data can be found at: http://www.jpepsy.oxfordjournals.org/.

Acknowledgments

The Generation R Study is conducted by the Erasmus Medical Center, Rotterdam in close collaboration with the School of Law and Faculty of Social Sciences of the Erasmus University Rotterdam, the Municipal Health Service, Rotterdam Homecare Foundation and Stichting Trombosedienst & Artsenlaboratorium Rijnmond. The authors acknowledge the contribution of participating mothers and their children, general practitioners, hospitals, midwives, and pharmacies.

Funding

The first phase of the Generation R Study was made possible by financial support from the Erasmus Medical Centre and

The Netherlands Organization for Health Research and Development (Zon MW Geestkracht Program 10.000.1003 and VIDI Grant 017.106.370 to HT). ERAWEB scholarship grant financed by the European Commission was granted to D.K. (grant agreement 2013-2548/001-001-EMA-2). O.H.F. works in ErasmusAGE, a center for aging research funded by Nestlé Nutrition (Nestec Ltd), Metagenics Inc, and AXA. Nestlé Nutrition, Metagenics Inc, and AXA had no role in design and conduct of the study; collection, analysis, and interpretation of the data; and preparation, review, or approval of manuscript.

Conflicts of interest: None declared.

References

Acebo, C., Sadeh, A., Seifer, R., Tzischinsky, O., Hafer, A., & Carskadon, M. A. (2005). Sleep/wake patterns derived from activity monitoring and maternal report for healthy 1- to 5-year-old children. *Sleep, 28*, 1568–1577.

Achenbach, T. M., & Rescorla, L. A. (2000). *Manual for ASEBA preschool forms and profiles*. Burlington: University of Vermont, Research Center for Children, Youth and Families.

Asher, M. I., Keil, U., Anderson, H. R., Beasley, R., Crane, J., Martinez, F., ... Williams, H. C. (1995). International study of asthma and allergies in childhood (isaac) - rationale and methods. *European Respiratory Journal, 8*, 483–491.

Auyeung, T. W., Lee, J. S., Leung, J., Kwok, T., Leung, P. C., Woo, J., & Wing, Y. K. (2013). Cognitive deficit is associated with phase advance of sleep-wake rhythm, daily napping, and prolonged sleep duration–a cross-sectional study in 2,947 community-dwelling older adults. *Age (Dordr), 35*, 479–486.

Beebe, D. W. (2011). Cognitive, behavioral, and functional consequences of inadequate sleep in children and adolescents. *Pediatric Clinic of North America, 58*, 649–665.

Blunden, S. L., & Beebe, D. W. (2006). The contribution of intermittent hypoxia, sleep debt and sleep disruption to daytime performance deficits in children: Consideration of respiratory and non-respiratory sleep disorders. *Sleep Medicine Reviews, 10*, 109–118.

Buchmann, A., Ringli, M., Kurth, S., Schaerer M., Geiger A., Jenni O.G., & Huber R. (2011). EEG sleep slow-wave activity as a mirror of cortical maturation. *Cerebral Cortex, 21*, 607–615.

Carskadon, M. A. (2011). Sleep's effects on cognition and learning in adolescence. *Human Sleep and Cognition, Pt Ii: Clinical and Applied Research, 190*, 137–143.

Chaput, J. P., Lambert, M., Gray-Donald, K., McGrath, J. J., Tremblay, M. S., O'Loughlin, J., & Tremblay, A. (2011). Short sleep duration is independently associated with overweight and obesity in Quebec children. *The Canadian Journal of Public Health, 102*, 369–374.

Dahl, R. E. (1996). The impact of inadequate sleep on children's daytime cognitive functioning. *Seminars in Pediatric Neurology, 3*, 44–50.

De Beurs, E. (2004). *Brief Symptom Inventory - Manual*. Leiden, The Netherlands: Pits Publishers.

Dionne, G., Touchette, E., Forget-Dubois, N., Petit, D., Tremblay, R. E., Montplaisir, J. Y., & Boivin, M. (2011). Associations between sleep-wake consolidation and language development in early childhood: A longitudinal twin study. *Sleep, 34*, 987–995.

Eide, E. R., & Showalter, M. H. (2012). Sleep and student achievement. *Eastern Economic Journal, 38*, 512–524.

Galland, B. C., Taylor, B. J., Elder, D. E., & Herbison, P. (2012). Normal sleep patterns in infants and children: A systematic review of observational studies. *Sleep Medicine Reviews, 16*, 213–222.

Geiger, A., Achermann, P., & Jenni, O. G. (2010). Association between sleep duration and intelligence scores in healthy children. *Developmental Psychology, 46*, 949–954.

Ghassabian, A., Rescorla, L., Henrichs, J., Jaddoe, V. W., Verhulst, F. C., & Tiemeier, H. (2014). Early lexical development and risk of verbal and nonverbal cognitive delay at school age. *Acta Paediatric, 103*, 70–80.

Haier, R. J., Sigel, B. V., Tang, C., Abel, L., & Buchsbaum, M. S. (1992). Intelligence and changes in regional cerebral glucose metabolic rate following learning. *Intelligence, 16*, 415–426.

Henrichs, J., Bongers-Schokking, J. J., Schenk, J. J., Ghassabian, A., Schmidt, H. G., Visser, T. J., ... Tiemeier, H. (2010). Maternal thyroid function during early pregnancy and cognitive functioning in early childhood: The generation R study. *The Journal of Clinical Endocrinology and Metabolism, 95*, 4227–4234.

Jaddoe, V. W., van Duijn, C. M., Franco, O. H., van der Heijden A. J., van Iizendoorn M. H., de Jongste J. C., ... Hofman, A. (2012). The generation R study: Design and cohort update 2012. *European Journal of Epidemiology, 27*, 739–756.

Jansen, P. W., Saridjan, N. S., Hofman, A., Jaddoe, V. W., Verhulst, F. C., & Tiemeier, H. (2011). Does disturbed sleeping precede symptoms of anxiety or depression in toddlers? The generation R study. *Psychosomatic Medicine, 73*, 242–249.

Leng, Y., Cappuccio, F. P., Wainwright, N. W., Surtees, P. G., Luben, R., Brayne, C., & Khaw, K. T. (2015). Sleep duration and risk of fatal and nonfatal stroke: A prospective study and meta-analysis. *Neurology, 84*, 1072–1079.

Luijk, M. P., Mileva-Seitz, V. R., Jansen, P. W., van Ijzendoorn, M. H., Jaddoe, V. W., Raat, H., ... Tiemeier, H. (2013). Ethnic differences in prevalence and determinants of mother-child bed-sharing in early childhood. *Sleep Medicine, 14*, 1092–1099.

Luijk, M. P., Sonnenschein-van der Voort, A. M., Mileva-Seitz, V. R., Jansen, P. W., Verhulst, F. C., Hofman, A., ... Tiemeier, H. (2015). Is parent-child bed-sharing a risk for wheezing and asthma in early childhood? *European Respiratory Journal, 45*(3), 661–669.

National Sleep Foundation. (2015). Children and Sleep. Retrieved December 28, 2015, from http://www.sleepfoundation.org

Nau, R. (2014). Statistical forecasting: notes on regression and time series analysis. Retrieved December 28, 2015, from http://people.duke.edu/~rnau/411log.htm

Netherlands Statistics. (2006). Begrippen. Allochten.

Nixon, G. M., Thompson, J. M., Han, D. Y., Becroft, D. M., Clark, P. M., Robinson, E., ... Mitchell, E. A. (2008).

Short sleep duration in middle childhood: Risk factors and consequences. *Sleep, 31*, 71–78.

O'Brien, L. M. (2009). The neurocognitive effects of sleep disruption in children and adolescents. *Child and Adolescent Psychiatric Clinics of North America, 18*, 813–823.

Prieler, J. (2003). *Raven's Advanced Progressive Matrices* (Vol. 24). Mödling, Austria: Schufried.

Sadeh, A. (2007). Consequences of sleep loss or sleep disruption in children. *Sleep Medicine Clinics, 2*, 513–520.

Sadeh, A., Gruber, R., & Raviv, A. (2003). The effects of sleep restriction and extension on school-age children: What a difference an hour makes. *Child Development, 74*, 444–455.

Sadeh, A., Mindell, J. A., Luedtke, K., & Wiegand B. (2009). Sleep and sleep ecology in the first 3 years: A web-based study. *Journal of Sleep Research, 18*, 60–73.

Shaw, P., Greenstein, D., Lerch, J., Clasen, L., Lenroot, R., Gogtay, N., ... Giedd J. (2006). Intellectual ability and cortical development in children and adolescents. *Nature, 440*, 676–679.

Spruyt, K., Molfese, D. L., & Gozal, D. (2011). Sleep duration, sleep regularity, body weight, and metabolic homeostasis in school-aged children. *Pediatrics, 127*, e345–e352.

Sterne, J. A., White, I. R., Carlin, J. B., Spratt, M., Royston, P., Kenward, M. G., ... Carpenter, J. R. (2009). Multiple imputation for missing data in epidemiological and clinical research: Potential and pitfalls. *BMJ, 338*, b2393.

Tellegen, P. J., Winkel, M., Wijnberg-Williams, B., & Laros, J. A. (2005). *Snijders-Oomen Niet-verbale intelligentietest: SON-R 2 1/2 -7*. Amsterdam: Boom Testuitgevers.

Touchette, E., Dionne, G., Forget-Dubois, N., Petit, D., Perusse, D., Falissard, B., ... Montplaisir, J. Y. (2013). Genetic and environmental influences on daytime and nighttime sleep duration in early childhood. *Pediatrics, 131*, e1874–e1880.

Touchette, E., Petit, D., Séguin, J. R., Boivin M., Tremblay R.E., & Montplaisir J.Y. (2007). Associations between sleep duration patterns and behavioral/cognitive functioning at school entry. *Sleep: Journal of Sleep and Sleep Disorders Research, 30*, 1213–1219.

van Bon, W. H. J. (1982). *TvK (Taaltest voor Kinderen)*. Lisse: Swets & Zeitlinger.

van den Berg, J. F., Knvistingh Neven, A., Tulen, J. H., Hofman, A., Witteman, J. C., Miedema, H. M., & Tiemeier, H. (2008). Actigraphic sleep duration and fragmentation are related to obesity in the elderly: The Rotterdam study. *International Journal of Obesity (London), 32*, 1083–1090.

Xu, L., Jiang, C. Q., Lam, T. H., Liu, B., Jin, Y. L., Zhu, T., ... Thomas, G. N. (2011). Short or long sleep duration is associated with memory impairment in older Chinese: The Guangzhou Biobank Cohort study. *Sleep, 34*, 575–580.

Commentary: Longitudinal Observational Research Informs Child Health Research

Robert D. Annett, PhD

University of Mississippi Medical Center, Children's of Mississippi

All correspondence concerning this article should be addressed to Robert D Annett, PhD, Department of Pediatrics, University of Mississippi Medical Center, 2500 North State Street, Jackson, MS 39216-4505, USA. E-mail: rannett@umc.edu

Received January 22, 2016; revisions received January 25, 2016; accepted January 26, 2016

Pediatric health outcomes research is informed by two fundamental research methodologies: randomized trials and observational research. Both inform researchers and families on treatment effects and vary with respect to how outcomes bias is controlled. Evidence-based interventions have routinely been included with the *Journal of Pediatric Psychology*, with two particularly notable journal issues devoted to presenting state-of-the-science evidence-based intervention research (24(2–4), 2009 and 39(8) 2012). Within the frame of evidence-based interventions, longitudinal observational research conducted with large cohorts is intimately linked to randomized trials and serves to inform randomized trials in several important ways. This brief commentary is provided to highlight the added value that longitudinal observational research provides to pediatric health research clinical trials.

Observational research has been broadly construed within a pyramid of scientific evidence as falling below meta-analyses of randomized trials and above unsystematic clinical expert opinion (Guyatt, Rennie, Meade, & Cook, 2008). Observational studies come in several forms, including case control studies, cross sectional studies, and cohort studies. Each of these methodological approaches provides scientific insights meant to inform subsequent research and yet is limited by the absence of randomization. Perhaps most important for the current discussion is the lack of control over the independent variables of interest to the investigator. However, an often overlooked advantage is that there is minimal risk to participants and, conversely, when compared with randomized trials, they offer little in the form of direct care benefit to participants. Despite these challenges, the significance of the contributions of longitudinal observational research to advancing our science is important to understand.

Longitudinal Observational Research Informs Outcomes Effectiveness Research

There are several ways in which observational research of pediatric cohorts informs outcomes effectiveness randomized trials. The *Journal of Pediatric Psychology* has provided numerous examples of longitudinal observational research that provide rich examples for this process. Perhaps the most important manner in which observational research guides clinical trial research is that observational studies provide a real-world understanding of practices and outcomes that occur for children. For example, understanding of early violence exposure subsequently impacts school-aged behavioral outcomes was enhanced by the study of Biggs-Gowan and colleagues (Briggs-Gowan, Carter, & Ford, 2012). In this study, both direct and mediated effects of early violence exposure in the home and community were demonstrated. These findings inform public health and inform subsequent intervention trials for at-risk school-aged children by clarifying risks conveyed by socioeconomic status and violence exposure.

Second, longitudinal observational research helps to isolate signals within a population that can become the target for a clinical trial. This is perhaps nowhere more obvious than in genome-wide association studies, a topic that has recently been addressed in the journal (McBride & Guttmacher, 2009). Another practical example includes, for example, a study of the gradation of child abuse experiences on health outcomes where there would be no feasible way to manipulate the exposure to determine net health effects.

A study by Clark and colleagues guides future hypotheses regarding these linkages (Clark, Thatcher, & Martin, 2010). Using adolescents recruited for the Pittsburgh Adolescent Alcohol Research Center prospective study, participants were characterized into trauma classes that were then examined at two future time points to determine the impact on both biomedical markers and psychological symptoms. In this study, classification of the continuum of trauma experiences increases the precision for group inclusion criteria for subsequent intervention research and provides a focus for salient outcomes.

In a similar fashion, longitudinal observational studies generate hypotheses for outcomes/intervention studies where little evidence exists. A study of children being admitted to a children's hospital setting informs us on how the nature of the admission (trauma vs. nontrauma-based admission) impacted traumatic stress symptoms (Murray, Kenardy, & Spence, 2008). These findings point out that accidental trauma admission increases risk for child PTSD symptoms and further raises several treatment-related hypotheses regarding intervention for acute versus more enduring child stress symptoms. These observations then raise potential hypotheses for an intervention study that can focus on the timing, duration, and intensity for a hospital-based stress symptom prevention or reduction study.

A final important contribution of longitudinal observational studies of child health is that they allow for systematic sampling of child health outcomes over the course of development. As pediatric researchers, we are typically interested in change over the course of a child's development as well as changes that can occur with the natural course of an illness. Psychological change in response to natural history of pediatric health and disease has been occurring through a number of large pediatric cohort studies, including those in Europe that have psychological components (e.g., Generation R Study, Growing Up in Ireland, to name two) and to a lesser extent in birth cohort studies in Africa (Campbell & Rudan, 2011) and Asia (e.g., Japan Environment and Children's Study; Kawamoto et al., 2014). Study outcomes of interest include a range of scientific concerns ranging from the impact of fetal exposures on subsequent child health and behavior to the effect of child rearing practices on cognitive function. While we often focus on identification of risks for illness and the consequences of illness, opportunities to examine the predictors of child health is often neglected in the literature. Within the *Journal of Pediatric Psychology*, there are several longitudinal studies that have reported on common developmental changes, including changes in sleep problems and fatigue (Luntamo, Sourander, Santalahti, Aromaa, & Helenius, 2012) as well as the evolution of psychological symptoms in children with diabetes (Rohan et al., 2015).

Conclusion

This brief commentary seeks to emphasize the rich research opportunities provided by longitudinal observational research. Pediatric health outcomes are informed by synergy between these approaches in several specific ways identified herein. Important to keep in mind, however, is that these alternative approaches can provide conflicting evidence. The potential for conflicting evidence can largely be controlled when a researcher examines the potential biases, confounders, and patterns of missingness in each method of scientific investigation. Yet, with current statistical methods, there are additional opportunities for controlling bias and thus discovering the multiple facets that contribute to disease outcomes as well as children's health. Longitudinal observational research contributions to the *Journal of Pediatric Psychology* provide the readership with thought-provoking information that is expected to stimulate conversations on many levels and provide a valuable guide for our research activities.

Conflicts of interest: None declared.

References

Briggs-Gowan, M. J., Carter, A. S., & Ford, J. D. (2012). Parsing the effects violence exposure in early childhood: Modeling developmental pathways. *Journal of Pediatric Psychology, 37*, 11–22. doi:10.1093/jpepsy/jsr063

Campbell, A., & Rudan, I. (2011). Systematic review of birth cohort studies in Africa. *Journal of Global Health, 1*, 46–58. Retrieved from http://www.ncbi.nlm.nih.gov/pubmed/23198102

Clark, D. B., Thatcher, D. L., & Martin, C. S. (2010). Child abuse and other traumatic experiences, alcohol use disorders, and health problems in adolescence and young adulthood. *Journal of Pediatric Psychology, 35*, 499–510. doi:10.1093/jpepsy/jsp117

Guyatt, G., Rennie, D., Meade, M. O., & Cook, D. J. (2008). *User's Guides to the Medical Literature: Essentials for Evidence-Based Practice* (2nd ed.). New York, NY: McGraw-Hill.

Kawamoto, T., Nitta, H., Murata, K., Toda, E., Tsukamoto, N., Hasegawa, M., ... Working Group of the Epidemiological Research for Children's Environmental, Health. (2014). Rationale and study design of the Japan environment and children's study (JECS). *BMC Public Health, 14*, 25. doi:10.1186/1471-2458-14-25

Luntamo, T., Sourander, A., Santalahti, P., Aromaa, M., & Helenius, H. (2012). Prevalence changes of pain, sleep problems and fatigue among 8-year-old children: Years 1989, 1999, and 2005. *Journal of Pediatric Psychology, 37*, 307–318. doi:10.1093/jpepsy/jsr091

McBride, C. M., & Guttmacher, A. E. (2009). Commentary: Trailblazing a research agenda at the interface of pediatrics and genomic discovery–a commentary on the psychological aspects of genomics and child health. *Journal of Pediatric Psychology, 34*, 662–664. doi:10.1093/jpepsy/jsn125

Murray, B. L., Kenardy, J. A., & Spence, S. H. (2008). Brief report: Children's responses to trauma- and non-trauma-related hospital admission: A comparison study. *Journal of Pediatric Psychology, 33*, 435–440. doi:10.1093/jpepsy/jsm078

Rohan, J. M., Huang, B., Pendley, J. S., Delamater, A., Dolan, L., Reeves, G., & Drotar, D. (2015). Predicting health resilience in pediatric Type 1 diabetes: A test of the resilience model framework. *Journal of Pediatric Psychology, 40*, 956–967. doi:10.1093/jpepsy/jsv061

Peer Victimization in Adolescents With Severe Obesity: The Roles of Self-Worth and Social Support in Associations With Psychosocial Adjustment

Jennifer Reiter-Purtill,[1] PhD, Marissa A. Gowey,[2] PhD, Heather Austin,[2] PhD, Kevin C. Smith,[3] PhD, Dana L. Rofey,[4] PhD, Todd M. Jenkins,[1] PhD, MPH, Beth H. Garland,[5] PhD, and Meg H. Zeller,[1] PhD, for the TeenView Study Group and in cooperation with Teen-LABS Consortium

[1]Cincinnati Children's Hospital Medical Center, Cincinnati, OH, USA, [2]University of Alabama at Birmingham, Birmingham, AL, USA, [3]Children's Mercy Kansas City, Kansas City, MO, USA, [4]University of Pittsburgh Medical Center, Pittsburgh, PA, USA, and [5]Baylor College of Medicine, Houston, TX, USA

All correspondence concerning this article should be addressed to Jennifer Reiter-Purtill, PhD, Division of Behavioral Medicine and Clinical Psychology, Cincinnati Children's Hospital Medical Center, 3333 Burnet Avenue, MLC3015, Cincinnati, OH 45229, USA. E-mail: jennifer.reiter-purtill@cchmc.org

Received December 21, 2015; revisions received July 19, 2016; accepted August 23, 2016

Abstract

Objective To examine the associations of peer victimization with internalizing symptoms, externalizing symptoms, social competence, and academic performance in a clinical sample of adolescents with severe obesity, and whether self-worth and social support affect these associations. **Methods** Multisite cross-sectional data from 139 adolescents before weight loss surgery (M_{age} = 16.9; 79.9% female, 66.2% White; $M_{Body\ Mass\ Index\ [BMI]}$ = 51.5 kg/m^2) and 83 nonsurgical comparisons (M_{age} = 16.1; 81.9% female, 54.2% White; M_{BMI} = 46.9 kg/m^2) were collected using self-reports with standardized measures. **Results** As a group, participants did not report high levels of victimization. Self-worth mediated the effects of victimization on a majority of measures of adjustment, and further analyses provided evidence of the buffering effect of social support for some mediational models. **Conclusions** Self-worth and social support are important targets for prevention and intervention for both victimization and poor adjustment in adolescent severe obesity.

Key words: adolescents; bariatric; severe obesity; surgery; victimization.

Introduction

A recent study of public perceptions of weight bias using a multinational sample suggested that adults believed weight was the most common reason for bullying and teasing among youth (Puhl et al., 2016). Peer victimization is highly prevalent among youth who are overweight/obese (Haines, Neumark-Sztainer, Hannan, van den Berg, & Eisenberg, 2008; Janssen, Craig, Boyce, & Pickett, 2004), with some studies suggesting that risk increases with body mass index (BMI; Puhl, Peterson, & Luedicke, 2013). Peer victimization has been associated with internalizing and externalizing symptoms, poor self-concept, loneliness, and academic difficulties, both in the developmental literature (Copeland, Wolke, Angold, & Costello, 2013; Hawker & Boulton, 2000; Nakamoto & Schwartz, 2010; Prinstein, Boergers, & Vernberg, 2001) and in community and clinic-based studies of youth with overweight/obesity (Adams & Bukowski, 2008; Gray, Kahhan & Janicke, 2009; Gunnarsdottir, Njardvik, Olafsdottir, Craighead, &

Bjarnason, 2012; Neumark-Sztainer et al., 2002; Puhl & Latner, 2007). These findings, coupled with evidence of a significant increase in levels of pediatric severe obesity (i.e., BMI $\geq$ 120% of the BMI-for-age 95th percentile) among youth in the United States (Skinner & Skelton, 2014), are concerning. Despite being a high-need population, the literature on the psychosocial comorbidities of adolescent severe obesity is in its infancy. Early evidence suggests that this group (BMI $\geq$ 99th percentile) may indeed present worse psychosocially than the obese counterpart (BMI = 95th to 98th percentile) (Phillips et al., 2012). However, there is also evidence of subgroups of youth with severe obesity reporting minimal psychopathology (Sysko, Zakarin, Devlin, Bush, & Walsh, 2011), including internalizing and externalizing symptoms (Rofey et al., 2015). Understanding this variability and identifying risk factors (e.g., victimization), as well as careful exploration of the mechanistic underpinnings and/or protective factors for adjustment, is imperative to intervention efforts.

Few studies have examined victimization specifically among adolescents with severe obesity. Preliminary evidence suggests that adolescents in residential treatment for severe obesity who report victimization and/or cyberbullying experienced greater psychological distress and more barriers to healthy lifestyle changes (DeSmet et al., 2014). Furthermore, limited research has examined potential mediators or moderators of the association of victimization with internalizing and externalizing symptoms and problems with social competence and academic performance among samples of youth who are overweight/obese. In the developmental literature, self-worth has been primarily identified as a mediator of peer victimization and difficulties, such as internalizing symptoms (Grills & Ollendick, 2002). Social information processing theory would posit that negative peer interactions such as experiences of victimization would lead some youth to develop negative self-perceptions (Crick & Dodge, 1994). These negative self-perceptions would in turn result in difficulties, particularly internalizing symptoms (e.g., anxiety; Grills & Ollendick, 2002) or less competent social behavior (i.e., withdrawn behavior, see Crick & Dodge, 1994). In contrast, the role of social support has been as a moderator, whereby social support provides protection against the damaging effects of life stressors (e.g., Moos, 2002). In particular, friendships (i.e., peer social support) have been found to provide a buffer against the effects of victimization, including the increase of internalizing and externalizing symptoms over time (Hodges, Boivin, Vitaro, & Bukowski, 1999). In the pediatric obesity literature, Adams and Bukowski (2008) found self-perceptions of appearance significantly mediated the association of victimization and depressive symptoms for a community sample of obese adolescent girls. Lim and colleagues (2011) demonstrated that peer social support appeared to moderate the associations of victimization and depressive symptoms for a clinical sample of obese girls, but not boys.

Victimization has been characterized as either direct such as overt victimization (i.e., physical aggression) or indirect such as relational victimization (i.e., social exclusion) and reputational victimization (i.e., damaging a person's social reputation), and these types have been suggested to have different implications for understanding the victim (see Garandeau & Cillessen, 2006, Prinstein et al., 2001). No studies were identified that specifically examined the associations of these types of peer victimization (i.e., overt, relational, or reputational) on a diverse set of clinically important outcomes such as internalizing symptoms, externalizing symptoms, social competence (i.e., one's perception of their own social behavior and acceptance), and academic performance for a sample of treatment-seeking adolescents with severe obesity, nor what factors might mediate or moderate those associations.

The current study used cross-sectional multisite data from a larger study (see Rofey et al., 2015; Zeller et al., 2015) of treatment-seeking adolescents with severe obesity and their caregivers, including 139 adolescents before undergoing weight loss surgery (WLS) and 83 adolescents who presented for behavioral weight loss treatment (nonsurgical comparisons, NSComps). The aim of the current study was to examine the associations of different types of adolescent victimization with internalizing symptoms, externalizing symptoms, social competence, and academic performance, and whether self-worth and social support affected these associations. Given that all participants were severely obese and treatment seeking, no between-group differences (i.e., WLS and NSComps) were expected, but were examined. Based on extant literature, we hypothesized that adolescent perceptions of greater victimization would be associated with greater internalizing symptoms, greater externalizing symptoms, lower social competence, and lower academic performance. We further tested separate models of mediation in which we expected that greater victimization (overt, relational, or reputational) would be associated with lower self-worth, which in turn would be associated with poorer adjustment (i.e., greater internalizing symptoms, greater externalizing symptoms, lower social competence, and lower academic performance; see Figure 1). Finally, we tested whether these individual mediational models were moderated by social support. Specifically, we expected that social support would moderate the pathways from victimization to poor self-worth as well as to measures of poor adjustment, such that in the presence

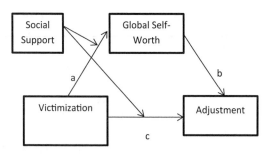

Figure 1 Conceptual model.

Note: "Victimization" could either be overt, relational, or reputational. "Adjustment" could be internalizing symptoms, externalizing symptoms, social competence, or academic performance. Pathways: a = (victimization type → global self-worth); Pathway b = (global self-worth → adjustment, with victimization type in the model), and Pathway c = (victimization type → adjustment with global self-worth in the model).

of greater perceived social support, the strength of the direct effects (i.e., from victimization to adjustment) and indirect effects (i.e., through self-worth) would be reduced to nonsignificance.

Methods

The present study used presurgical/baseline data from the TeenView study, which examines the psychosocial health of adolescents with severe obesity undergoing WLS. TeenView is an ancillary to the Teen Longitudinal Assessment of Bariatric Surgery consortium (Teen-LABS; NCT00474318), a prospective observational cohort study executed at five academic tertiary care centers in the United States to document the safety and efficacy of WLS in 242 adolescent patients (enrollment 2007–2011; Inge et al., 2007; Michalsky et al., 2014). Consecutive patients at each care center who were undergoing WLS were approached for Teen-LABS study participation. TeenView recruited two cohorts (enrollment 2008–2011): (1) Teen-LABS participants ("WLS"), and (2) demographically similar comparison adolescents with severe obesity in nonsurgical behavioral weight loss programs at the same five academic medical centers. TeenView was not designed as a comparative intervention trial (i.e., WLS vs. behavioral weight loss), but to examine psychosocial benefits and risks associated with adolescent WLS relative to a more "natural course" for adolescent severe obesity. The institutional review board at each institution approved study protocols.

Participants and Procedures

TeenView participants and procedures have been reported on previously (see Rofey et al., 2015; Zeller et. al., 2015) but are summarized below. Baseline/preoperative data from 222 TeenView adolescents and a caregiver were used. Eligibility criteria required that the Teen-LABS adolescent: (1) had a BMI $\geq 40 \text{ kg/m}^2$; (2) was 13–18 years of age; (3) was not receiving full-time special education services owing to the high reading demand; (4) had a caregiver willing to participate; and (5) was able to speak/read English. Eligible participants were approached about TeenView participation during a presurgical clinic visit at each care center. Of the 159 eligible WLS participants, 14 declined and 4 (consented) were unable to participate before surgery, leaving 141 participating adolescents (recruitment: 88.7%). For sibling pairs ($n = 2$), the older sibling was excluded from analyses. In addition, one caregiver consented but did not complete forms before surgery, resulting in a final WLS cohort of 139 adolescents and 138 caregivers, who completed baseline data collection within 30 days before surgery.

NSComps were recruited from TeenView research registries that identified study eligible youth presenting at lifestyle modification programs at each care center and whose families agreed to be contacted for study enrollment should the adolescent become a demographic match (i.e., gender, race, ±6 months in age) to a WLS participant at any site. Once a family was identified as a potential match, they were contacted via phone and asked to participate in the study. During enrollment, 86 eligible NSComps were approached, of whom 3 declined, resulting in a final sample of 83 adolescents/caregivers (recruitment: 96.5%).

Assessments were completed at in-person clinic visits by study trained personnel. Adolescents and caregivers independently completed paper/pencil measures. Adolescent and caregiver heights and weights were measured by certified research staff, using digital scales and stadiometers provided at each care center. Participants were weighed and measured in street clothing without shoes, with weight and height measurements taken in triplicate.

Measures
Revised Peer Experiences Questionnaire
Victimization was assessed using the 18-item victim version of the Revised Peer Experiences Questionnaire (Prinstein et al., 2001), a self-report measure of overt (three items, e.g., "a teen hit, kicked, or pushed me in a mean way"), relational (three items, e.g., "a teen left me out of what they were doing"), and reputational (three items, e.g., "another teen gossiped about me so others would not like me") victimization. Adolescents rated each item regarding past year frequency of occurrence (1 = *never* to 5 = *a few times a week*), with scales computed as the average across items. This measure has acceptable psychometrics (Prinstein et al., 2001; De Los Reyes & Prinstein, 2004) with internal consistencies for the current sample ranging from $\alpha = 0.65$ to $\alpha = 0.84$.

Youth Self-Report
Adolescent-reported internalizing and externalizing symptoms in the past 6 months were obtained via two

broadband scales of the Youth Self-Report (YSR; Achenbach & Rescorla, 2001). The Social Competence (e.g., participation in organizations and groups, number and contact with friends, and behavior with others) and the Academic Performance scales (mean performance in academic subjects from *failing* [0] to *above average* [3]) were also used. The strong psychometric properties of the YSR are well-established (Achenbach & Rescorla, 2001; Song, Singh, & Singer, 1994), and it has been used extensively with youth with chronic medical conditions (Pinquart & Shen, 2011).

Self-Perception Profile for Adolescents
The Self-Perception Profile for Adolescents is 45-item self-report measure assessing adolescent self-perceptions of competence in specific domains as well as a global perception of self-worth (Harter, 2012). Each item is rated from 1 (*low perceived competence*) to 4 (*high perceived competence*), with domains scored as the average across items. The global self-worth scale was used (five items), which serves as a general assessment of how happy adolescents are with themselves or their lives. This measure has demonstrated good validity (Harter, 2012), as well as good internal consistency ($\alpha = 0.80$) for global self-worth for the current sample.

Children's Social Support Questionnaire
The Children's Social Support Questionnaire measured adolescent perception of the size and quality of their social support network (Bogat, Chin, Sabbath, & Schwartz, 1985). Adolescents were asked to list people who were part of their "social network" and rate how happy they were with each relationship (1 = *very unhappy* to 5 = *very happy*). Network size was obtained by summing all individuals listed, and the average of their happiness rating across all individuals was computed. If no individuals were listed, a "0" was entered for happiness with social support. This measure has acceptable psychometrics (Bogat et al., 1985).

Other Measures
Caregivers completed a demographic questionnaire to assess caregiver gender, age, level of education, and family composition. Adolescents were asked about current school enrollment. Mean height and weight were used to calculate BMI (kg/m^2).

Analyses
Missing data ranged from 0.5% to 2.7% for all variables and were handled via maximum likelihood estimation in Mplus (Version 7.3). The nesting of participants within the five data collection sites was controlled in hypothesized analyses via specialized variable and analysis commands in Mplus to avoid possible Type-1 errors. Preliminary analyses using two-tailed independent t tests or Chi-square tests for demographic factors and BMI as well as analyses of covariance (ANCOVA) for variables of interest compared groups (WLS vs. NSComps). Demographic variables for which significant differences were found were controlled in group comparison analyses. To test proposed models of mediation, separate path analyses were completed with the significance of each indirect effect (i.e., the effect of victimization [overt, relational, or reputational] on adjustment [internalizing, externalizing, social competence, or academic performance] through global self-worth) evaluated using the "Indirect" command in Mplus with bootstrapped confidence intervals (CI). Bootstrapping with 5,000 resamples was used to create CI, as this strategy provides a nonparametric approach that can be effectively used with small samples. Tests of whether these individual models of mediation were moderated (i.e., moderated mediation) by social support (i.e., adolescent perception of happiness with social support) were also completed in Mplus using path analysis and "Model Constraint" commands as suggested in the Mplus user's guide (Muthen & Muthen, 1998–2012). For each model, CI for the conditional indirect effects (i.e., at +1 SD or −1 SD of the moderator) were also generated with a bootstrapping procedure.

Results

Descriptives
Adolescents were primarily female, White, and living in two-caregiver homes (Table I). WLS participants were significantly older and had a higher mean BMI relative to NSComps. No other significant demographic differences were identified. Table II presents descriptive information for all variables of interest for the total sample and by group. The means for relational and reputational victimization were similar to those found for a sample of high school students, although slightly lower for overt victimization (De Los Reyes & Prinstein, 2004). Of those participants who had not yet graduated high school, the majority attended school with their peers (i.e., not home schooled/early leaving), with mean social competence T scores indicating good adjustment. A number of significant group (WLS vs. NSComp) differences were identified using ANCOVA after controlling for adolescent age and BMI. NSComps reported greater experiences of relational victimization and lower academic performance relative to the WLS group. Groups were similar for measures of global self-worth and social support. Finally, although not included in Table II, group differences have been reported previously for internalizing symptoms and externalizing symptoms, which are dependent variables in the current study's

Table I. Demographic Characteristics of WLS Adolescents and NSComp Adolescents and their Families

Demographics	Total (N = 222) Mean ± SD%	WLS (n = 139) Mean ± SD%	NSComp (n = 83) Mean ± SD%	p[a]
Adolescent				
BMI	49.77 ± 7.89	51.52 ± 8.32	46.85 ± 6.12	<.001
Age	16.59 ± 1.44	16.86 ± 1.39	16.11 ± 1.40	<.001
% Female	80.6%	79.9%	81.9%	.71
% White[b]	61.7%	66.2%	54.2%	.08
Caregiver[c]				
BMI	38.05 ± 9.63	37.84 ± 9.35	38.35 ± 10.08	.71
Age	44.27 ± 7.50	44.47 ± 6.41	43.93 ± 9.05	.63
% Female	93.6%	93.4%	94.0%	.86
Education				.18
% ≤ High School Graduation	42.5%	39.0%	48.2%	
% 1+ years after secondary	57.5%	61.0%	51.8%	
Family				
% Single caregiver home	33.3%	31.6%	36.1%	.49

Note: BMI = Body mass index; NSComp = nonsurgical comparison; WLS = weight loss surgery.
[a]p-values are based on two-tailed independent t tests when examining mean values and on Chi-square tests when examining percentages.
[b]The remaining self-identified as Black (26.1%), more than one race (5.4%), or Hispanic (6.8%).
[c]Demographic information was available for 136 WLS caregivers, with the exception of caregiver BMI, which was available for 123 caregivers. Demographic information was available for all 83 comparison caregivers.

Table II. Mean Levels of Adolescent Victimization, Level of Social Disengagement and Competence, Academic Performance, Self-Perceptions and Social Support for WLS Adolescents and NSComp Adolescents

Adolescent Self Report	Total Mean ± SD n (%)	WLS (n = 137–139) Mean ± SD n (%)	NSComp (n = 82–83) Mean ± SD n (%)	p[a]	Cohen's d[b]	Range of scores Total N
General victimization (RPEQ)						
Overt victimization	1.19 ± 0.39	1.15 ± 0.35	1.25 ± 0.44	.45	0.26	1–3, N = 221
Relational victimization	1.97 ± 0.90	1.87 ± 0.85	2.13 ± 0.95	.03	0.29	1–5, N = 222
Reputational victimization	1.72 ± 0.89	1.62 ± 0.83	1.90 ± 0.98	.17	0.32	1–5, N = 221
Social competence/academic						
% Home schooled/not in school[c]	23 (10.8%)	15 (11.5%)	8 (9.8%)	.98	0.99	
% In school with peers	190 (89.2%)	116 (88.5%)	74 (90.2%)			
Social competence (YSR)[d]	45.56 ± 10.63	45.96 ± 10.59	44.88 ± 10.73	.08	0.10	22–65, N = 218
Academic performance (YSR)[d]	2.20 ± 0.54	2.25 ± 0.52	2.13 ± 0.56	.01	0.21	0.50–3.00, N = 205
Self-Perceptions (SPPA)						
Global Self-Worth	2.76 ± 0.72	2.84 ± 0.70	2.64 ± 0.75	.48	0.28	1–4, N = 220
Social Support (CSSQ)						
Total Network Size	8.05 ± 4.04	8.33 ± 3.98	7.58 ± 4.11	.08	0.19	0–17, N = 222
Total Happiness	4.25 ± 0.86	4.33 ± 0.87	4.14 ± 0.84	.18	0.22	0–5, N = 222

Note: CSSQ = Child Social Support Questionnaire; NSComp = nonsurgical comparison; RPEQ = Revised Peer Experiences Scale; SPPA = Self-Perception Profile for Adolescents; WLS = weight loss surgery; YSR = Youth Self Report.
[a]For mean levels, p-values were based on analyses of covariance. For prevalence estimates, p-values were based on logistic regressions. Adolescent age and BMI were used as covariates in both sets of analyses.
[b]Effect sizes are reported as Cohen's d, and are defined at small = 0.20, medium = 0.50, and large = 0.80.
[c]For the analyses comparing those participants home schooled/not in regular school versus those in school, participants who graduated high school (7 WLS, 1 NSComp) were excluded. One WLS participant was missing data for this question. The effect size for this variable is given as an odds ratio.
[d]For the YSR, means and SDs are provided as T scores for Social Competence in the table to aid in interpretation, but all analyses were completed using raw scores. T scores are not computed for academic performance. For academic performance, those participants who were not attending any school/educational training were excluded from analyses (n = 11), leaving 205 of 211.

analyses. Specifically, NSComps had significantly higher levels of self-reported internalizing symptoms and externalizing symptoms on the YSR (see Rofey et al., 2015).

Intercorrelations of Victimization With Adjustment and Social Support

Using Pearson correlations (Table III), associations were in the expected directions with greater victimization correlated with greater internalizing symptoms and externalizing symptoms as well as lower global self-worth. Few significant associations were identified with measures of social competence, academic performance, or social support.

Models of Mediation

Separate models of mediation tested whether the indirect effects of victimization (i.e., either overt, relational, or reputational) on various measures of self-reported adjustment (internalizing symptoms, externalizing symptoms, social competence, or academic performance) through global self-worth were significant (Figure 1). Given significant group (WLS vs. NSComp) differences noted above, group was controlled for in all models. Standardized beta estimates for pathways "a," "b," and "c" for these individual models as shown in Figure 1, as well as unstandardized beta estimates of all indirect effects with 95% CIs, are presented in Table IV.

For all models involving internalizing symptoms, indirect effects were significant, suggesting that greater victimization, regardless of type, was associated with lower global self-worth, which in turn was associated with greater internalizing symptoms. As indicated by the standardized betas for path c, the association for reputational victimization remained significant even with global self-worth in the model. In addition, R^2 values suggest that these models explain a substantial amount of variance. For externalizing symptoms, indirect effects for models involving overt victimization or relational victimization were significant. The indirect effect for reputational victimization was nonsignificant, although its association with externalizing symptoms (pathway c) remained significant even with global self-worth in the model. Finally, although zero-order correlations indicated few significant associations between types of victimization with social competence and academic performance (Table III), tests of mediation indicated that the majority of indirect effects through global self-worth were significant, with the only exception involving reputational mediation with academic performance. Little variance was explained by these models, particularly for academic performance.

Moderation by Social Support

For mediational models with significant indirect effects, moderation by adolescent perception of social support network happiness was tested. Moderation was tested for both direct effects (pathway "c" in Figure 1: interaction of social support and victimization type → adjustment) and indirect effects (pathway "a": effect of social support and victimization type through global self-worth) at low (−1 SD) and high (+1 SD) values of the moderator.

Results suggested that several mediational models were significantly moderated by social support. In these cases, the independent variable was relational victimization, with no significant moderation for models including overt or reputational victimization. In addition, significant moderation occurred only for the indirect paths but not for the direct paths. For relational victimization → global self-worth → internalizing, the indirect effect was nonsignificant at high levels of social support ($\beta = 0.63$; 95% CI = −0.30 to 0.99) but remained significant at low levels ($\beta = 1.12$; 95% CI = 0.56 to 1.81). For relational victimization → global self-worth → social competence, the indirect effect remained significant at low levels of social support ($\beta = -0.21$; 95% CI = −0.38 to −0.07), but at high levels, was nonsignificant ($\beta = -0.12$; 95% CI = −0.20 to 0.04). For all other mediation models tested for potential moderation, indirect effects

Table III. Intercorrelations of Measures of Victimization With Adolescent Adjustment, Self-Perceptions and Social Support for Severely Obese Adolescents (N = 218–221)

Adolescent Self Report	Overt victimization	Relational victimization	Reputational victimization
Psychopathology (YSR)			
Internalizing symptoms	.19*	.32**	.34**
Externalizing symptoms	.13	.22*	.31**
Social/academic competence[a]			
Social competence (YSR)	−.03	−.07	−.13
Academic performance (YSR)	−.05	.04	−.01
Home schooled/not in regular school	.19**	−.07	−.06
Self-perceptions (SPPA)			
Global self-worth	−.26*	−.30**	−.33**
Social support (CSSQ)			
Network size	.06	−.004	−.01
Happiness	−.04	−.13	−.21

Note: CSSQ = Children's Social Support Questionnaire; SPPA = Self-Perception Profile for Adolescents; YSR = Youth Self Report. To control for Type I error, the significance level was set at $p < .01$. $p < .01$; **$p < .001$.

[a]Sample size for social competence was from $n = 218$. For academic performance, those participants who were not attending any school/educational training were excluded from analyses ($n = 11$), leaving a sample size of $n = 205$.

Table IV. *Mediation Analyses Testing the Indirect Effects of Victimization Type (i.e., Overt, Relational, or Reputational) on Adjustment (i.e., Internalizing Symptoms, Externalizing Symptoms, Social Competence, or Academic Performance) Through Global Self-Worth for 222 Adolescents With Severe Obesity*

Mediational models	Standardized B			Indirect effect[a]	R^2
	A	b	c	(95% CI)	
1. Overt/internalizing	−.27***	−.50***	.05	3.09 (1.65 – 4.92)	0.27
2. Relational/internalizing	−.30***	−.45***	.17	1.36 (0.95 – 1.79)	0.30
3. Reputational/internalizing	−.33***	−.45***	.18**	1.48 (1.02 – 2.39)	0.30
4. Overt/externalizing	−.27**	−.18**	.06	0.87 (0.35 – 1.96)	0.09
5. Relational/externalizing	−.30***	−.14**	.15	0.32 (0.13 – 0.50)	0.11
6. Reputational/externalizing	−.33***	−.11*	.24*	0.28 (−0.06 – 0.85)	0.14
7. Overt/social competence	−.26**	.33***	.06	−0.59 (−1.21 – −0.26)	0.11
8. Relational/social competence	−.30***	.33***	.03	−0.30 (−0.41 – −0.22)	0.11
9. Reputational/social competence	−.33***	.31***	−.03	−0.30 (−0.56 – −0.22)	0.11
10. Overt/academic[b]	−.27**	.19	.01	−0.07 (−0.18 – −0.01)	0.04
11. Relational/academic[b]	−.30***	.21**	.12	−0.04 (−0.06 – −0.003)	0.05
12. Reputational/Academic[b]	−.34***	.20	.05	−0.04 (−0.09 – 0.00)	0.04

Note: Pathways: a = (victimization type → global self-worth); Pathway b = (global self-worth → measure of adjustment, with victimization type in the model), and Pathway c = (victimization type → measure of adjustment with global self-worth in the model). Group status (Weight Loss Surgery and Nonsurgical Comparisons) was controlled for in all models.
*$p < .05$;
**$p < .01$;
***$p < .001$.
[a]Unstandardized beta estimates with 95% confidence intervals are provided for all indirect effects.
[b]For academic performance, those participants who were not attending any school/educational training were excluded from analyses ($n = 11$).

through global self-worth remained significant regardless of the level of social support. These results suggest that an adolescent's happiness with social support may be protective against the effects relational victimization operating through global self-worth, but that social support did not have an impact for other types of victimization.

Discussion

The present study extends the literature by providing a comprehensive assessment of overt, relational, and reputational peer victimization and their associations with a diverse set of clinically important outcomes for a sample of treatment-seeking adolescents with severe obesity at known risk. Consistent with the literature (Copeland et al., 2013; Hawker & Boulton, 2000), adolescent perception of greater victimization was associated with greater levels of adolescent internalizing symptoms and externalizing symptoms as well as lower global self-worth, although there were few significant associations with social competence or academic performance.

When testing mediational models, indirect effects involving overt victimization and relational victimization through global self-worth on each dependent variable (e.g., internalizing, externalizing, social competence, and academic performance) were significant, whereas the pathways from victimization to the dependent variables were nonsignificant when global self-worth was also in the model. These results are consistent with social information processing theory (Crick & Dodge, 1994), which would suggest that negative peer interactions such as experiences of victimization would lead some youth to develop negative self-perceptions, which in turn could result in difficulties. In contrast, mediational results for reputational victimization were more complex. For the model involving externalizing symptoms, there was no significant indirect effect of reputational victimization through global self-worth, but instead, a significant direct effect after controlling for self-worth. Thus, adolescents who perceive this type of victimization, which involves others spreading rumors and gossip about them, also endorse greater externalizing symptoms regardless of their level of global self-worth. Perhaps these adolescents might have a more confrontational style noticeable to others, making them more likely to be gossiped about by a group of individuals. In addition, some aggressive youth have been characterized as "provocative victims" (Garandeau & Cillessen, 2006). These youth are less likely to hold negative self-perceptions but instead respond to negative peer interactions with hostile attribution biases, which results in more externalizing behaviors.

When examining results for academic performance, zero-order correlations indicated no significant associations between victimization and academic performance in contrast to the general developmental literature (Nakamoto & Schwartz, 2010). Moreover, the indirect effect of reputational victimization on academic performance through self-worth was not significant, which is inconsistent with a recent study, in which Jenkins and Demaray (2015) found significant mediation of victimization on academic performance through academic self-concept for a sample of middle school girls, but not boys. Although significant indirect effects were found for models involving overt and reputational victimization, the amount of variance explained by these models was small. Given the multidimensional structure of self-concept and consistent with findings by Jenkins and Demaray (2015), it may be that the indirect paths from victimization to academic performance are not through global self-worth but through self-perceptions in specific domains (i.e., self-perception of scholastic competence). Alternatively, the physical limitations of adolescents with severe obesity might prevent them from being fully engaged with their peers, including attending school. Approximately 11% of youth in the current sample who had not yet graduated high school were homeschooled/not in regular school, and as such, victimization might have less of an effect on their grades. Future research will need to address these issues. Taken together, these data suggest that the associations of peer victimization on adjustment are complex, and further, seem to indicate self-worth as an important target for prevention and intervention for some types of victimization as well as for poor adjustment in adolescent severe obesity.

Analyses provided some evidence of the buffering effect of social support on some indirect pathways, consistent with literature regarding the benefits of social support (Lim et al., 2011; Moos, 2002). Higher levels of happiness with social support may be protective against negative outcomes such as greater internalizing symptoms and lower social competence from victimization that is relational in nature. However, social support did not appear to have an impact on the effects of overt or reputational victimization. Perhaps for this sample of severely obese adolescents, social support is a more effective buffer against less confrontational styles of victimization such as relational victimization (e.g., social exclusion) as compared with styles of victimization characterized as more confrontational (e.g., overt) or group-based (e.g., reputational), requiring the cooperation of a group of others to spread rumors or gossip. Still, it is encouraging that among youth with severe obesity, often characterized as socially isolated, there is a subsample with social resources available to protect them from some adverse effects.

Unexpectedly, BMI was negatively associated with measures of general victimization. Explaining these associations proves more difficult, as the literature seems to suggest the opposite effect (Puhl et al., 2013). As was stated earlier, it may be that youth at the highest levels of BMI have more physical limitations that keep them from being fully engaged with their peers, and thus, have fewer opportunities to perceive victimization. This could also potentially explain why mean levels of victimization for the current sample appeared similar to levels reported in the literature for the general adolescent population (De Los Reyes & Prinstein, 2004), in contrast to previously reported high rates of victimization in pediatric overweight/obesity.

Strengths of the present study include the multisite and controlled design and a focus on adolescents who have reached severe levels of obesity. We also took a multidimensional approach to understanding victimization and its associations with a diverse set of outcomes using measures with well-established psychometrics. However, this study has several limitations. First, the reliance on self-report of victimization limited potentially important peer insights to understanding victimization. Second, the WLS sample was primarily female and White, limiting our ability to generalize findings to males and other racial/ethnic groups known to be at heightened risk for severe obesity (Kelly et al., 2013) and adolescents in less severe excess weight status ranges or community settings. Further, adolescents who demographically "matched" and participated in the nonoperative comparison group may have been different than those who did not match, or those who initially declined being listed as potential matches on the registry. Third, the cross-sectional nature of the present study limits our ability to draw causal or directional conclusions. Although a temporal ordering of associations was assumed in tests of mediation based on theory, longitudinal studies are needed to test this ordering and to address potential reciprocal effects between victimization and adjustment. Future studies should examine the impact of victimization over time as adolescents enter young adulthood. Finally, although we examined several domains of traditional victimization, future research might address cyberbullying as well, particularly given the implication of the current study's finding that social support did little to buffer the impact of reputational victimization (i.e., rumors or gossip).

Clinical Implications

Although few group differences were identified, the NSComp group was characterized by poorer functioning when differences were significant. We have documented similar group differences for this cohort in other domains (Rofey et al., 2015; Zeller et al., 2015). While beyond current aims and thus speculative, we argue that unlike adolescents presenting for first-line behavioral weight treatment, adolescents who undergo WLS may be a unique clinical group. Achieving WLS candidacy involves navigating a complex process with multiple levels of decision-makers (i.e., adolescent motivation, supportive caregivers, a referring physician, the clinical team, insurance coverage and approval). It is possible that adolescents with greater psychosocial impairment (i.e., psychopathology, family dysfunction, victimization) or fewer financial resources are less likely to pursue or be referred for surgery. Moreover, adolescents with greater psychosocial impairment who do pursue WLS may drop out of the intensive WLS clinical care pathway during the preoperative phase, or are deferred or denied access to surgery by the clinical team. These are important areas for future research. In addition, youth who do achieve candidacy may benefit from the support and attention from their families and medical team as they prepare for WLS.

Pediatric psychologists or other mental health practitioners involved in pre-WLS evaluations or behavioral weight management programs may want to assess the adolescent's self-worth and social support as part of intake, to further inform the treatment of psychosocial difficulties, and should be wary of stereotypes that all youth with obesity have significant social difficulties and impaired self-worth. For patients who already express a strong self-worth and/or social support network, mental health practitioners should support and foster the influences contributing to these strengths, while focusing therapy on other issues of importance to the patient. For adolescents experiencing peer difficulties, cognitive behavioral therapies may be useful to deal with victimization proactively, improve self-esteem, and educate the adolescent regarding the value of social support. In particular, adolescents could be encouraged to engage in activities (e.g., volunteering) that provide opportunities for building social support and increasing self-worth not tied to weight management or body esteem. Finally, future work will be necessary to examine group differences in the associations among the variables in this study over time, after one group (WLS) likely experiences significant weight loss while the other group (NSComp) likely maintains or gains weight over time.

Acknowledgments

The authors acknowledge the contributions of additional TeenView Study Group Co-Investigators and staff. Cincinnati Children's Hospital Medical Center: Faye Doland, BS, Ashley Morgenthal, BS, Taylor Howarth, BS, Shelley Kirk, PhD, Thomas H. Inge, MD, PhD, Michael Helmrath, MD, PhD; Texas Children's Hospital, Baylor Medical Center: Margaret Callie Lee, MPH, David Allen, BS, Gia Washington, PhD, Carmen Mikhail, PhD, Mary L. Brandt, MD; University of Pittsburgh Medical Center: Ronette Blake, BS, Nermeen El Nokali, PhD, Silva Arslanian, MD, Anita P. Courcoulas, MD, MPH, Children's Hospital of Alabama University of Alabama: Krishna Desai, MD, Amy Seay, PhD, Beverly Haynes, BSN, Carroll Harmon, MD, PhD; Nationwide Children's Hospital Medical Center: Melissa Ginn, BS, Amy E. Baughcum, PhD, Marc P. Michalsky, MD; Temple University: David Sarwer, PhD; Teen-LABS Data Coordinating Center: Michelle Starkey Christian, Jennifer Andringa, BS, Carolyn Powers, RD, Rachel Akers, MPH. The authors also acknowledge the significant contributions made by the parent Teen-LABS Consortium (U01DK072493, UM1DK072493l; PI: Inge, MD, PhD), the Teen-LABS Data Coordinating Center (UM1DK095710; PI: Ralph Buncher, ScD), and the NIDDK/Teen-LABS Project Scientist, Mary Horlick, MD.
Methods for this study were first reported in (1) Zeller, M. H., et al. (2015). Child maltreatment and the adolescent patient with severe obesity: Implications for clinical care. *Journal of Pediatric Psychology*, 40, 640–648 and (2) Rofey, D. L., et al. (2015). A multi-site view of psychosocial risks in patients presenting for bariatric surgery. *Obesity*, 23, 1218–1225.

Funding

This research was supported by a grant from the National Institutes of Health (R01DK080020, PI: Zeller).
All authors were supported by a grant from the National Institutes of Health (R01DK080020, PI: Zeller), with the exception of Dr Gowey who was funded by a NIH training grant (T32DK062710).

Conflicts of interest: None declared.

References

Achenbach, T. M., & Rescorla, L. A. (2001). *Manual for the ASEBA school-age forms & profiles*. Burlington, VT: University of Vermont, Research Center for Children, Youth & Families.

Adams, R. E., & Bukowski, W. M. (2008). Peer victimization as a predictor of depression and body mass index in obese and non-obese adolescents. *Journal of Child Psychology and Psychiatry*, 49, 858–866. doi: 10.1111/j.1469-7610.2008.01886.

Bogat, G. A., Chin, R., Sabbath, W., & Schwartz, C. (1985). *The children's social support questionnaire (Technical report #3)*. East Lansing: Michigan State University.

Copeland, W. E., Wolke, D., Angold, A., & Costello, E. J. (2013). Adult psychiatric outcomes of bullying and being bullied by peers in childhood and adolescence. *JAMA Psychiatry*, 70, 419–426.

Crick, N. R., & Dodge, K. A. (1994). A review and reformulation of social information-processing mechnisms in children's social adjustment. *Psychological Bulletin*, 115, 74–101.

De Los Reyes, A., & Prinstein, M. J. (2004). Applying depression-distortion hypotheses to the assessment of peer victimization in adolescents. *Journal of Clinical Child and Adolescent Psychology*, 33, 325–335. doi: 10.1207/s15374424jccp3302_14

DeSmet, A., Deforche, B., Hublet, A., Tanghe, A., Stremersch, E., & De Bourdeaudhuij, I. (2014). Traditional and cyberbullying victimization as correlates of psychosocial distress and barriers to a healthy lifestyle among severely obese adolescents–a matched case–control study on prevalence and results from a cross-sectional study. *BMC Public Health*, 14, 224.

Garandeau, C. F., & Cillessen, A. H. N. (2006). From indirect aggression to invisible aggression: A conceptual view on bullying and peer group manipulation. *Aggression and Violent Behavior, 11*, 641–654.

Gray, W. N., Kahhan, N. A., & Janicke, D. M. (2009). Peer victimization and pediatric obesity: A review of the literature. *Psychology in the Schools, 46*, 720–727. doi:Doi 10.1002/Pits.20410

Grills, A. E., & Ollendick, T. H. (2002). Peer victimization, global self-worth, and anxiety in middle school children. *Journal of Clinical Child and Adolescent Psychology, 31*, 59–68.

Gunnarsdottir, T., Njardvik, U., Olafsdottir, A. S., Craighead, L. W., & Bjarnason, R. (2012). Teasing and social rejection among obese children enrolling in family-based behavioural treatment: Effects on psychological adjustment and academic competencies. *International Journal of Obesity, 36*, 35–44. doi: 10.1038/ijo.2011.181

Haines, J., Neumark-Sztainer, D., Hannan, P. J., van den Berg, P., & Eisenberg, M. E. (2008). Longitudinal and secular trends in weight-related teasing during adolescence. *Obesity, 16 (Suppl 2)*, S18–S23. doi: 10.1038/oby.2008.447

Harter, S. (2012). *Self-perception profile for adolescents: Manual and questionnaires*. Denver, CO: University of Denver, Department of Psychology.

Hawker, D. S., & Boulton, M. J. (2000). Twenty years' research on peer victimization and psychosocial maladjustment: A meta-analytic review of cross-sectional studies. *Journal of Child Psychology and Psychiatry, 41*, 441–455.

Hodges, E. V. E., Boivin, M., Vitaro, F., & Bukowski, W. M. (1999). The power of friendship: Protection against an escalating cycle of peer victimization. *Developmental Psychology, 35*, 94–101.

Inge, T. H., Zeller, M. H., Harmon, C. M., Helmrath, M. A., Bean, J., Modi, A. C., & Courcoulas, A. (2007). Teen-longitudinal assessment of bariatric surgery: Methodological features of the first prospective multicenter study of adolescent bariatric surgery. *Journal of Pediatric Surgery, 42*, 1969–1971.

Janssen, I., Craig, W. M., Boyce, W. F., & Pickett, W. (2004). Associations between overweight and obesity with bullying behaviors in school-aged children. *Pediatrics, 113*, 1187–1194.

Jenkins, L. N., & Demaray, M. K. (2015). Indirect effects in the peer victimization-academic achievement relation: The role of academic self-concept and gender. *Psychology in the Schools, 52*, 235–247.

Kelly, A. S., Barlow, S. E., Rao, G., Inge, T. H., Hayman, L. L., Steinberger, J., & Daniels, S. R. (2013). Severe obesity in children and adolescents: Identification, associated health risks, and treatment approaches: A scientific statement from the American Heart Association. *Circulation, 128*, 1689–1712.

Lim, C. S., Graziano, P. A., Janicke, D. M., Gray, W. N., Ingerski, L. M., & Silverstein, J. H. (2011). Peer victimization and depressive symptoms in obese youth: The role of perceived social support. *Childrens Health Care, 40*, 1–15. doi: 10.1080/02739615.2011.537929

Michalsky, M. P., Inge, T. H., Teich, S., Eneli, I., Miller, R., Brandt, M. L. . . . , , , , , , & Buncher, R. C.; Teen-LABS Consortium. (2014). Adolescent bariatric surgery program characteristics: The Teen Longitudinal Assessment of Bariatric Surgery (Teen-LABS) study experience. *Seminars in Pediatric Surgery, 23*, 5–10.

Moos, R. H. (2002). Life stressors, social resources, and coping skills in youth: Applications to adolescents with chronic disorders. *Journal of Adolescent Health, 30 (Suppl 4)*, 22–29.

Muthen, L. K., & Muthen, B. O. (1998–2012). *Mplus user's guide*. (7th ed.). Los Angeles, CA: Muthen & Muthen.

Nakamoto, J., & Schwartz, D. (2010). Is peer victimization associated with academic achievement? A meta-analytic review. *Social Development, 19*, 221–242.

Neumark-Sztainer, D., Falkner, N., Story, M., Perry, C., Hannan, P. J., & Mulert, S. (2002). Weight-teasing among adolescents: Correlations with weight status and disordered eating behaviors. *International Journal of Obesity, 26*, 123–131.

Pinquart, M., & Shen, Y. (2011). Behavior problems in children and adolescents with chronic physical illness: A meta-analysis. *Journal of Pediatric Psychology, 36*, 1003–1016. doi: 10.1093/jpepsy/jsr042

Prinstein, M. J., Boergers, J., & Vernberg, E. M. (2001). Overt and relational aggression in adolescents: Social-psychological adjustment of aggressors and victims. *Journal of Clinical Child Psychology, 30*, 479–491. doi: 10.1207/S15374424JCCP3004_05

Puhl, R. M., & Latner, J. D. (2007). Stigma, obesity, and the health of the nation's children. *Psychological Bulletin, 133*, 557–580. doi: 10.1037/0033-2909.133.4.557

Puhl, R. M., Latner, J. D., O'brien, K., Luedicke, J., Forhan, M., & Danielsdottir, S. (2016). Cross-national perspectives about weight-based bullying in youth: Nature, extent, and remedies. *Pediatric Obesity, 11*, 241–250.

Puhl, R. M., Peterson, J. L., & Luedicke, J. (2013). Weight-based victimization: Bullying experiences of weight loss treatment-seeking youth. *Pediatrics, 131*, e1–e9. doi: 10.1542/peds.2012-1106

Phillips, B. A., Gaudette, S., McCracken, A., Razzaq, S., Sutton, K., Speed, L., & Ward, W. (2012). Psychosocial functioning in children and adolescents with extreme obesity. *Journal of Clinical Psychology in Medical Settings, 19*, 277–284.

Rofey, D. L., Zeller, M. H., Brode, C., Reiter-Purtill, J., Mikhail, C., Washington, G. . . . , , , , , & Courcoulas, A. P.; TeenView Writing Group in cooperation with the Teen-LABS Consortium. (2015). A multi-site view of psychosocial risks in patients presenting for bariatric surgery. *Obesity, 23*, 1218–1225.

Skinner, A. C., & Skelton, J. A. (2014). Prevalence and trends in obesity and severe obesity among children in the United States, 1999-2012. *JAMA Pediatr, 168*, 561–566. doi: 10.1001/jamapediatrics.2014.21

Song, L. Y., Singh, J., & Singer, M. (1994). The youth self-report inventory: A study of its measurement fidelity. *Psychological Assessment, 6*, 326–345.

Sysko, R., Zakarin, E. B., Devlin, M. J., Bush, J., & Walsh, B. T. (2011). A latent class analysis of psychiatric symptoms among 125 adolescents in a bariatric surgery program. *International Journal of Pediatric Obesity*, 6, 289–297. doi: 10.3109/17477166.2010.545411

Zeller, M. H., Noll, J. G., Sarwer, D. B., Reiter-Purtill, J., Rofey, D. L., Baughcum, A. E. ..., , , , , & Becnel, J.; TeenView Study Group and in Cooperation With Teen-LABS Consortium. (2015). Child maltreatment and the adolescent patient with severe obesity: Implications for clinical care. *Journal of Pediatric Psychology*, 40, 640–648.

Group-Based Trajectory Modeling of Distress and Well-Being Among Caregivers of Children Undergoing Hematopoetic Stem Cell Transplant

Stephen A. Sands,[1] PsyD, Laura Mee,[2] PhD, Abraham Bartell,[3] MD, Sharon Manne,[4] PhD, Katie A. Devine,[4] PhD, Mirko Savone,[1] and Deborah A. Kashy,[5] PhD

[1]Clinical Psychology Departments of Pediatrics and Psychiatry, Columbia University School of Medicine, [2]Department of Pediatrics, Emory University School of Medicine, [3]Memorial Sloan-Kettering Cancer Center, [4]Population Science, Rutgers Cancer Institute of New Jersey and [5]Department of Psychology, Michigan State University

All correspondence concerning this article should be addressed to Sharon Manne, PhD, Rutgers Cancer Institute of New Jersey, 195 Little Albany Street, New Brunswick, NJ 08903, USA. E-mail: mannesl@cinj.rutgers.edu

Received February 15, 2016; revisions received June 21, 2016; accepted June 21, 2016

Abstract

Objective To examine the trajectories of caregiver psychological responses in the year following their child's hematopoetic stem cell transplant (HSCT), and whether cognitive and social processing strategies differentiated between trajectories. **Method** One hundred and eight caregivers randomized to the control condition of a cognitive-behavioral intervention study completed measures of distress, coping, and social support at baseline, 1 month, 6 months, and 1 year post HSCT of their child. **Results** The majority reported moderate or low anxiety, depression, or distress that decreased over time, but a small group demonstrated high anxiety, depression, or distress that persisted or increased over time. Maladaptive coping was highest among caregivers in the high-persistent distress subgroup compared with the moderate-decreasing and low-stable groups. Adaptive coping was minimally associated with trajectory subgroups. **Conclusions** Screening HSCT caregivers for distress and maladaptive coping may be useful in identifying caregivers likely to experience persistently high distress who may benefit from psychological intervention.

Key words: behavioral intervention; caregivers; distress; parents; pediatric transplantation.

Parents providing care to children undergoing hematopoetic stem cell transplant (HSCT) experience extreme stress. In addition to the emotional toll of having one's child diagnosed with a potentially life-threatening disease, watching one's child endure the grueling HSCT process is in itself stressful (Heinze et al., 2015). Pediatric HSCT is associated with short-term side effects such as mouth sores and infection, as well as long-term risks including failed engraftment, graft-versus-host disease (GvHD), systemic infection, and cardiopulmonary, endocrine, and neurological issues (Bresters et al., 2009; Han et al., 2009). Over the course of the next several decades of the child's life, even children who have a successful HSCT remain at increased risk for disease recurrence, second cancers, and/or mortality (Mehta et al., 2015). Each of these issues place parent caregivers at significant risk for psychological distress. Distress is particularly high during the pretransplant and acute hospitalization phases. Studies have shown elevated levels of psychological distress among 47% of fathers and 60% of mothers during preadmission (Dermatis & Lesko, 1990; Streisand, Rodrigue, Houck, Graham-Pole, & Berlant, 2000). At the time of HSCT, prior work found that 22% of mothers met criteria for major depressive, generalized anxiety, and/or panic disorder (Manne et al, 2002; Virtue et al., 2014), and an additional 16% to 21% reported clinically significant anxiety and depression

(Manne et al., 2004; Virtue et al., 2014). It is important to note that these levels of emotional distress are elevated compared with the incidence level reported in the general population, where the depression prevalence is 6.7% among U.S. adults (Pratt & Brody, 2008), while the prevalence rate of anxiety among U.S. adults is >10% annually (Kessler et al., 2009).

Longitudinal research suggests that distress declines steadily post-HSCT for the majority of parents (Manne et al., 2004; Phipps, Long, Hudson, & Rai, 2005; Streisand et al., 2000), but remains elevated for a subset of parent caregivers up until 18 months after HSCT (Manne et al., 1996; Sloper, 2000). Few studies have characterized the patterns of distress among parent caregivers over time. The most common approach to examining change over time is to summarize averages at serial time points using repeated measures designs (Phipps et al., 2012) or use average growth curves and individual variations around the mean scores. However, analyses that assume that caregivers' responses are homogenous over time can be misleading when the population contains distinct subgroups, as this sample may. Trajectory analysis, or group-based trajectory modeling, simultaneously estimates patterns over time and identifies unobserved subpopulations. These analyses can also examine trajectory shapes (nonlinear changes) and can elucidate a number of subgroups. Although group-based trajectory modeling is increasing in its usage, to our knowledge it has not been used to characterize distress among caregivers of children undergoing HSCT. Toward this end, the primary goal of this study was to determine whether there are distinct patterns of parent caregiver distress over the year after HSCT. We proposed that the majority of parent caregivers would exhibit a pattern of high anxiety, depression, and traumatic distress that declined steadily over the 1 year post-HSCT period and that most caregivers' well-being would increase over that time. However, we proposed that there would also be a group of parent caregivers who would exhibit persistently high distress and low well-being over the 1 year post-HSCT period and a group of parents who would have low, stable levels of distress.

The second goal was to evaluate the demographic, medical, and psychological factors that may be associated with distress trajectories subgroups. The guiding framework was cognitive-social processing theory of adjustment to traumatic events (Creamer, Burgess, & Pattison, 1992; Tait & Silver, 1989), which has been supported in this population. This theory posits that traumatic experiences cause people to question core beliefs about themselves, their relationships, and their world (Janoff-Bulman, 1992). Cognitive-processing, which involves confronting, contemplating, and reevaluating the traumatic event and its meaning, may help people integrate the meaning of the traumatic event into their mental model and reduce distress (Lepore, 2001; McCann & Pearlman, 1990). In the context of HSCT, cognitive processing involves approaching one's fears, finding meaning in the child's HSCT, or integrating the threatening aspects of the HSCT into a coherent conceptual framework. Social processing, which involves talking with supportive family or friends (Lepore, 2001), facilitates cognitive processing (Albrecht, Burleson, & Goldsmith, 1994; Rime, 1995), and experiencing unsupportive responses from family and friends hinders adaptive cognitive processing (Manne & Glassman, 2000; Tait & Silver, 1989).

Research has provided evidence for the role of cognitive and social processing for caregivers of children undergoing HSCT. With regard to cognitive processing, fewer bone marrow transplant (BMT)-related fears (Manne et al., 2002, 2003) and greater use of cognitive reappraisal such as acceptance, positive reappraisal, and humor is associated with decreases in depressive symptoms post-HSCT (Manne et al., 2003; Nelson, Miles, & Belyea, 1997). Emotional disengagement coping such as self-blame and avoidance is associated with higher distress post-HSCT (DuHamel et al., 2004; Kronenberger et al., 1998), whereas use of active engagement through problem-solving is associated with lower distress (Nelson & Gleaves, 2003). In terms of social processing, sharing feelings with supportive family and friends (Manne et al., 2003), receiving social support (Manne et al., 2003; Phipps et al., 2005), and lower levels of unsupportive responses (Manne et al., 2002; Phipps et al., 2005) are associated with less caregiver distress post-HSCT. Thus, we expected that self-blame, holding back, worry frequency, and unsupportive responses would be associated with higher anxiety, depression, and distress, but humor, distraction, positive reappraisal, acceptance, problem solving, and enacted support would be associated with lower anxiety, depression, and distress. In terms of demographic and medical factors, we proposed that younger caregivers (Manne et al., 2004) and caregivers whose children have more medical complications (Terrin et al., 2013) and caregivers whose children do not survive would be more likely to be in the persistently elevated distress trajectory subgroup.

The current study was an analysis of participants from the usual care condition, called Best-Practice Psychosocial Care (BPC), of a randomized clinical trial evaluating the efficacy of a brief cognitive-behavioral intervention, called the parent social-cognitive intervention program (P-SCIP; Manne et al., 2016). P-SCIP was delivered to parent caregivers during HSCT. P-SCIP reduced caregiver's distress significantly more than BPC between the pretransplant assessment and the 1 month follow-up assessment. However, at the 1-year follow-up, significant differences between P-SCIP and BPC were only seen among caregivers who reported higher anxiety pretransplant and whose children had GvHD at the HSCT discharge. Because P-SCIP did not show long-term effects for the majority of the sample, the current study represents an opportunity to understand patterns of change in distress over time as well as predictors of these changes.

Methods

Participants

The sample consisted of the participants in the control condition of a randomized clinical trial evaluating a cognitive-behavioral intervention for primary caregivers of children undergoing HSCT (Manne et al., 2016). Parents were randomized to the one of two study conditions after informed consent and baseline assessment were completed. Details about the larger randomized clinical trial are contained in the parent intervention publication (Manne et al., 2016).

The control condition was labeled "Best-Practice Psychosocial Care" (BPC). BPC was administered in a brief meeting held immediately after the HSCT infusion day in in the inpatient unit. BPC was delivered by the study research assistant and consisted of: (1) a DVD developed by the National Marrow Donor Program (NMDP) titled, "Discovery to Recovery: A Child's Guide to Bone Marrow Transplant," which is a 62-min video that covers medical information about the HSCT procedure, common emotional reactions children have during the HSCT, advice from parents about coping with the hospitalization, and family testimonials about psychological reactions during the HSCT; (2) a pamphlet covering caregiver issues during HSCT created by the National Bone Marrow Transplant Link titled, "Top Tips for Parent Caregivers during the BMT Process," which was eight pages in length; (3) the offer of 5 hr of respite care (e.g., watching the child while the caregiver left the room); and (4) the provision of a walkie-talkie to communicate with the child while not in the room.

P-SCIP was an individually delivered intervention that consisted of five 60-min sessions where stress management, coping, and support skills were taught over a span of 2–3 weeks after HSCT. Participants also received an interactive CD-ROM that reviewed these skills.

Participants were recruited from four HSCT centers across the United States. Participating centers offered similar treatment regimen, participate in the American Society of Blood and Bone Marrow Transplantation, and collaborate with the NMDP. Participating centers also offer similar psychosocial care. Eligible participants were primary caregivers (biological or foster parents) of children <19 years of age who were scheduled for HSCT within the next month. When both parents provided primary care, they decided which one would participate. Additional eligibility criteria were: (a) child could not have a diagnosis of medulloblastoma or other cancer of the brain; (b) caregiver must have phone service; and (c) caregiver had to speak, read, and write in English or Spanish (two of the four HSCT centers were equipped to enroll Spanish-speakers). All scales that did not have a valid Spanish version were translated and back-translated by an agency specializing in translation. Parents of children who had undergone one or more prior HSCTs were eligible for the study.

Procedure

Eligible caregivers were identified by the transplant teams and were approached in the week before the child's scheduled transplant. After the study was described, interested caregivers signed the site-specific institutional review board-approved consent and survey. Caregivers completed four assessments: one at baseline (before randomization for the larger study) and three follow-ups at 1, 6, and 12 months postbaseline. Baseline surveys were completed in hospital and follow-ups completed at home. Caregivers were paid $25 each for the first two assessments and $50 each for the third and fourth assessments. Recruitment began in October 2008 and ended in December 2013. Of the 381 caregivers approached, 218 consented and completed the Time 1 survey (57.2%), 151 caregivers refused (39.6%), and 12 caregivers consented but dropped out after consenting and did not complete the Time 1 survey (3.1%). The most common reasons participants refused were "study would take too much time" (20%), "not interested" (23%) and "too overwhelmed/stressed" (20%). Of the 13 caregivers who dropped after consenting, the reasons were: caregiver was too tired (n = 5), the caregiver did not have time (n = 1), the HSCT occurred before the Time 1 survey was completed (n = 3), the HSCT was canceled (n = 1), the survey was upsetting (n = 2), and the caregiver was not proficient in English (n = 1). Comparisons between study participants and refusers with available data indicated that there were no significant differences with regard to caregiver or child demographics. The acceptance rate was lower at one site (Memorial Sloan Kettering Cancer Center (MSKCC); 50%) versus the other sites (62–68%) (Chi-square = 8.5, $p < .05$).

Of the 218 participants, 108 were randomly assigned to the BPC arm. Of these, 99 (91.6%) completed the 1-month follow-up, 78 (72.2%) completed the 6-month follow-up, and 72 (66.7%) completed the 1-year follow-up. It is important to note that by the 1-year follow-up assessment, 25 participants' children *of* BPC *participants* (23.1%) had passed away and were no longer included in the study. Excluding drop out owing to the child's death, completion rates were 98% at the 1-month, 88.4% at the 6-month, and 88.9% at the 1-year follow-up.

Outcome Measures (All Time Points)

Depressive Symptoms. The Beck Depression Inventory (BDI; Beck, Steer, & Brown, 1996) was used. The BDI contains 21 items rated on a 4-point Likert scale (0–3). Cronbach's alphas ranged from .89 to .94 across the time points.

Anxiety. The Beck Anxiety Inventory (BAI; Beck, Epstein, Brown, & Steer, 1988) was used. The BAI contains 21 items rated on a 4-point Likert scale (0 = *not at all*, 4 = *severely, I could barely stand it*). Cronbach's alphas ranged from .82 to .94 across the time points.

Traumatic Distress. The Impact of Events Scale-Revised (IES-R; Weiss & Marmar, 1997) was used. The IES-R is a 22-item self-report measure that assesses subjective distress caused by traumatic events. Caregivers were asked to rate symptoms associated with the child's transplant on a 5-point Likert scale (0 = *Not at all*, 5 = *often*). Cronbach's alphas ranged from .91 to .94 across the time points.

Positive Well-Being. The positive well-being scale from the Mental Health Inventory was used (Veit & Ware, 1983). This 14-item scale assessed satisfaction with life and positive affect. Items were rated on a 6-point Likert scale (1 = *none of the time*, 6 = *all of the time*). Cronbach's alphas ranged from .90 to .94 across the time points.

Demographic, Medical, and Psychosocial Variables

Demographic and Medical Variables

Caregivers reported ethnicity, relationship to child, marital status, education level, and age. Child variables included child age, child sex, time since diagnosis. The medical risk factors were selected by the transplant physicians involved in this study to reflect the key risk factors for an unsuccessful medical outcome. These included time since diagnosis, whether the child was diagnosed with GvHD by the hospital discharge, whether the child remained hospitalized at Time 2, GvHD status, and whether the child died over the course of the study. At baseline, parents completed a measure of psychiatric history (ever seen a mental health professional for emotional issues, participated in substance treatment, hospitalized for psychiatric care, psychotropic medication) and psychosocial care in the past month (psychologist, psychiatrist, social worker, group therapy, psychotropic medication). Two dichotomous variables were created for the analyses (yes/no).

Initial Adaptive and Maladaptive Coping Strategies (Baseline Only)

Coping

Five adaptive coping subscales of the Brief COPE (Carver, 1997) were used: Adaptive coping includes humor, distraction, positive reappraisal/growth, acceptance, and problem solving. The maladaptive coping scale of self-blame was included. Each scale consisted of two items, and caregivers were asked to rate the extent to which they used each coping strategy in dealing with the child's HSCT on a 4-point Likert scale. Cronbach's alphas ranged from .62 (distraction) to .73 (humor).

Fear Appraisals

Two components of fear appraisals were included (DuHamel et al., 2004). First, one item assessed caregivers' perception of their own *potential for future suffering* ("How scared are you that you'll never be able to put the transplant experience behind you?") rated on a scale from 0 to 8. Second, caregivers listed the number of worries for the child's future in six life domains (e.g., social life) and then rated *the frequency of the caregiver's worry* on a scale from 1 to 7. Cronbach's alpha for the worry frequency scale was .90.

Perceived Unsupportive Behavior of Family and Friends

The family and friends version of the Perceived Negative Behaviors Scale (Manne & Glassman, 2000; Norton et al., 2005) was adapted for the HSCT context to assess unsupportive behaviors of family and friends. Items (e.g., "Criticized the way you handle your child's transplant and/or treatment") were rated on a 4-point scale (1 = *never responded this way* to 4 = *often responded this way*). Scores ranged from 19 to 76, with higher scores indicating more unsupportive behavior. Cronbach's alpha was .89.

Holding Back Sharing With Family and Friends

Holding back was assessed using a previously developed measure (Porter et al., 2005) that we adapted for this study. The measure consisted of nine areas of concern related to the child's transplant (e.g., child's physical symptoms). Caregivers rated the degree to which they hold back from sharing concern in each domain on a 6-point scale (0 = *not at all* to 5 = *a lot*). Scores ranged from 0 to 45, with higher scores indicating greater holding back from family and friends. Cronbach's alpha was .91.

Family/Friend Support

Using an adapted version of the Cancer Support Inventory (Manne & Schnoll, 2001), caregivers rated the degree to which family and friends responded in supportive ways in the past week on a 4-point scale (1 = *never* to 4 = *often*). Scores ranged from 13 to 52, with higher scores indicating more support. Cronbach's alpha was .92.

Analytic Approach

Analyses were conducted using a group-based trajectory modeling approach, which is a specialized application of finite mixture modeling. The PROC TRAJ (name of statistical procedure on the statistical package) procedure in SAS Version 9.4 was used for the primary analyses (Jones, Nagin, & Roeder, 2001). In a nontechnical sense, this approach is a combination of multilevel growth modeling and cluster analysis in that it is designed to identify subgroups of individuals who show similar trajectories on an outcome over time. Time was coded such that a 1 unit change corresponded to a 1 month increase, and took on values of 0, 1, 6, and 12 for the four waves of data collection. Thus the intercept refers to the initial assessment. Models were developed by sequentially testing 1, 2, 3, and 4 group models, allowing for both linear and quadratic fixed effects for time. A common random intercept variance was specified across the groups, and the Bayesian information criterion (BIC) and an evaluation of the parameter estimates as suggested by Ram and Grimm (2009) were used for model selection. Nonsignificant terms were dropped from the model and maximum likelihood was used as the estimation method. The PROC TRAJ procedure generates subgroup membership classification for each participant in the study, and we used that information to examine the extent to which there were differences between the groups. Because 24 of the 108 children died during the study, we reran the trajectory models to evaluate whether the subgroups differed if caregivers of children who died were eliminated from the analysis. No major differences emerged (i.e., similar estimates, same statistically significant effects, similar membership in subgroups). Therefore, we present the results based on the full data set.

We used SPSS Version 22 to evaluate group differences on a variety of variables including demographics (caregiver race—non-Hispanic White/other race, married/not married, after high school/before high school, caregiver age, child age, child sex), medical risk variables (whether the child remained hospitalized at Time 2, whether the child died, GvHD status, and time since diagnosis), psychiatric care variables (dichotomous variable for prior and current care), study site, and Time 1 coping, fear appraisals, and perceived support. For the categorical variables we tested trajectory subgroup differences using Fisher Exact tests to correct for the relatively small sample size, which resulted in some cells with expected cell frequencies lower than 5. Between-subjects analysis of variance (ANOVA) were used to test for subgroup differences on the continuous variables, and significant ANOVAs were followed up using post hoc Fisher's least significant difference (LSD) tests to correct for family-wise error.

Table I. Demographic, Medical, and Psychosocial Data for Study Participants (N = 108)

Variable Quantitative variables	M	SD	Range
Caregiver age	37.8	8.5	18–62
Child age	8.1	5.3	<1–19
Qualitative variables	N	%	
Household income			
0–$19,999	17	15.9	
$20,000–$49,000	41	19.7	
$50,000–$79,000	14	13.0	
Above $80,000	35	32.4	
Missing	1	.9	
Relationship to patient			
Mother	96	88.9	
Father	7	6.5	
Other	5	4.6	
Caregiver race			
Non-Hispanic White	50	45.5	
Non-Hispanic Black	31	28.2	
Hispanic/Latino	24	21.8	
Other	5	4.5	
Caregiver education level			
<High School	8	7.4	
High school graduate/GED	18	16.7	
Greater than High School	82	75.9	
Caregiver marital status			
Married	74	68.5	
Never married	19	17.6	
Widowed/divorced/separated	15	13.8	
Child gender			
Male	61	56.5	
Female	47	43.5	
Child-type of SCT			
Autologous	21	19.4	
Allogeneic-sibling donor	34	31.5	
Allogeneic-other donor	53	49.1	
Child-Diagnosis Group			
Acute lymphoblastic leukemia	22	20.4	
Acute myelogenous leukemia	26	24.1	
Hodgkin's disease/non-Hodgkin's lymphoma	5	4.6	
Solid tumor	17	15.7	
Non-malignancy	38	35.2	
Child-graft vs. host disease at discharge (yes)	17	17.3	
Child-number of relapses			
0	71	65.7	
1	19	17.6	
2	4	3.7	
Prior psychiatric care (yes)	55	50.9	
Current psychiatric care (yes)	46	42.6	

Results

Descriptive Information

The majority of caregivers were the mother (88.9%), married (68.8%), had completed at least some college (75.9%), with the racial breakdown composed of 49% White, non-Hispanic, 24% African American, 15% Hispanic/Latino and 12% other. The mean caregiver age was 38 years. Approximately half the

Table II. *Regression Equations for the Trajectories of Anxiety, Depression, Distress, and Positive Well-Being Over Time*

Variable	Subgroup	Intercept		Linear slope		Quadratic slope		% of sample
		B	t	B	T	b	t	
Anxiety	(1) Low-decreasing	4.87	6.91**	−0.17	2.16*	0[a]	–	75.57
	(2) High-decreasing	23.29	13.69**	−4.06	6.25**	0.23	4.39**	17.1
	(3) High-stable	25.96	11.48**	0[a]	–	0[a]	–	7.3
Depression	(1) Low-decreasing	5.77	7.00**	−0.31	3.03**	0[a]	–	60.5
	(2) High-decreasing	16.25	9.84**	−0.42	2.24*	0[a]	–	31.2
	(3) High-increasing	16.58	9.04**	1.34	5.66*	0[a]	–	8.3
Distress	(1) Low-stable	−1.28	0.23	0[a]	–	0[a]	–	19.2
	(2) Moderate-decreasing	32.07	10.51**	−3.32	3.08**	0.22	2.52*	65.9
	(3) High-stable	52.19	8.87**	0[a]	–	0[a]	–	14.9
Positive Well-being	(1) Moderate-increasing	42.39	33.13**	4.78	5.82**	−0.27	4.20**	65.7
	(2) Moderate-decreasing	46.86	25.68**	−3.35	3.10**	0.20	2.29*	34.3

*$p < .05$, **$p < .01$.

[a]Indicates that this parameter was fixed to zero because it was not statistically significant and nested model testing indicated that dropping it did not worsen model fit.

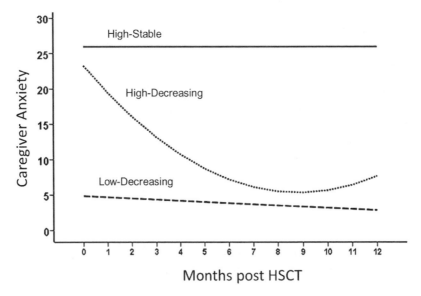

Figure 1. Trajectories of caregiver anxiety after child has HSCT. Coefficients for the trajectory equations as a function of time are in Table II.

children undergoing HSCT were male (56.5%) and the average child age was about 8 years. For most children, this was the first HSCT, and the most common HSCT type was allogeneic (68.5%). Detailed information is presented in Table I.

Trajectory Analysis Results

Table II presents the trajectory results for anxiety, depression, traumatic distress, and positive well-being over time, and Figures 1–4 illustrate the equations for the subgroup trajectories. The BIC values, along with statistical significance tests of the model parameters, indicated that the best models for anxiety, depression, and distress included three subgroups, and the model for positive well-being included two subgroups. For anxiety (Figure 1), the first subgroup (Low-decreasing), comprising 75.6% of the sample, was relatively low in anxiety at the first assessment and decreased modestly in a linear fashion over time. The second subgroup (High-decreasing), comprising 17.1% of the sample, began the study with high initial anxiety, but that anxiety decreased over time. Both the linear and quadratic parameters were significant for this second subgroup and as shown in Figure 1, these components combined such that the linear decrease moderated over time with a slight increase in anxiety by 12 months. The final subgroup (High-stable), comprising 7.3% of the sample, was characterized by an intercept-only model: These individuals started with high anxiety that did not decrease over time.

For depression, the three subgroups each had significant linear effects (see Figure 2). The first subgroup (Low-decreasing), comprising 60.5% of the sample,

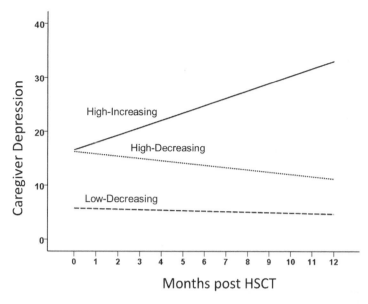

Figure 2. Trajectories of caregiver depression after child has HSCT. Coefficients for the trajectory equations as a function of time are in Table II.

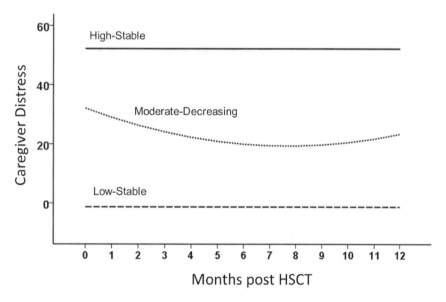

Figure 3. Trajectories of caregiver distress after child has HSCT. Coefficients for the trajectory equations as a function of time are in Table II.

started the study relatively low in depression and decreased in depression over time. The second subgroup (High-decreasing), comprising 31.2% of the sample, started relatively high in depression but decreased over time. The third subgroup (High-increasing), comprising 8.3% of the sample, started high in depression, but depression increased significantly over time. For traumatic distress the three subgroups were distinct across time (see Figure 3). The first subgroup (19.2%; Low-stable) started and stayed low in traumatic distress. The second subgroup (65.9%) started at moderate distress, had linear decreases in distress (i.e., Moderate-decreasing), but the quadratic component suggests that the linear decrease moderated over time.

The final group (14.9%; High-stable) started and stayed relatively high in distress. Finally, analyses of positive well-being resulted in two subgroups (see Figure 4): 66% began with moderate well-being and then increased significantly over time, and 34% began with similarly moderate well-being but decreased significantly over time.

Demographic, Medical, and Psychiatric Care Variables Related to Trajectory Subgroup Membership

As noted, we examined whether the trajectory subgroups differed on a number of caregiver and child demographic, medical, and psychiatric care variables

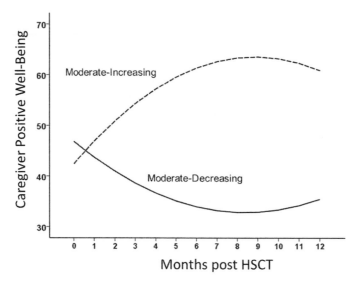

Figure 4. Trajectories of caregiver positive well-being after child has HSCT. Coefficients for the trajectory equations as a function of time are in Table II.

Table III. *Demographic and Medical Variables Associated With Anxiety, Depression, Distress, and Positive Well-Being Trajectory Subgroups*

Variable	Subgroup		Caregiver mother		Caregiver married		Caregiver post High-School Education		Child gender		GvHD		Child died	
			No	Yes	No	Yes	No	Yes	Female	Male	No	Yes	No	Yes
Anxiety	(1) Low-decreasing	N	8	73	25	56	20	47	28	53	61	11	60	20
		(%)	(67)	(76)	(73)	(76)	(59)	(83)	(60)	(87)	(75)	(65)	(72)	(83)
	(2) High-decreasing	N	1	19	4	16	12	8	14	6	17	2	16	4
		(%)	(8)	(20)	(12)	(22)	(35)	(14)	(30)	(10)	(21)	(12)	(19)	(17)
	(3) High-stable	N	3	4	5	2	2	2	5	2	3	4	7	0
		(%)	(25)	(4)	(15)	(3)	(6)	(3)	(11)	(3)	(4)	(24)	(8)	(0)
	Fisher's exact test		5.94*		5.81*		6.26*		10.34**		6.69*		1.87	
Depression	(1) Low-decreasing	N	8	58	22	44	17	37	29	37	54	5	48	17
		(%)	(67)	(60)	(65)	(59)	(50)	(65)	(62)	(61)	(67)	(29)	(58)	(71)
	(2) High-decreasing	N	3	32	7	28	17	16	14	21	23	9	28	7
		(%)	(25)	(33)	(21)	(38)	(50)	(28)	(30)	(34)	(28)	(53)	(34)	(29)
	(3) High-increasing	N	1	6	5	2	0	4	4	3	4	3	7	0
		(%)	(8)	(6)	(15)	(3)	(0)	(7)	(8)	(5)	(5)	(18)	(8)	(0)
	Fisher's exact test		0.67		6.92*		5.52		0.77		8.98**		2.10	
Distress	(1) Low-stable	N	1	18	10	9	7	9	8	11	13	2	10	9
		(%)	(8)	(19)	(29)	(12)	(21)	(16)	(17)	(18)	(16)	(12)	(12)	(38)
	(2) Moderate decreasing	N	9	68	19	58	23	42	34	43	60	11	61	15
		(%)	(75)	(71)	(56)	(78)	(68)	(74)	(72)	(70)	(74)	(65)	(74)	(62)
	(3) High-stable	N	2	10	5	7	4	6	5	7 (12)	8	4	12	0
		(%)	(16)	(10)	(15)	(10)	(12)	(10)	(11)		(10)	(24)	(14)	(0)
	Fisher's exact test		1.11		6.10*		0.55		0.10		2.41		9.92**	

Note. GvHD = graft versus host disease.
*$p < .05$, **$p < .01$. Fisher Exact tests have $df = 2$.

(see Table III). Positive well-being subgroup membership was not associated with any of these variables, and there were no differences in anxiety, depression, or distress subgroups for caregiver ethnicity, age, psychiatric history, psychosocial care, child age, or time since diagnosis.

Anxiety

Fisher's exact tests indicated that nonmaternal caregivers (fathers, grandparents, foster parents) were relatively more likely to fall into the high-stable anxiety subgroup than maternal caregivers, and maternal caregivers were more likely to be in either the low-decreasing or high-decreasing subgroups. A similar pattern emerged for caregiver marital status such that unmarried caregivers were more likely to be in the high-stable anxiety subgroup. The caregiver's education was also associated with anxiety subgroups such that caregivers with after high-school education were most likely to be in the low-decreasing group, but caregivers with a high-school degree or lower education were more likely to be in the high-decreasing or high-stable groups. Child gender and GvHD status were also associated with anxiety subgroups. Caregivers of boys were most likely to fall into the low-decreasing subgroup, but caregivers of girls were somewhat more likely to fall into the high-decreasing subgroup. Caregivers of children with GvHD were more likely to show the high-stable anxiety trajectory than caregivers of children who did not have GvHD.

Depression
Caregiver depression trajectory subgroups were associated with caregiver marital status and child's GvHD status. Specifically, unmarried caregivers were more likely to show high-increasing depression compared with married caregivers, and married caregivers were more likely to show high-decreasing depression compared with unmarried caregivers. In terms of GvHD status, caregivers of children who had GvHD were more likely to be in the high-decreasing or high-increasing subgroups, and caregivers of children who did not have GvHD were most likely to be in the low-decreasing subgroup.

Distress
Membership in the traumatic distress subgroups was associated with both caregiver marital status and whether the child died during treatment. Married caregivers were most likely to show moderate distress that decreased over time but unmarried caregivers were somewhat more likely to either show low-stable distress or high-stable distress. Caregivers of children who died were primarily in the low-stable or moderate but decreasing subgroups. There were no caregivers of children who died who fell into the high-stable distress subgroup. Caregivers of children who did not die were primarily in the moderate-decreasing subgroup.

Maladaptive and Adaptive Coping Strategies Associated With Trajectory Subgroups
Table IV presents the means, standard deviations, and F-tests assessing the extent to which there were mean-level differences in initial coping in the different subgroups. No significant differences between the subgroups were found for humor, distraction, positive reappraisal, acceptance, or the number of worries. Results for these variables are not included in the Table.

Anxiety
Results indicated a consistent pattern across initial self-blame, potential for suffering, holding back sharing concerns, worry frequency, and perceived unsupportive responses from family and friends. Across all of these variables, caregivers who showed a pattern of anxiety that started relatively low and decreased over time were significantly lower in each of these maladaptive coping strategies than caregivers in the high-decreasing subgroup for anxiety. A similar difference emerged for problem solving such that caregivers in the low-decreasing anxiety subgroup reported lower levels of problem solving than caregivers in the high-decreasing subgroup. Notably, caregivers in the high-stable anxiety subgroup did not differ significantly from those in the high-decreasing subgroup on any of the initial coping variables, and they differed from those in the low-decreasing subgroup only on holding back concerns.

Depression
Caregivers who began the study low in depression and continued to decrease over time were significantly lower than caregivers who started high in depression but then decreased over time in self-blame, potential for suffering, holding back concerns, and worry frequency. There was also evidence that caregivers in the low-decreasing depression subgroup received greater family support than those in the high-decreasing subgroup. Similar to results for anxiety, caregivers in the high-increasing subgroup did not differ from those in the high-decreasing subgroup for any of the variables. However, the high-increasing depression subgroup was significantly higher than the low-decreasing subgroup on potential for suffering, holding back sharing concerns, and family support.

Distress
There were significant mean differences between caregivers in each of the three distress trajectory subgroups on self-blame, potential for suffering, and holding back sharing concerns. Caregivers in the low-stable group were lowest on these maladaptive coping strategies, caregivers in the moderate-decreasing group were significantly higher, and caregivers in the high-stable distress group were highest. Worry frequency also showed mean-level differences; the low-stable group was significantly lower in worry frequency than the other two groups.

Positive Well-Being
Caregivers who started at moderate well-being and increased were significantly lower in self-blame, potential for suffering, holding back sharing concerns, and worry frequency than caregivers who started at moderate well-being but decreased over time. In parallel,

Table IV. Initial Coping Strategies Associated With Anxiety, Depression, Distress, and Positive Well-Being Trajectory Subgroups

Variable	Subgroup	Self-blame M (SD)	Potential for suffering M (SD)	Holding back concerns M (SD)	Worry frequency M (SD)	Family criticism M (SD)	Planful problem solving M (SD)	Family support M (SD)
Anxiety	(1) Low-decreasing	2.57_a (1.14)	9.94_a (2.88)	1.75_a (1.51)	4.10_a (1.14)	26.55_a (10.35)	5.21_a (1.88)	42.99 (8.75)
	(2) High-decreasing	3.85_b (2.11)	11.60_b (3.50)	2.58_b (1.17)	5.15_b (0.89)	36.54_b (15.42)	6.40_b (1.70)	40.55 (9.34)
	(3) High-stable	3.29_{ab} (2.21)	11.71_{ab} (2.69)	2.55_b (1.52)	4.65_{ab} (1.26)	32.14_{ab} (14.38)	5.71_{ab} (1.60)	39.86 (5.98)
	F	6.69^{**}	3.20^{*}	3.29^{*}	7.11^{**}	6.18^{**}	3.44^{*}	0.93
Depression	(1) Low-decreasing	2.45_a (1.03)	9.43_a (2.68)	1.37_a (1.36)	3.98_a (1.14)	26.98 (12.85)	5.50 (1.93)	44.05_a (7.94)
	(2) High-decreasing	3.66_b (2.01)	11.70_b (3.12)	2.86_b (1.19)	4.84_b (1.05)	30.51 (9.60)	5.54 (1.79)	40.37_b (9.22)
	(3) High-increasing	2.57_{ab} (0.98)	12.86_b (2.73)	2.88_b (1.28)	4.82_{ab} (1.05)	36.82 (15.15)	4.71 (1.89)	36.00_b (9.56)
	F	8.34^{**}	9.92^{**}	16.84^{**}	7.54^{**}	2.67	0.60	4.26^{*}
Distress	(1) Low-stable	2.05_a (0.23)	8.63_a (2.39)	1.14_a (1.46)	3.82_a (1.34)	23.61 (6.69)	5.05 (2.22)	41.58 (9.30)
	(2) Moderate decreasing	2.82_b (1.37)	10.44_b (2.99)	2.01_b (1.43)	4.31_a (1.06)	29.18 (12.98)	5.49 (1.78)	42.85 (8.28)
	(3) High-stable	4.33_c (2.39)	12.91_c (2.88)	2.93_c (1.26)	5.16_b (1.23)	34.23 (11.79)	5.92 (1.93)	40.25 (10.82)
	F	9.78^{**}	7.76^{**}	5.95^{**}	4.94^{**}	3.04	0.81	0.54
PWB	(1) Moderate increasing	2.76 (1.38)	9.93 (3.16)	1.71 (1.47)	4.18 (1.21)	27.58 (12.20)	5.56 (1.93)	44.09 (7.78)
	(2) Moderate decreasing	3.67 (1.63)	11.52 (2.50)	2.59 (1.33)	4.70 (0.99)	31.83 (11.98)	5.20 (1.73)	37.78 (9.51)
	F	8.53^{**}	5.88^{**}	8.15^{**}	4.19^{*}	2.64	0.81	12.54^{**}

Note. PWB = Positive well-being. For Anxiety, Depression, and Distress means within outcome variable subgroups with subscripts in common did not differ significantly using a Fisher's LSD post hoc test. Degrees of freedom for the F-tests for Anxiety, Depression, and Distress were $df_{numerator} = 2$, and $df_{denominator}$ ranged between 100 and 105, and for positive well-being, the degrees of freedom were $df_{numerator} = 1$, and $df_{denominator}$ ranged between 101 and 106.
$^{*}p < .05, ^{**}p < .01$.

those who were moderate but increasing reported significantly higher family support than those who were moderate but decreasing in well-being.

Discussion

This study extends the literature by describing the natural trajectory of the emotional functioning of parents, who were randomized to the nonintervention arm of a cognitve-behavioral study, from the time immediately before their child's HSCT through 1 year after the HSCT. Three distinct subgroups emerged consistently across the anxiety, depression, and distress outcomes. For anxiety and depression, the majority of caregivers had low-decreasing or low-stable symptoms, while a moderate percentage of caregivers began with high anxiety or depression that decreased over time, and a small group of caregives began with high symptoms that persisted or incrased over time. For distress, the majority of caregivers had moderate distress that decreased over time, with a moderate percentage of caregivers showing low-stable distress, and a small percentage of caregivers showing high-stable distress. These findings closely resemble the trajectories of previously reported emotional functioning of parents of children newly diagnosed with cancer—high-declining, moderate-stable, and low-stable (Dolgin et al., 2007) or high, moderate, declining, and low (Steele, Dreyer & Phipps, 2004). Moreover, the distribution of primary caregivers in each subcaetory is consistent with the Pediatric Psychosocial Preventative Health Model (Kazak et al., 2006) and screening using the Psychosocial Assessment Tool–2, which has found that most caregivers fall into a univeral risk category, with a moderate percentage demonstrating acute distress that may benefit from intervention, and a small percentage demonstrating persistent and/or escalating distress that warrant proactive clinical intervention (Pai et al., 2008).

There were only a few demographic and medical factors significantly associated with trajectory subgroup membership. Consistent with some previous work (Dolgin et al., 2007), there were more unmarriered caregivers in the high-stable or high-increasing anxiety, depression, and distress subgroups, and caregivers with lower education were more likely to be in the high-stable or high-decreasing anxiety subgroups. Further, caregivers of children with GvHD were more likely to be in the high-stable anxiety subgroup and high-increasing or high-descreasing depression subgroups. These results are in contrast with a study by Terrin and colleagues (2013), who found GvHD was associated with decreased parental emotional functioning acutely but not longitudinally at 12 months post-HSCT.

This study advances previous work by evaluating the relationship between social and cognitive processing factors and trajectories of emotional functioning. Our hypotheses were paritally supported in that maladaptive coping strategies (self-blame, potential for suffering, holding back concerns, and worry frequency) were consistenly associated with the high-stable or high-increasing subgroup compared with the low-stable group. However, for anxiety and depression, these strategies did not differentiate between those who started high and either persisted or decreased in anxiety or depression. Thus, scores on the maladaptive coping strategies can identify those who will not be in the low-stable group but does not appear to be able to distinguish between those who start high and then decrease in anxiety or depression from those who will start high and either remain elevated or get worse in functioning. Therefore, only in the distress trajectories did we see a clear pattern of higher levels of maladaptive coping between each trajectory. These results are consistent with previous work linking avoidant and disengagement coping with depression (Kroenenberger, 1998) and family criticism with post-trauamatic stress (Manne et al., 2002). Our hypotheses regarding adaptive coping strategies and distress trajectories were only minimally supported. Problem-solving was higher among caregivers in the high-decreasing versus low-decreasing anxiety subgroups, suggesting that these caregivers may have had more problems to solve and used the skill effectively. Family support was higher among caregivers in the low-decreasing versus high-increasing depression and among caregivers who showed an increase in positive well-being over time. However, none of the other adaptive coping strategies were significantly associated with outcomes for this nonintervention group.

Taken together, these results suggest that the majority of caregivers will adjust well without intervention; however, a discrete subgroup will experience persistent or increased distress following their child's HSCT. Furthermore, the three distinct trajectories may be interpreted within a conceptual framework of caregiver repsonse to stressful events. The low-stable trajectores may be interpreted as caregiver resilience with consistently low symptoms over time. The moderate-decreasing trajectories may be framed as the development of resilience or stress-related growth with the dimunition of symptoms over time. The high-stable or high-increasing trajectories represent the group at greatest risk of clinically significant distress.

This study had some limitations. First, this study was a secondary analysis of a clinical trial examining caregivers in a control condition of a larger clinical trial. Thus, the sample may have differed from an observational study in terms of distress and well-being, both at the time of recruitment and over time. Second, the 20% of the participants who were approached for this trial and refused the study owing to being stressed or overloaded may have been more distressed caregivers. Thus, the current sample may underrepresent the percentage of parents in the persistently high distress trajectory. A third limitation is the small sample size ($N = 108$) for trajectory analyses, and, accordingly, the small number of parents who demonstrated high and persistent negative emotional responses. Given the small sample size, it was difficult to identify factors that distinguished between those who started with high distress that declined over time from those who started with high distress that remained high or worsened. Replication in larger samples is needed. Fourth, because only type of maladaptive coping was assessed (self-blame), future studies should assess other types of maladaptive coping. Fifth, our study focused only on caregiver functioning. Future studies would benefit from examining the interrelationship between caregiver and child functioning over time.

Clinically, these results support the use of screening of caregivers of children undergoing HSCT. Screening for maladaptive coping strategies such as self-blame, potential for suffering, holding back concerns, and worry frequency may be particularly useful for identifying caregivers likely to experience high-stable distress who may benefit from intervention. Screening on these coping strategies may also help distinguish between caregivers likely to display low-decreasing anxiety and depression versus those who will start high and persist, increase, or decrease, but these measures do not seem sensitive enough to identify those at highest risk from those who start high and go on to improve. Other screening tools, such as the PAT 2.0 (Pai et al., 2008), may also be useful for this population and warrant further integrated research. Early intervention for at-risk caregivers could lead to improvements in both caregiver and child functioning. Examples of currently available parent interventions include the Parent Social-Cognitive Processing Intervention Program (Manne et al., 2016), the Bright IDEAS Problem-Solving Skills Training (Sahler et al.,

2013), and Surviving Cancer Competently Intervention Program (Kazak et al., 2005).

In conclusion, this study found three distinct trajectories for caregiver anxiety, depression, and distress in the year following their child's HSCT. Although the majority of parents will experience low-stable or moderate-decreasing negative emotions, a small subgroup will experience significant persistent symptoms and may benefit from screening and intervention before the HSCT.

Acknowledgments

The authors acknowledge Tara Bohn, Caraline Craig, Ayxa Calero-Breckeimer, Sara Frederick, Tina Gajda, Laura Goorin, Merav Ben Horin, Bonnie Maxson, Julia Randomski, Mirko Savone, Kristen Sorice, Kate Volipicelli, and Octavio Zavala. They thank the caregivers who participated, the pediatric HSCT teams at all sites, and the P-SCIP interventionists. Ernie Katz participated in this study for the first year.

Funding

This work was supported by grant CA127488 awarded by the National Cancer Institute to Sharon Manne.

Conflicts of interest: None declared.

References

Albrecht, T., Burleson, R., & Goldsmith, D. (1994). Supportive communication. In M. Knapp & G. Miller (Eds.), *Handbook of interpersonal communication* (2nd ed., pp. 419–499). Thousand Oaks, CA: Sage.

Beck, A., Steer, R., & Brown, G. (1996). *Manual for the Beck Depression Inventory–II*. San Antonio, TX: Psychological Corporation.

Beck, A. T., Epstein, N., Brown, G., & Steer, R. A. (1988). An inventory for measuring clinical anxiety. *Journal of Consulting and Clinical Psychology*, 56, 893.

Bresters, D., van Gils, I., Kollen, W., Ball, L., Oostdijk, W., van der Bom, J., & Egeler, R. (2009). High burden of late effects after haematopoietic stem cell transplantation in childhood. A single-centre study. *Bone Marrow Transplant*, 43, S169–S170.

Creamer, M., Burgess, P., & Pattison, P. (1992). Reaction to trauma: A cognitive processing model. *Journal of Abnormal Psychology*, 101, 452–459.

Carver, C. (1997). You want to measure coping but your protocol's too long: Consider the Brief COPE. *International Journal of Behavioral Medicine*, 4, 92–100.

Dermatis, H., & Lesko, L. M. (1990). Psychological distress in parents consenting to child's bone marrow transplantation. *Bone Marrow Transplant*, 6, 411–417.

Dolgin, M. J., Phipps, S., Fairclough, D. L., Sahler, O. J., Askins, M., Noll, R. B. … Katz, E. R. (2007). Trajectories of adjustment in mothers of children with newly diagnosed cancer. *Journal of Pediatric Psychology*, 32, 771–782.

DuHamel, K.N., Manne, S., Nereo, N., Ostroff, J., Martini, R., Parsons, S. … Redd, W. H. (2004). Cognitive processing among mothers of children undergoing bone marrow/stem cell transplantation. *Psychosomatic Medicine*, 66, 92–103.

Han, J., Kwon, S., Won, S., Shin, Y., Ko, J., & Lyu, C. (2009). Comprehensive clinical follow up of late effects in childhood cancer survivors shows the need for early and well-timed intervention. *Annals of Oncology*, 20, 1170–1177.

Heinze, K., Rodday, A., Nolan, M., Bingern, K., Kupst, M., Patel, S. K. … Parsons, S. (2015). The impact of pediatric blood and marrow transplant on parents. *Health and Quality of Life Outcomes*, 13, 46–1186. Doi: 10./s12955-015-0240-6.

Janoff-Bulman, R. (1992). *Shattered assumptions*. New York, NY: Free Press.

Jones, B. L., Nagin, D. S., & Roeder, K. (2001). A SAS procedure based on mixture models for estimating development trajectories. *Sociological Methods & Research*, 29, 374–393.

Kazak, A. E., Kassam-Adams, N., Schneider, S., Zelikovsky, N., Alderfer, M. A., & Rourke, M. (2006). An integrative model of pediatric medical traumatic stress. *Journal of Pediatric Psychology*, 31, 343–355.

Kazak, A. E., Simms, S., Alderfer, M. A., Rourke, M. T., Crump, T., McClure, K. … Reilly, A. (2005). Feasibility and preliminary outcomes from a pilot study of a brief psychological intervention for families of children newly diagnosed with cancer. *Journal of Pediatric Psychology*, 30, 644–655.

Kessler, R. C., Aguilar-Gaxiola, S., Alonso, J., Chatterji, S., Lee, S., Ormel, J. … Wang, P. S. (2009). The global burden of mental disorders: An update from the WHO World Mental Health (WMH) surveys. *Epidemiologia E Psichiatria Sociale*, 18, 23–33.

Kronenberger, W. G., Carter, B. D., Edwards, J., Morrow, C., Stewart, J., & Sender, L. (1998). Psychological adjustment of mothers of children undergoing bone marrow transplantation: The role of stress, coping, and family factors. *Children's Health Care*, 27(2), 77–95. doi: DOI 10.1207/s15326888chc2702_1

Lepore, S. (2001). A social cognitive-processing model of emotional adjustment to cancer. In A. Baum & B. Andersen (Eds.), *Psychological interventions for cancer* (pp. 99–116). Washington, DC: American Psychological Association.

Manne, S., DuHamel, K., Nereo, N., Ostroff, J., Parsons, S., Martini, R. … Redd, W. H. (2002). Predictors of PTSD in mothers of children undergoing bone marrow transplantation: The role of cognitive and social processes. *Journal of Pediatric Psychology*, 27, 607–617.

Manne, S., Duhamel, K., Ostroff, J., Parsons, S., Martini, D. R., Williams, S. E. … Redd, W. H. (2003). Coping and the course of mother's depressive symptoms during and after pediatric bone marrow transplantation. *Journal of American Academy of Child and Adolescent Psychiatry*, 42, 1055–1068.

Manne, S., DuHamel, K., Ostroff, J., Parsons, S., Martini, D. R., Williams, S. E. … Redd, W. H. (2004). Anxiety, depressive, and posttraumatic stress disorders among mothers of pediatric survivors of hematopoietic stem cell transplantation. *Pediatrics*, 113, 1700–1708.

Manne, S., & Glassman, M. (2000). Perceived control, coping efficacy, and avoidance coping as mediators between spouses' unsupportive behaviors and cancer patients' psychological distress. *Health Psychology, 19*, 155–164.

Manne, S., Miller, D., Meyers, P., Wollner, N., Steinherz, P., & Redd, W.H. (1996). Depressive symptoms among parents of newly diagnosed children with cancer: A 6-month follow-up study. *Children's Health Care, 25*, 191–209.

Manne, S., & Schnoll, R. (2001). Measuring supportive and unsupportive responses during cancer treatment. *Journal of Behavioral Medicine, 24*, 297–321.

Manne, S. L., Mee, L., Bartell, A., Sands, S., & Kashy, D. (2016). A randomized clinical trial of a parent-focused social-cognitive processing intervention for caregivers of children undergoing hematopoetic stem cell transplantation. *Journal of Consulting and Clinical Psychology, 84*, 389–401.

McCann, I., & Pearlman, L. (1990). *Psychological trauma and the adult survivor.* New York, NY: Brunner/Mazel.

Mehta, P., Zhang, M., Eapen, M., He, W., Seber, A., Gibson, B. . . . Davies, S. (2015). Transplant outcomes for children with hypodiploid acute lymphoblastic leukemia. *Biology of Blood and Marrow Transplantation, 21*, 1273–1277.

Nelson, A., & Gleaves, L. (2003). Mothers' responses during the child's stem cell transplantation: Pilot Study. *Pediatric Nursing, 29*, 219–223.

Nelson, A., Miles, M., & Belyea, M. (1997). Coping and support effects on mothers' stress responses to their child's hematopoietic stem cell transplantation. *Journal of Pediatric Oncology Nursing, 14*, 202–212.

Norton, T., Manne, S., Rubin, S., Hernandez, E., Carlson, J., Bergman, C., & Rosenblum, N. (2005). Ovarian cancer patients' psychological distress. *Health Psychology, 24*, 143–152.

Pai, A., Patino-Fernandez, A., McSherry, M., Beele, D., Alderfer, M., Reilly, A., & Kazak, A. (2008). The psychosocial assessment tool. *Journal of Pediatric Psychology, 33*, 50–62.

Phipps, S., Long, A., Hudson, M., & Rai, S. N. (2005). Symptoms of post-traumatic stress in children with cancer and their parents: Effects of informant and time from diagnosis. *Pediatric Blood and Cancer, 45*, 952–959.

Phipps, S., Peasant, C., Barrera, M., Alderfer, M. A., Huang, Q. L., & Vannatta, K. (2012). Resilience in children undergoing stem cell transplantation: Results of a complementary intervention trial. *Pediatrics, 129*, E762–E770.

Porter, L., Keefe, F., Hurwitz, H., & Faber, M. (2005). Dislcosure between patients with gastrointestinal cancer and their spouses. *Psycho-Oncology, 14*, 1030–1042.

Pratt, L. A., & Brody, D. J. (2008). Depression in the United States household population, 2005–2006. *NCHS Data Brief, 7*, 1–8.

Ram, N., & Grimm, K. J. (2009). Growth mixture modeling: A method for identifying differences in longitudinal change among unobserved groups. *International Journal of Behavioral Development, 33*, 565–576.

Rime, B. (1995). Mental rumination, social sharing, and the recover from emotional exposure. In J. Pennebaker (Ed.), *Emotion, disclosure, and health* (pp. 271–292). Washington, DC: American Psychological Association.

Sahler, O. J., Dolgin, M., Phipps, S., Fairclough, D., Askins, M., Katz, R. . . . , Butler, R. (2013). Specificity of problem-solving skills training in mothers of children newly diagnosed with cancer: Results of a multi-site randomized clinical trial. *Journal of Clinical Oncology, 31*, 1329–1335.

Sloper, P. (2000). Predictors of distress in parents of children with cancer: A prospective study. *Journal of Pediatric Psychology, 25*, 79–91.

Steele, R., Dreyer, M., & Phipps, S. (2004). Patterns of maternal distress among children with cancer and their association with child emotional and somatic distress. *Journal of Pediatric Psychology, 29*, 507–517.

Streisand, R., Rodrigue, J., Houck, C., Graham-Pole, J., & Berlant, N. (2000). Parents of children undergoing bone marrow transplantation: Documenting stress and piloting a psychological intervention program. *Journal of Pediatric Psychology, 25*, 331–337.

Tait, R., & Silver, R. C. (1989). Coming to terms with major negative life events. In J. S. Uleman & J. A. Bargh (Eds.), *Unintended thought* (pp. 351–382). New York, NY: Guilford Press.

Terrin, N., Rodday, A. M., Tighiouart, H., Chang, G., & Parsons, S. K.; Journeys to Recovery Study. (2013). Parental emotional functioning declines with occurrence of clinical complications in pediatric hematopoietic stem cell transplant. *Supportive Care in Cancer, 21*, 687–695.

Veit, C., & Ware, J. (1983). The structure of psychological distress and well-being in general populations. *Journal of Consulting and Clinical Psychology, 51*, 730–742.

Virtue, S., Manne, S., Mee, L., Bartell, A., Sands, S., Gajda, T., & Darabos, K. (2014). Psychological distress and psychiatric diagnoses among primary caregivers of children undergoing hematopoietic stem cell transplant. *General Hospital Psychiatry, 36*, 620.

Weiss, D. S., & Marmar, C. R. (1997). In J. Wilson & T. Keane (Eds.), *The Impact of Event Scale – Revised.* New York, NY: Guilford Press.

Evaluating Parents' Self-Efficacy for Diabetes Management in Pediatric Type 1 Diabetes

Amy E. Noser,[1] MS, Susana R. Patton,[2] PhD, CDE, Jason Van Allen,[3] PhD, Michael B. Nelson,[4] MD, MPH, and Mark A. Clements,[5] MD, PhD, CPI

[1]Clinical Child Psychology Program, University of Kansas, [2]Department of Pediatrics, University of Kansas Medical Center, [3]Clinical Psychology Program, Department of Psychological Sciences, Texas Tech University, [4]Department of Pediatrics, University of Utah School of Medicine, [5]Division of Endocrinology and Diabetes, Department of Pediatrics, Children's Mercy Kansas City

All correspondence concerning this article should be addressed to Susana R. Patton, PhD, CDE, University of Kansas Medical Center, Mailstop 4004, 3901 Rainbow Boulevard, Kansas City, KS 66160, USA. E-mail: spatton2@kumc.edu

Received April 29, 2016; revisions received July 28, 2016; accepted July 29, 2016

Abstract

Objective To examine the factor structure and construct validity of the Maternal Self-Efficacy for Diabetes Management Scale (MSED) in 135 youth ($M_{age} = 13.50 \pm 1.83$ years), with type 1 diabetes mellitus. **Method** The study used exploratory factor analysis (EFA) to examine the factor structure and correlations to examine relationships among MSED factors and select parent and child diabetes-related health behaviors and outcomes. **Results** EFA identified an 11-item three-factor solution ($\chi^2_{(25, n=133)} = 40.22$, $p < .03$, RMSEA $= 0.07$, CFI $= 0.98$, TLI $= 0.97$), with factors corresponding to parents' perceived ability to manage their child's diabetes (MSED-M), problem-solve issues surrounding glycemic control (MSED-P), and teach their child about diabetes care (MSED-T). Correlational analyses revealed significant associations between the MSED-M and MSED-T and parent-reported optimism and youth's diabetes-specific self-efficacy. The MSED-T was also associated with glycated hemoglobin and self-monitoring blood glucose. **Conclusion** Results provide preliminary evidence for the reliability and validity of a three-factor solution of the MSED.

Key words: adherence; adolescents; assessment; diabetes; parents.

Proper management of type 1 diabetes mellitus (T1DM) poses significant challenges for youth, as it involves frequent blood glucose monitoring, insulin injections or use of an insulin pump, and close monitoring of diet and physical activity (e.g., Silverstein et al., 2005). Given these demands, effective diabetes management generally requires substantial parental involvement through childhood with a gradual shift in responsibility to youth during adolescence (e.g., Anderson, Auslander, Jung, Miller, & Santiage, 1990; King, Berg, Butner, Butler, & Wiebe, 2014). Despite the importance of parental involvement, the demands of diabetes regimens are often burdensome and stressful for parents (e.g., Mellin, Neumark-Sztainer, & Patterson, 2004; Streisand, Swift, Wickmark, Chen, & Holmes, 2005). However, parental self-efficacy for diabetes management is one mechanism that has been shown to help parents overcome the challenges and stressors associated with T1DM in order to facilitate better management of their child's diabetes, as well as to foster their child's development of acceptable diabetes management skills (Streisand et al., 2005, 2008). Indeed, available research suggests that high parental self-efficacy for diabetes management may be associated with positive parent outcomes, including lower levels of stress and anxiety when compared to parents with low self-efficacy (Streisand et al., 2005, 2008). Likewise, the research shows that parental self-efficacy for diabetes is associated with better glycemic control (e.g., Leonard, Skay, & Rheinberger, 1998) and higher perceived competency for diabetes management among youth (Kaugars, Kichler, & Alemzadeh, 2011; Leonard et al., 1998).

Thus, these associations underscore the potential benefit treatments that promote greater parental self-efficacy for diabetes management could have for families.

However, in a recent integrative review that critically evaluated self-efficacy measures developed for youth with T1DM and their caregivers (Rasbach, Jenkins, & Laffel, 2015), the authors noted that the most commonly used measures of parental self-efficacy (e.g., Grossman, Brink, & Hauser, 1987; Iannotti et al., 2006) were adaptations of youth measures. This is a notable point because accurate assessment of self-efficacy requires tailoring measures to the relevant domains of functioning for individuals (Bandura, 2006). Thus, measures developed for persons with T1DM should typically assess their competence in diabetes-specific domains, such as diabetes self-care and problem-solving (Frei, Svarin, Steurer-Stey, & Puhan, 2009; Iannotti et al., 2006), while measures designed for parents should focus on domains directly related to parenting a child with T1DM, such as the parents' ability to teach their child about T1DM or to give effective commands (e.g., Mitchell, & Fraser, 2011; Ranganathan & Montemayor, 2014). Despite these differences in parent and youth self-efficacy for diabetes management, parental self-efficacy measures adapted from youth measures primarily focus on domains of self-care (e.g., "Follow a consistent schedule for diabetes management [eating meals, snacks, giving insulin]," Grossman et al., 1987) and problem-solving (e.g., "Recognize patterns of blood glucose levels that indicate a need for insulin dose/basal rate adjustment," Grossman et al., 1987; "Adjust your child's insulin or food accurately based on how much exercise he/she gets," Iannotti et al., 2006), but do not include items directly relevant to parenting a child with T1DM, therefore weakening their ability to measure the specific domain of parental self-efficacy.

There is only one measure specifically designed for use among parents, the Maternal Self-Efficacy for Diabetes Scale (MSED; Leonard et al., 1998). A strength of the MSED is that it includes items that elicit parents' perceived self-efficacy for teaching diabetes management skills (e.g., "I can teach my child how to take more responsibility for diabetes management"). To develop the MSED, parents of youth with diabetes as well as nurse practitioners reviewed potential items to ensure good content validity. Then, a sample of mothers of youth attending a diabetes summer camp completed the MSED to obtain preliminary psychometrics. While previous research using the MSED has scored the measure based on a single summary score (i.e., summing all 17 items), thus assuming it only examines one dimension of parental self-efficacy, the diversity of items makes it likely that the MSED may represent more than one underlying construct. Thus, the primary purpose of this study was to conduct an exploratory factor analysis (EFA) of the MSED to examine its underlying factor structure. We determined that this was an important next step for this measures ongoing development because identifying underlying factors of the MSED would provide a more refined interpretation of the scale and would make it possible to explore individual differences in parental self-efficacy across domains, which may better identify potential treatment targets. Moreover, a factor structure with more than one underlying construct would also be more consistent with Bandura's original concept, which presupposed that beliefs in personal efficacy could differ across domains of functioning (Bandura, 2006). To assess for convergent and criterion validity, respectively, we also examined latent associations between the MSED factor(s) and parents' self-reported optimism as well as youths' glycated hemoglobin levels (HbA1c), daily self-monitoring blood glucose (SMBG), and diabetes-specific self-efficacy. These variables were selected based on published results which show direct associations between parents' perceived self-efficacy and parents' level of optimism (Bretherton & McLean, 2014), youth's management of T1DM (e.g., Leonard et al., 1998), and youth self-efficacy (e.g., Kaugars et al., 2011).

Method

Participants

This study reports on a subset of data collected during a larger trial, which recruited youth and their primary caregiver from two pediatric diabetes centers in the mid-western United States. Families were eligible to participate if youth had a T1DM diagnosis of greater than 6 months, youth were between 10 and 16 years old, and the family was English speaking. The study had an exclusion criterion for youth who had a concurrent developmental delay (i.e., autism, cerebral palsy, or mental retardation), as well as any psychiatric hospitalization within the last year. One hundred thirty-five families completed study measures (89% recruitment rate); each of which had one participating caregiver (82% mothers; 16% fathers; 1% caregivers; 2% of caregivers did not report their relationship to the youth). Youth had a mean age of 13.5 ± 1.83 years (range: 10–16 years), 54.9% were female, and their racial/ethnic composition was 76.7% Caucasian, 11.6% Hispanic, 6.2% African American, 2.3% Asian, and 3.2% other. At the time of data collection, the HbA1c target in youth 8–13 years old was $< 8.0\%$ and it was $< 7.5\%$ in youth 13–17 years old (Silverstein et al., 2005). The HbA1c values for the present sample of youth ranged from 5.20 to 15.30% ($M = 9.17$, $SD = 2.16$; 37.9% of HbA1c were in the recommended range) and the majority (89.4%) reported using insulin pump therapy.

Procedure
The study recruited parent–youth dyads during their routine diabetes clinic appointments. Participants completed all study measures on a tablet during their scheduled clinic visit and were compensated $25. Prior to patient enrollment, the institutional review boards at each of the participating hospitals reviewed and approved all study procedures.

Measures
Maternal Self-Efficacy for Diabetes Management Scale
This is a 17-item scale, which asks parents or the primary caregiver to rate their confidence in independently managing diabetes-related tasks on a 5-point scale ranging from 1 (*not at all confident*) to 5 (*very confident without help*) (Leonard et al., 1998). Although we initially tested the MSED in only the 104 mothers included in the sample, we elected to expand the sample to include all familial caregivers, as the items do not reference mothers specifically.

Self-Efficacy for Diabetes Scale—Diabetes
The Self-Efficacy for Diabetes Scale—Diabetes (SED-D) is a 24-item measure (Grossman et al., 1987). For each item, youth report their perceived ability for a specific task (e.g., "Keep myself free of high blood sugar levels") using a 6-point scale ranging from 1 (*very sure I can't*) to 6 (*very sure I can*). Past research shows the SED-D has adequate internal consistency ($\alpha = .90$; Kaugars et al., 2011); the internal consistency in the present study was .83.

The Life Orientation Test-Revised
The Life Orientation Test-Revised (LOT-R) is a 6-item measure (Scheier, Carver, & Bridges, 1994). For each item, parents reported their agreement (e.g., "In uncertain times, I usually expect the best") on a 5-point scale from 0 (*strongly disagree*) to 4 (*strongly agree*). Previous studies using the LOT-R provide evidence of its internal consistency ($\alpha = .85$; Lipińska-Grobelny, 2011); the internal consistency in the present study was .86.

Glycated Hemoglobin Levels
As part of the medical appointment, all youth had a point-of-care HbA1c performed and reported to the electronic medical record (EMR), which we later extracted to use as a study demographic variable.

Self-Monitoring Blood Glucose
As part of the medical appointment, all youth provided SMBG data via an electronic download from their glucometer and reported to the EMR, which we later extracted to use as a study demographic variable. Using the most recent 14 days of data, we calculated youth's SMBG score by computing an average of the number of checks performed each day over the 14-day period.

Analytic Plan
Prior to conducting the EFAs, we screened the data for outliers and violations of normality and removed two univariate outliers. However, further evaluation revealed a negative skew for responses on all MSED items. As such, we elected to treat these data as categorical (Brown, 2006). There were two exceptions. For item 12 ("I can change my child's doctor if I don't like him/her") and item 13 ("I can adjust my child's management plan to allow for an overnight stay away from home without parents"), their distribution fell beyond the recommended guidelines for skewness (−3.51 and −2.26, respectively) and kurtosis (12.06 and 4.59, respectively), suggesting that these items may not accurately capture behaviors relevant to this population. Therefore, we elected to omit these items from all subsequent analyses.

To assess the underlying factor structure of the MSED, the present study used EFAs with Mplus 7.2 (Muthén & Muthén, 2012) using weighted least squares mean and variance adjusted (WLSMV) estimator and an oblique Geomin rotation. To evaluate each EFA model, we used multiple fit indices: chi-square (χ^2), the comparative fit index (CFI), the Tucker-Lewis index (TLI), and the root mean square error of approximation (RMSEA). The CFI and TLI values range from 0 to 1; values >.90 represent an acceptable model fit and values >.95 represent a good model fit (Bollen, 1989; Little, 2013). We used the RMSEA to indicate population error variance, with values between .08 and .05 indicative of acceptable model fit and values <.05 indicative of good fit (Hu & Bentler, 1999; Little, 2013). As a first step, we conducted EFAs specifying one to four factors, and retained factor solutions based on their fit indices and interpretability. Then, we reviewed these initial factor solutions examining their item loadings and any Heywood cases (i.e., factor loading >1; negative residual variance; Heywood, 1931), which can occur when solutions extract too many factors or trivial factors with only a few salient loadings. A priori, we had decided to remove any items with loadings ≤0.40 and double loadings ≥0.40. We had also decided to remove items resulting in a Heywood case in order to avoid multicollinearity. Thus, as a final step, we ran a new set of EFAs with items removed that either met our criteria for their loading or represented a

Table I. Fit Statistics for Exploratory Factor Analyses for MSED Models with One to Four Factors

Model	χ^2(df)	p	CFI	TLI	RMSEA
		15-item models			
One-factor	399.18/90	<.001	.78	.74	.16
Two-factor	229.28/76	<.001	.89	.85	.12
Three-factor	157.89/63	<.001	.93	.89	.11
Four-factor	87.76/51	<.001	.97	.95	.07
		14-item models			
One-factor	291.49/90	<.001	.84	.82	.13
Two-factor	149.32/64	<.001	.92	.89	.10
Three-factor	82.46/52	<.001	.97	.95	.07
		13-item model			
Three-factor	63.36/42	.02	.98	.96	.06
		11-item model			
Three-factor	40.22/25	.03	.98	.97	.07

	Number of items	Mean (SD)	Range	α
MSED total score	11	44.69 (6.82)	25–55	.83
MSED-M	2	7.77 (1.76)	4–10	.79
MSED-P	6	25.27 (4.44)	14–30	.79
MSED-T	3	11.65 (2.93)	3–15	.76

Note: 15-item models omit items 12 and 13; 14-item models omit items 12, 13, and 17; 13-item model omits items 12, 13, 17, and 8; and the 11-item model omits items 12, 13, 17, 8, 11 and 16.

Heywood case. We selected our final model based on our predetermined analytical plan, fit, and theoretical content. Once we had selected a final model, we used Mplus 7.2 (Muthén & Muthén, 2012) to determine the convergent and discriminant validity of the MSED (Campbell & Fiske, 1959; Holmbeck et al., 2008) based on correlations among the MSED factors, and between the MSED factors and parents' LOT-R scores, youth's SMBG, HbA1c, and youth's self-efficacy scores. To examine the alpha coefficients of the final model, we used SPSS Version 22 (IBM Corporation., 2013).

Results

In the first step, the EFAs used 15 items of the original MSED (items: 1, 2, 3, 4, 5, 6, 7, 8, 9, 10, 11, 14, 15, 16, and 17), and specified one to four factors (see Table I). Fit statistics suggested that the four-factor EFA model provided an acceptable fit to the data. However, in this factor solution, a Heywood case emerged for item 17 (i.e., factor loading = 1.19; residual variance = −0.40); thus we removed this item and conducted a subsequent set of EFAs estimating one-, two-, and three-factors (see Table I). Results of these analyses revealed an acceptable fit for a 14-item three-factor model (see Table I). Yet, there were three items (i.e., items 8, 11, and 16) with low factor loadings (<0.40) across two iterations, so we removed these items. Thus, the final model was an 11-item three-factor model (see Table I). Notably, item 9 cross-loaded onto factor 2 (.40) and factor 3 (.79); however, this item was retained on factor 3 given its sustainably high loading and theoretical fit with the remaining items loading on factor 3. A conceptual evaluation of the final 11-item three-factor model suggested factors evaluating parents' perceived ability to manage their child's diabetes (MSED-M), problem-solve issues surrounding glycemic control (MSED-P), and teach their child about diabetes care (MSED-T). Factor loadings of the final MSED items are presented in Table II.

Reliability and Validity

The MSED-M, MSED-P, MSED-T, and MSED total score all demonstrated adequate internal consistency (see Table I; Nunnally & Bernstein, 1994). The MSED demonstrated good convergent validity based on significant correlations between the MSED-M and MSED-T and LOT-R (see Table III). Further, significant associations among the MSED-M and MSED-T and youth's diabetes-specific self-efficacy, as well as between MSED-T and youth's SMBG and HbA1c levels, provide evidence of criterion-related validity (see Table III).

Discussion

A lack of validated research on measures of parental self-efficacy for diabetes management and limited availability of measures developed specifically for parents, underscored the importance of examining the

Table II. Factor Loadings of the Final MSED Items Based on Exploratory Factor Analysis

Study variable	Factor 1 (MSED-M)	Factor 2 (MSED-P)	Factor 3 (MSED-T)
1. I am confident in my ability to help my child manage diabetes	**.91**	.00	.00
2. I can help my child fit his/her diabetes management plan into a normal lifestyle	**.77**	.01	.16
5. I can adjust my child's management plan when s/he is more active than usual	−.02	**.85**	.07
4. I can determine what to do if my child's blood sugar is higher that it should be	.01	**.76**	−.11
7. I can adjust my child's management plan to avoid low blood sugar (insulin reactions)	.18	**.66**	−.06
6. I can adjust my child's insulin dose based on the results of blood or urine tests	.06	**.63**	.05
3. I can adjust my child's management plan if s/he gets a cold or the flu	.30	**.55**	.00
14. I can adjust my child's management plan with changes in schedule (for example, from school to summer schedule)	−.02	**.55**	.37
9. I can teach my child how to take more responsibility for diabetes management	.00	.40	**.79**
15. I can be successful in getting my child to follow his/her management plan, even when s/he may be reluctant or resistant at first	.38	−.01	**.74**
10. I can talk to my child about the realities of long-term complications without undue upset	.01	.34	**.59**
8. I can advocate for my child's best care in community settings[a]	−.03	.31	.37
11. Can advocate for better health care for my child if I am concerned about unfairness or unreasonableness[a]	−.05	.30	.39
16. I can organize our family mealtimes and schedule so that my child can eat most meals at the same time each day[a]	.09	.33	.40

Note: Items retained on each factor indicated in bold. MSED-M = parental self-efficacy to manage youth's diabetes; MSED-P = parental self-efficacy to problem-solve issues surrounding glycemic control; MSED-T = parental self-efficacy to teach their child diabetes care.
[a]Loadings reported for item 8 are from the 13-item model, whereas loadings reported for items 11 and 16 are from the 14-item model.

Table III. Intercorrelations Among MSED Factors and Parent and Child Outcomes

Study variable	1	2	3	4	5	6	7
1. MSED-M	—						
2. MSED-P	.62***	—					
3. MSED-T	.61***	.51***	—				
4. LOT-R	.28**	.05	.31***	—			
5. SED-D	.29**	.16	.42***	.11	—		
6. HbA1c	−.17	.06	−.32***	−.05	−.30***	—	
7. SMBG	.05	.00	.21*	−.12	.05	−.41***	—

Note. MSED-M = parental self-efficacy to manage youth's diabetes; MSED-P = parental self-efficacy to problem-solve issues surrounding glycemic control; MSED-T = parental self-efficacy to teach their child diabetes care; LOT-R = parents' self-reported optimism; SED-D = youth's diabetes-specific self-efficacy; SMBG = self-monitoring blood glucose.
*$p < .05$,
**$p < .01$,
***$p < .001$.

factor structure of the MSED (Rasbach et al., 2015), which was the focus of the present study. As mentioned previously, the MSED has previously been scored as a single-factor. However, current findings suggest a three-factor structure best represents the MSED. Model fit of the three-factor solution was good with factors corresponding to parents' perceived ability to manage their child's diabetes, problem-solve issues surrounding glycemic control, and teach their child about diabetes care.

It is notable that our results suggest that several of the original MSED items may not contribute to the measurement of parental self-efficacy for diabetes management. For instance, limited variability on two items (i.e., items 12 and 13) suggests that parents may have perceived these as low challenge items (Bandura, 2006). Indeed, the literature supports that most parents report a high level of confidence in their ability to communicate concerns or redirect their child's physician (Janicke & Finney, 2003). As such, it seems reasonable that parents of youth with T1DM would also report a high level of confidence for these items. Furthermore, the emergence of a Heywood case (i.e., item 17), and insufficient factor loadings for several items (i.e., 8, 11, and 16) indicates that these items may not provide meaningful information for the measurement of parental self-efficacy for diabetes management. For example, it is possible that a parent could interpret the use of "unfairness and unreasonableness" in item 11 differently or fail to see this as related to illness status versus another characteristic (e.g., child's age or ethnicity), which would limit this item's relevance to parental self-efficacy for diabetes management.

Reliability and validity analyses provided further support for the MSED three-factor solution. Internal consistency was adequate for all three factors, indicating that items loading onto the factors served as an appropriate measure of the construct. Further, examination of latent correlations among the factors suggests that MSED factors represent related, yet distinct constructs. In addition, latent correlations between the MSED-M and MSED-T and a measure of parents' self-report optimism provided support for the convergent validity of the scale. Consistent with previous research (e.g., Bretherton & McLean, 2014; Caprara & Steca, 2006; Magaletta & Oliver, 1999), self-efficacy was positively correlated with parents' reported levels of optimism. The results also showed evidence of criterion-related validity through the positive correlation found between MSED-T and SMBG as well as the negative correlation between MSED-T and youth's HbA1c. This is logical, as it suggests that youth may demonstrate greater frequency of SMBG and better glycemic control when their parents demonstrate greater confidence in diabetes management and/or in teaching youth about their diabetes care. In addition, youth's diabetes-specific self-efficacy was positively associated with the MSED-M and MSED-T. This suggests that high parental self-efficacy for diabetes management and teaching management skills may positively influence youth's confidence for managing their diabetes.

The MSED's proposed three-factor structure appears adequate and to contribute relevant information on the domains of parental self-efficacy for diabetes management. Although additional confirmatory research is necessary to establish whether covariance among MSED factors are best accounted for by a higher order factor, it is notable that correlations between the factors suggest this possibility, making it plausible to still report a total MSED score. Interpretation of the total score would likely provide a useful overview of parents' confidence surrounding diabetes management, and therefore, may be informative for screening purposes in both research and clinical practice. For example, researchers and clinicians may turn to the MSED total score to screen a large number of parents and identify those with lower self-efficacy who could benefit from further evaluation or intervention. Then within this smaller subset of parents, the MSED subscale scores could be used to identify specific areas of concerns and guide treatment.

Clinical Implications

The MSED is a practical and accessible measure of parental self-efficacy for diabetes management which can be easily administered in the context of clinical care, especially now in the proposed 11-item length. Use of the MSED as a screening tool may help clinicians identify parents with low levels of self-efficacy for diabetes management, an important component of maintaining youth's diabetes care. Further, the proposed three-factor structure may help clinicians identify the unique treatment needs of families, rather than broadly addressing parents' perceived abilities for managing their child's diabetes. For example, low scores on the MSED-P may prompt clinicians to discuss problem-solving skills with parents. In addition, MSED subscales may provide a better understanding of intervention targets that enhance adherence to pediatric diabetes regimens. Specifically, MSED subscales could be used by clinicians and researchers to identify intervention targets, track progress over time, assess treatment outcomes, and would allow for comparisons of subscale scores across various individual (e.g., parent depression, education) and family (e.g., conflict, cohesiveness) characteristics.

Limitations

A significant strength of the study was the examination of the MSED's relation with youth's diabetes-specific self-efficacy as well as an objective assessment of SMBG and HbA1c. However, there are also some limitations. First, similar to studies using other measures of diabetes-specific self-efficacy (Kappen, van der Bijl, & Vaccaro-Olko, 2001) as well as measures of academic self-efficacy (Diseth, Meland, & Breidablik, 2014; Toland & Usher, 2015), MSED items demonstrated limited variation, indicating that the instrument may be vulnerable to response biases. This is problematic because it can limit researchers' ability to detect potentially meaningful differences in parents' self-efficacy. Alternatively, the MSED may suffer from method effects due to its format, which may influence participant response. For example, participant responding tends to show greater acquiescence with items, irrespective of item content, when response scales include a midpoint, perhaps because the midpoint leads to movement of otherwise negative responses in a positive direction (Weijters, Cabooter, & Schillewaert, 2010). However, research has also shown greater acquiescence for fully labeled response scales, perhaps because the labels increase the clarity and salience of items, which, in turn, leads to a greater positive response bias (Tourangeau, Rips, & Rasinski, 2000). The MSED includes both a midpoint and fully labeled responses. Thus, in the future, it may be valuable to test an updated form of the MSED to see if an optimal number of response items and number of labels can be determined to promote greater response variation. Second, the present study used a relatively homogeneous sample of parents, which also limits its generalizability. Therefore, future research is needed evaluating the MSED in parents from diverse racial-ethnic backgrounds as well as parents of both older and younger children. Third, it is notable that correlations between the factors suggest the presence of a higher order factor, making it possible to report a total MSED score. However, we believe future studies are needed to examine the stability of a MSED total score in the context of confirmatory factor analysis. Similarly, future studies are needed to establish the test–retest reliability and divergent validity of the MSED.

Conclusion

In conclusion, this study provided preliminary evidence for the reliability and validity of a MSED three-factor solution assessing parental self-efficacy for diabetes management. The MSED is the only measure of diabetes self-efficacy developed specifically for parents, and this study represents the only EFA validation of the measure. Unique associations among the three MSED subscales and parent- and child-report of diabetes-related health outcomes suggest that assessing domains of parental self-efficacy may be useful for clinicians and researchers alike. Moreover, use of the MSED in practice and research may provide an advantage over adapted measures given its ability to assess parents' unique efficacy beliefs for diabetes management. Therefore, we recommend that future research rely on the three-factor solution of the MSED for examining parental self-efficacy for diabetes management. Additionally, researchers are encouraged to conduct further assessment of the MSED's validity, particularly through confirmatory work with diverse parent–youth samples.

Funding

This research was supported in part by a grant from the Diabetes Institute of the University of Kansas Medical Center (to S.R.P.), and by a grant R01-DK100779 (to S.R.P.) from the National Institutes of Health/National Institute of Diabetes and Digestive and Kidney Diseases.

Conflicts of interest: None declared.

References

Anderson, B. J., Auslander, W. F., Jung, K.C., Miller, J.P., & Santiago, J.V. (1990). Assessing family sharing of diabetes responsibilities. *Journal of Pediatric Psychology*, 15, 477–492. doi:10.1093/jpepsy/15.4.477

Bandura, A. (2006). Guide for constructing self-efficacy scales. In F. Pajares,& T. Urdan (Eds.), *Self-efficacy beliefs of adolescents* (pp. 307–337). Greenwich, CT: Information Age Publishing.

Bollen, K. A. (1989). A new incremental fit index for general structural equation models. *Sociological Methods and Research*, 17, 303–316.

Bretherton, S. J., & McLean, L. A. (2014). Mediating effects of perceived control in the relationship between optimism and adjustment in parents of children with disabilities. *Journal of Developmental and Physical Disabilities*, 26, 357–369. doi:10.1007/s10882-014-9371-7

Brown, T. A. (2006). *Confirmatory factor analysis for applied research*. New York, NY: Guildford Press.

Campbell, D. T., & Fiske, D. W. (1959). Convergent and discriminant validation by the multitrait-multimethod matrix. *Psychological Bulletin*, 56, 81–105. doi:10.1037/h0046016

Caprara, G. V., & Steca, P. (2006). The contribution of self-regulatory efficacy beliefs in managing affect and family relationships to positive thinking and hedonic balance. *Journal of Social and Clinical Psychology*, 25, 603–627. doi:10.1521/jscp.2006.25.6.603

Diseth, A., Meland, E., & Breidablik, H. J. (2014). Self-beliefs among students: Grade level and gender differences in self-esteem, self-efficacy and implicit theories of intelligence. *Learning and Individual Differences*, 35, 1–8. doi:10.1016/j.lindif.2014.06.003

Frei, A., Svarin, A., Steurer-Stey, C., & Puhan, M. A. (2009). Self-efficacy instruments for patients with chronic diseases suffer from methodological limitations: A systematic review. *Health and Quality of Life Outcomes*, 7, 86–95. doi:10.1186/1477-7525-7-86

Grossman, H. Y., Brink, S., & Hauser, S. T. (1987). Self-efficacy in adolescent girls and boys with insulin-dependent diabetes mellitus. *Diabetes Care*, 10, 324–329.

Heywood, H. B. (1931). On finite sequences of real numbers. *Proceedings of the Royal Society of London. Series a, Containing Papers of a Mathematical and Physical Character*, 134, 486–501.

Holmbeck, G. N., Thill, A. W., Bachanas, P., Garber, J., Miller, K. B., Abad, M. ..., & Zukerman, J. (2008). Evidence-based assessment in pediatric psychology: Measures of psychosocial adjustment and psychopathology. *Journal of Pediatric Psychology, 33*, 958–980. doi:10.1093/jpepsy/jsm059

Hu, L.-t., & Bentler, P. M. (1999). Cutoff criteria for fit indexes in covariance structure analysis: Conventional criteria versus new alternatives. *Structural Equation Modeling: A Multidisciplinary Journal, 6*, 1–55.

Iannotti, R. J., Schneider, S., Nansel, T. R., Haynie, D. L., Plotnick, L. P., Clark, L. M ..., , & Simons-Morton, B. (2006). Self-efficacy, outcome expectations, and diabetes self-management in adolescents with type 1 diabetes. *Journal of Developmental and Behavioral Pediatrics, 27*, 98–105.

IBM Corporation. (2013). *IBM SPSS Statistics for Windows, Version 22.0.* Armonk, NY: IBM Corporation.

Janicke, D. M., & Finney, J. W. (2003). Children's primary health care services: Social-cognitive factors related to utilization. *Journal of Pediatric Psychology, 28*, 547–558. doi:10.1093/jpepsy/jsg045

Kappen, M. J., van der Bijl, J. J., & Vaccaro-Olko, M. J. (2001). Self-efficacy in children with diabetes mellitus: Testing of a measurement instrument. *Scholarly Inquiry for Nursing Practice, 15*, 209–221.

Kaugars, A. S., Kichler, J. C., & Alemzadeh, R. (2011). Assessing readiness to change the balance of responsibility for managing type 1 diabetes mellitus: Adolescent, mother, and father perspectives. *Pediatric Diabetes, 12*, 547–555. doi:10.1111/j.1399-5448.2010.00737.x

King, P. S., Berg, C. A., Butner, J., Butler, J. M., & Wiebe, D. J. (2014). Longitudinal trajectories of parental involvement in type 1 diabetes and adolescents' adherence. *Health Psychology, 33*, 424–432. doi:10.1037/a0032804

Leonard, B. J., Skay, C. L., & Rheinberger, M. M. (1998). Self-management development in children and adolescents with diabetes: The role of maternal self-efficacy and conflict. *Journal of Pediatric Nursing, 13*, 224–233. doi:10.1016/S0882-5963(98)80049-3

Lipińska-Grobelny, A. (2011). Effects of gender role on personal resources and coping with stress. *International Journal of Occupational Medicine and Environmental Health, 24*, 18–28. doi:10.2478/s13382-011-0002-6

Little, P. T. D. (2013). *Longitudinal structural equation modeling.* New York, NY: Guilford Press.

Magaletta, P. R., & Oliver, J. M. (1999). The hope construct, will, and ways: Their relations with self-efficacy, optimism, and general well-being. *Journal of Clinical Psychology, 55*, 539–551. doi:10.1002/(SICI)1097-4679(199905)55:5

Mellin, A. E., Neumark-Sztainer, D., & Patterson, J. M. (2004). Parenting adolescent girls with type 1 diabetes: Parents' perspectives. *Journal of Pediatric Psychology, 29*, 221–230. doi:10.1093/jpepsy/jsh023

Mitchell, A. E., & Fraser, J. A. (2011). Parents' self-efficacy, outcome expectations, and self-reported task performance when managing atopic dermatitis in children: Instrument reliability and validity. *International Journal of Nursing Studies, 48*, 215–226. doi:10.1016/j.ijnurstu.2010.06.008

Muthén, L. K., & Muthén, B. O. (2012). *Mplus user's guide* (7th ed.). Los Angeles, CA: Muthén & Muthén.

Nunnally, J. C., & Bernstein, I. R. (1994). *Psychometric theory.* New York: McGraw-Hill.

Ranganathan, C., & Montemayor, R. (2014). Parental efficacy, parental monitoring efficacy, and monitoring among Asian-Indian parents of adolescents living in Chennai, India. *Journal of Adolescence, 37*, 1363–1372. doi:10.1016/j.adolescence.2014.10.002

Rasbach, L., Jenkins, C., & Laffel, L. (2015). An integrative review of self-efficacy measurement instruments in youth with type 1 diabetes. *The Diabetes Educator, 41*, 43–58. doi:10.1177/0145721714550254

Scheier, M. F., Carver, C. S., & Bridges, M. W. (1994). Distinguishing optimism from neuroticism (and trait anxiety, self-mastery, and self-esteem): A re-evaluation of the life orientation test. *Journal of Personality and Social Psychology, 67*, 1063–1078. doi:10.1037/0022-3514.67.6.1063

Silverstein, J., Klingensmith, G., Copeland, K., Plotnick, L., Kaufman, F., Laffel, L ..., & Clark, N. (2005). Care of children and adolescents with type 1 diabetes a statement of the American Diabetes Association. *Diabetes Care, 28*, 186–212. doi:10.2337

Streisand, R., Mackey, E. R., Elliot, B. M., Mednick, L., Slaughter, I. M., Turek, J., & Austin, A. (2008). Parental anxiety and depression associated with caring for a child newly diagnosed with type 1 diabetes: Opportunities for education and counseling. *Patient Education and Counseling, 73*, 333–338. doi:10.1016/j.pec.2008.06.014

Streisand, R., Swift, E., Wickmark, T., Chen, R., & Holmes, C. S. (2005). Pediatric parenting stress among parents of children with type 1 diabetes: The role of self-efficacy, responsibility, and fear. *Journal of Pediatric Psychology, 30*, 513–521. doi: 10.1093/jpepsy/jsi076

Toland, M. D., & Usher, E. L. (2015). Assessing mathematics self-efficacy: How many categories do we really need? *The Journal of Early Adolescence, 36*, 1–29. http://jea.sagepub.com.www2.lib.ku.edu/content/early/2015/06/09/0272431615588952.full.pdf+html doi:10.1177/0272431615588952

Tourangeau, R., Rips, L. J., & Rasinski, K. (2000). *The psychology of survey response.* Cambridge, UK: Cambridge University Press.

Weijters, B., Cabooter, E., & Schillewaert, N. (2010). The effect of rating scale format on response styles: The number of response categories and response category labels. *International Journal of Research in Marketing, 27*, 236–247. doi:10.1016/j.ijresmar.2010.02.004

Maternal and Paternal Distress and Coping Over Time Following Pediatric Traumatic Brain Injury

Megan E. Narad,[1] PHD, Keith O. Yeates,[2] PHD, H. Gerry Taylor,[3] PHD, Terry Stancin,[4] PHD, and Shari L. Wade,[1] PHD

[1]Cincinnati Children's Hospital Medical Center, Cincinnati, OH, [2]Department of Psychology, Alberta Children's Hospital Research Institute, Hotchkiss Brain Institute, University of Calgary, [3]Rainbow Babies & Children's Hospital, University Hospitals Case Medical Center, Case Western Reserve University, and [4]MetroHealth Medical Center, Case Western Reserve University

All correspondence concerning this article should be addressed to Megan E. Narad, PHD, Division of Physical Medicine and Rehabilitation & Behavioral Medicine and Clinical Psychology, Cincinnati Children's Hospital Medical Center, 3333 Burnet Avenue, Cincinnati, OH 45229, USA. E-mail: megan.narad@cchmc.org

Received December 28, 2015; revisions received August 15, 2016; accepted August 23, 2016

Abstract

Objective Examine differences in maternal and paternal coping and distress following traumatic brain injury (TBI) and orthopedic injuries (OI). **Method** Concurrent cohort/prospective design with five assessments between 1 and an average of 7 years after injury of children aged 3–6 years hospitalized for TBI ($n = 87$) or OI ($n = 119$). Mixed models analyses were used to examine hypotheses. **Results** Overall, fathers reported greater depression and general distress than mothers 18 months after injury, but not at long-term follow-up. Active and acceptance coping were unrelated to parental sex, injury factors, or time since injury. A group × rater × time interaction was noted for Denial coping. Following severe TBI, fathers reported greater denial at 18 months, whereas mothers reported greater denial at the long-term follow-up. Denial coping did not differ between mothers and fathers following OI and moderate TBI. **Conclusions** Parental response to early TBI is complex and may warrant clinical intervention even years after injury.

Key words: accidents and injuries; children; coping; parent stress.

Pediatric traumatic brain injury (TBI) is one of the leading causes of morbidity and mortality in childhood, and the most common source of acquired disability in children (Thurman, 2014). Moderate to severe TBI in childhood is associated with significant cognitive and behavioral sequelae (Babikian, Merkley, Savage, Giza, & Levin, 2015). Parents of children with TBI are faced with unique stressors regarding their child's recovery, including adjustment to emerging behavioral difficulties and concern over long-term functioning and implications for independence (Babikian et al., 2015). As such, TBI and recovery following injury are significant stressors for families, resulting in increased caregiver burden and psychological distress even years after the injury (Ganesalingam et al., 2008; Rivara et al., 1992; Rivara et al., 1996; Verhaeghe, Defloor, & Grypdonck, 2005; Wade et al., 2002). More than one-third of parents of children with TBI report clinically elevated levels of anxiety and depression (Hawley, Ward, Magnay, & Long, 2003; Wade, Taylor, Drotar, Stancin, & Yeates, 1998), and researchers have identified a reciprocal relationship between levels of parental distress and child behaviors (Taylor et al., 2001), further reflecting the importance of addressing parent and family outcomes following childhood TBI.

The impact of TBI on caregivers and families is well documented (Aitken et al., 2009; Shudy et al., 2006); however, these findings are most often based on mothers' reports with little attention given to fathers' response to injury. Fathers' roles within the family and involvement in child rearing have increased in recent years (Lamb, 2013). Additionally, pediatric research has demonstrated that fathers' involvement does have an impact on all aspects of child development and behavior (Phares, Lopez, Fields, Kamboukos, & Duhig, 2005), highlighting the importance of understanding how fathers experience stressors related to their child's health and well-being. Moreover, most investigations examining caregiver response and family adaptation to injury focus on the initial year after injury or are cross-sectional in nature, therefore neglecting the long-term outcomes for parents and families and limiting the ability to examine the change in functioning over time. A better understanding of trajectories of maternal and paternal coping and distress is crucial for developing interventions that are responsive to the needs of both mothers and fathers.

Parental distress appears to be related to the type of injury as well as the age at which the child was injured. Research indicates that parents of children who sustain a TBI in the preschool years report greater general distress during the initial 18 months postinjury compared with parents of children with orthopedic injuries (OI), and levels of parental distress are higher for parents of children injured later in childhood than for those injured in the preschool years (Fay et al., 2009; Stancin, Wade, Walz, Yeates, & Taylor, 2010). These findings provide insight into parental distress following injury of preschool-aged children during early childhood but fail to inform us about potential longer-term changes in parental distress (beyond 18 months after injury) as the injured child progresses through the school-age years. Increasing demands for self-regulation and executive function skills during middle school may contribute to emerging neurocognitive and behavioral deficits and concomitant parental distress as the child ages (Anderson et al., 1997; Anderson et al., 2006; Catroppa, Anderson, Morse, Haritou, & Rosenfeld, 2008; Ewing-Cobbs et al., 2006; Fay et al., 2009), with children injured at younger ages especially prone to these adverse effects (Ewing-Cobbs et al., 2006).

How parents cope with and manage ongoing stressors is an important determinant of their distress (Wade et al., 2001). Lazarus and Folkman (1984) define coping as cognitive and/or behavioral efforts to manage the demands of a stressor or emotional response to a stressor. Coping styles are often divided into two distinct categories: emotion focused strategies, aimed at managing the emotional distress created by stressors, and problem-focused strategies, aimed at managing distress by modifying the source of the problem. While problem-focused coping strategies have been theoretically and empirically linked with more positive psychological outcomes than emotion-focused or denial/disengagement coping strategies (Compas & Boyer, 2001), the effectiveness of a given coping style may vary depending on the nature of the stressor (Baker & Berenbaum, 2007; Wade et al., 2001). Although avoidant coping/disengagement has been consistently linked with negative outcomes and increased distress (Aldwin & Revenson, 1987; Billings & Moos, 1984; Felton & Revenson, 1984; Felton, Revenson, & Hinrichsen, 1984; Holahan & Moos, 1987; Wade et al., 2001), problem-focused coping may be most beneficial in situations that can be changed, whereas emotion-focused coping may be healthier in unalterable situations. For example, parents of children with OI face sequelae that can be addressed through problem-focused strategies such as attending medical appointments, having casts removed, and completing physical therapy. On the other hand, the neurological complications associated with TBI are unlikely to improve in response to the parents' active efforts to change the situation. Wade et al. (2001) showed that active coping strategies were reported more frequently by parents of children with TBI compared with parents of children with OI; however, active coping was associated with increased parental distress in the TBI group. Therefore, for parents of children with TBI, managing one's own emotional reactions to the stressors may be more successful in reducing caregiver distress than active coping directed at changing the neurological consequences (Wade et al., 2001).

While parental burden and distress are common consequences of childhood injuries, Perlesz & O'loughlan (1998) point out that relatives of individuals with TBI are not universally distressed, underscoring the need to identify factors associated with positive adjustment. Research on parental coping, burden, and distress following childhood TBI is most often based on primary caregiver (typically mother's) report. Findings are mixed regarding how mothers and fathers differ in response to their child's illness, injury, or disability (Holmbeck et al., 1997; Macias, Saylor, Haire, & Bell, 2007; Sloper, 2000; Wade et al., 2010). Wade et al. (2010) found that fathers endorsed greater distress than mothers following both severe TBI and OI. Further, Benn and McColl (2004) noted that mothers were more likely than fathers to use coping strategies aimed at altering the perception of the injury and its aftermath. Wade et al. (2010) found that during the first 18 months after injury, mothers reported using more acceptance-based coping regardless of type of injury or time since injury, while fathers' coping varied over time in relation to the type and severity of the injury. This lack of consensus, coupled with evidence of a bidirectional relationship between parental functioning and child outcomes following TBI (Raj et al., 2014; Taylor et al., 2001), warrant further research to examine both maternal and paternal distress and coping over longer periods following TBI in childhood.

The current project builds on a previous report by Wade et al. (2010) regarding parental coping, injury-related burden, and psychological distress in mothers and fathers of preschool-aged children with TBI during the first 18 months after injury. The present study extends this prospective longitudinal investigation to a long-term follow-up assessment of parental coping and psychological outcomes when the child entered early adolescence and experienced increased demands on academic and social functioning. Although Wade et al (2010) examined only ratings from parent dyads, the current study considered data from all parents in the sample regardless of whether ratings were obtained from one or both parents. Based on the findings reported in Wade et al. (2010), we hypothesized that fathers would report higher levels of distress than mothers regardless of injury characteristics. In view of the persisting effects of TBI on children's behavior and the potential for associated increases in parent distress over time (Taylor et al., 2001), we also hypothesized that parental distress would increase over time for parents of children with TBI (with a greater increase in families of children with severe TBI than those with moderate TBI), while decreasing among parents of children with OI. Similar to Wade et al. (2010), we further expected fathers of children with TBI to report greater use of denial than mothers, with more pronounced effects in the severe TBI group than the moderate TBI and OI groups, while mothers of children in all injury groups would report using more positive coping strategies (acceptance and active coping) than fathers. Finally, we anticipated that parents of children with TBI would report more changes in coping strategies over time than parents of children with OI, given the potential for persisting cognitive and behavioral consequences of TBI to erode parent satisfaction with strategies used more immediately after injury. Further it is hypothesized that parents of children with severe TBI would report more changes in strategies over time than parents of children with moderate TBI.

This report focuses on maternal and paternal coping and distress in early adolescence from a 12-year, prospective longitudinal study of early TBI that has resulted in >30 papers focusing largely on predictors of child cognitive and behavioral outcomes. Only two previous papers focused on early parental coping or distress, with one of these considering both paternal and maternal responses (Stancin et al., 2010; Wade et al., 2010). Thus, the focus of the current paper on paternal and maternal response is relatively unique both within our research and the broader pediatric TBI literature. Given the variability of recovery trajectory following TBI (Narad et al., 2016), understanding how parents cope with varying stressors long-term after injury is an important/unique contribution to the literature. Further, there is scant literature regarding fathers' response to injury or chronic illness. Most research focuses on primary caregivers, most often mothers, with fathers not assessed or treated as secondary caregivers. To situate the current findings in the extant literature and identify potential avenues for intervention, we have chosen to examine maternal and paternal ratings together. In a separate report, currently under review, we have examined the cross-lagged associations between maternal distress and child behavior (Petranovich et al., under review). Focusing the present article on maternal and paternal outcomes, rather than child outcomes, allows us to address critical gaps in the literature.

Method

Research Design

The study used a prospective, concurrent cohort research design to examine the long-term coping and distress of mothers and fathers of children with TBI relative to a comparison group of parents of children with OI. The study was approved by the institutional review boards at each of the participating medical centers.

Participants

Participants were parents of children hospitalized between 2003 and 2006 for TBI or OI between the ages of 3 and 7 years at three children's hospitals and one general hospital in Ohio. Assessments were completed at multiple time points, including post-discharge baseline (0–3 months after injury), more immediate follow-ups at 6, 12, and 18 months after injury, and a long-term follow-up an average of 6.7 years after injury (2013–2015). This long-term follow-up was timed to coincide with middle-school/early adolescents to examine the potential for emerging deficits. The time since injury for this long-term follow up ranged from 4.47 to 10.58 years. Inclusion criteria included the absence of evidence of child abuse or a history of neurological problems or developmental delays before injury and English as the primary language at home. The OI group included children who sustained a bone fracture (excluding skull fracture), had an overnight stay in the hospital, and did not exhibit alterations in consciousness or other signs or symptoms of head trauma or brain injury. The severity of TBI was characterized using the lowest postresuscitation Glasgow Coma Scale (GCS) score. Severe TBI was defined as a GCS score <9 and moderate TBI as a GCS score of 9–12 or a higher GCS score accompanied by abnormal brain imaging.

Families of 87 children with TBI (53.40% of those identified as potentially eligible) and 119 with OI

(35.10% of those identified as potentially eligible) completed informed consent and were enrolled. Of the total sample, 67.33% had married parents, and 64.85% had reports from both caregivers at baseline. See Table I for sample demographics and Table II for the number of mothers and fathers who completed ratings of coping and distress at each time point.

Procedure and Measures

At each follow-up assessment, parents completed ratings of their coping in response to the injury and of their psychological distress. The strategies used by the caregiver to cope with their child's injury and its sequelae were assessed with the COPE (Carver, Scheier, & Weintraub, 1989). The COPE is a 60-item self-report inventory that measures a variety of aspects of coping behavior. The situational version of the COPE was used and included the following statement in the instructions: "We are *specifically* interested in how you are dealing with the stress that has been created by your child's injury." Three coping summary scales were created based on previous research, theory, and statistical confirmation. The three summary scales include active coping (active coping, planning, suppression of competing activities); acceptance coping (acceptance, restraint coping, positive reinterpretation, and growth); and denial/disengagement (denial, mental disengagement, behavioral disengagement). Active coping was interpreted as reflecting problem-focused strategies, acceptance coping was interpreted as capturing emotion-focused strategies, and denial/disengagement was interpreted as representing maladaptive strategies. The average standardized Cronbach's alphas over time for each of the coping factors were as follows: active coping = .88, acceptance coping = .74, denial/disengagement = .70.

Parent psychological distress at the baseline and initial four follow-up visits was assessed using the Brief Symptom Inventory (BSI) (Derogatis, 1993a), a 53-item questionnaire assessing a wide range of psychological symptoms with well-established reliability and validity. Psychological distress at the extended follow-up visit was assessed using the Symptom Checklist-90-R, a 90-item self-report questionnaire. The SCL-90-R is the parent, longer version of the BSI (Derogatis, 1993b). There is support for the equivalence of the SCL-90-R and BSI, and correlations between scales on the two measures are high (.92–.99; Derogatis, 1993a; Derogatis, 1993b; Derogatis & Melilsaratos, 1983). Both scales yield nine dimension scores as well as three summary scales. Depressive symptoms are a common parental response following pediatric TBI; therefore, both the depression scale (DEP) and General Severity Index were examined. The DEP was used to assess levels of depression and includes items related to dysphoric affect and mood, loss of interests, loss of energy, and feelings of hopelessness. The GSI combines the number of symptoms endorsed with the intensity of reported distress, and was used as an index of global psychological distress. In both cases, higher scores are indicative of greater distress. GSI and DEP scales are presented as T-scores, with scores ≥63 indicative of clinically elevated symptoms (Derogatis, 1993a; Derogatis & Melilsaratos, 1983).

Data Analysis

Linear mixed models were used to examine parental coping and distress over time in relation to injury

Table I. Demographics Table

	Severe traumatic brain injury ($n = 22$)	Moderate traumatic brain injury ($n = 63$)	Orthopedic injuries ($n = 117$)	p-value
Age at injury	4.88 (0.96)	5.04 (1.20)	5.11 (1.07)	.40
Sex (%) males	68.18	58.73	57.26	.63
Race (%) non-White	31.82	33.33	22.22	.16
Marital status (%) married	45.45	55.56	77.78	.002
Rater (%) with two raters	45.45	55.56	73.50	.01

Table II. Depicts the Number of Patients With Mother Only Report, Father Only Report, and Both Mother and Father Report by Injury Group Over Time

	Baseline			6 months			12 months			18 months			Long term		
	Severe	Mod	OI	Severe	Mod	OI	Severe	Mod	OI	Severe	Mod	OI	Severe	Mod	OI
Mother only	11	25	30	9	23	27	12	21	20	10	24	23	5	18	17
Father only	1	1	1	1	1	1	0	2	0	0	0	0	1	2	2
Mother and father	10	35	86	9	32	71	9	31	67	11	27	64	9	21	52
Total N	22	63	117	20	56	99	21	54	87	21	51	87	16	42	72

Note: Severe = severe traumatic brain injury, Mod = moderate traumatic brain injury, OI = orthopedic injury.

group (severe TBI, moderate TBI, OI) and rater (mother vs. father). Fully saturated models were run, and all interactions were retained in the final model, regardless of level of significance. Mixed models were run using PROC MIXED in Statistical Analysis System (SAS), which uses maximum likelihood estimation making use of all data available. Separate models were examined for each of the three coping summary scores (active, acceptance, denial/disengagement), GSI, and DEP scores for a total of five analyses, and post hoc comparisons within the models were used to understand significant findings. Family socioeconomic status (SES), defined by the average of the z-scores for maternal education and median income for the census tract in which the family resided, was included as covariate in analyses. Time since injury was treated as a continuous variable in the primary analysis but was classified by visit number to examine interactions involving time. To adjust for multiple comparisons, we used a p level of .025 for the significance level for parental distress models as measured by the BSI (0.05/2 scales), and .0167 for the significance level for coping style models as assessed by the COPE (0.05/3 styles).

Additionally, to better understand the factors associated with elevated parental distress, a binary variable was created using the GSI and DEP scales of the BSI, with scores ≥63 indicative of clinically elevated symptoms. It is possible that for the most part parents are reporting levels of distress within normal limits; therefore, examining factors associated with clinical elevations will help to identify parents/families under greatest distress and at most need for intervention. Logistic regression using PROC GENMOD in SAS was completed to determine whether rater sex, injury severity, or time since injury impacted whether parents reported clinically elevated levels of distress. The mixed models analyses discussed above will allow the examination of factors associated with the full range of reported parental distress, while the logistic regression will allow for the examination of these factors in the most at-risk parent group.

Models were also run using only participants with two parent ratings, and all results remained the same. Interestingly, parents of children with TBI were more likely to be unmarried at the time of injury. Models were run controlling for marital status, and all injury-related findings became nonsignificant. Because marital status at the time of injury was used to define this variable, this differential marital status was not a result of the injury but instead seems to be intrinsic in the population (possibly related to SES). For this reason, we decided not to control for marital status in the presented analyses.

Results

SES, injury severity, and child sex did not change over time, suggesting that attrition was not impacted by these demographic variables.

Parent Psychological Distress
Depression

Analysis of the depression subscale from the BSI and SCL-90 revealed a significant main effect of rater, $F(1,151) = 43.95$, $p < .01$, and rater × time interaction, $F(1,1138) = 6.84$, $p = .01$ (Table III). The effect of rater is best understood within the context of the rater × time interaction. Regardless of injury type or severity, fathers reported greater levels of depression than mothers during the initial 18 months after injury (Baseline: $p < .01$, 6 months: $p < .01$, 12

Table III. Mean, Standard Error, and n for Parent-Reported Levels of Depression and General Distress

	Depression					
	Mother	n		Father	n	Comparison
Baseline	50.64 (0.93)	198		55.78 (1.19)	130	F > M
6 months	50.84 (0.97)	171		55.20 (1.20)	131	F > M
12 months	50.50 (0.96)	159		55.55 (1.28)	108	F > M
18 months	50.16 (0.96)	159		53.17 (1.20)	102	F > M
Long term	53.35 (1.09)	121		54.87 (1.26)	83	F = M
Comparison	BL = 6 months = 12 months = 18 months < 72 months			BL = 6 months = 12 months = 18 months = 72 months		
	General distress					
Baseline	51.42 (1.08)	198		56.79 (1.34)	130	F > M
6 months	51.50 (1.12)	171		56.01 (1.35)	131	F > M
12 months	50.16 (1.11)	159		55.70 (1.43)	108	F > M
18 months	49.88 (1.12)	159		53.33 (1.35)	102	F > M
Long-term	52.13 (1.24)	121		53.79 (1.41)	83	F = M
Comparison	BL = 6 months = 12 months = 18 months = LT			BL > 18 months; BL > LT		

Note: F = father, M = mother, BL = baseline, LT = long-term followup.
Comparisons reflect simple effects from Significant Rater × Time interaction.

months: $p < .01$, 18 months: $p = .02$). However, this difference was no longer significant at the long-term follow-up, as a result of a significant increase in maternal-reported depression, such that maternal depression at the long-term follow up was significantly greater than all other time points (Baseline: $p < .02$, 6 months: $p < .03$, 12 months: $p < .02$, 18 months: $p = .01$).

General Severity Index
Analyses of the GSI scale resulted in a significant main effect of rater, $F(1,151) = 44.22$, $p < .01$, and rater × time interaction, $F(1,1132) = 6.03$, $p = .01$ (Table III). The effect of rater is best understood through examination of the rater × time interaction. Regardless of injury type, fathers reported consistent levels of distress during the first 12 months after injury, with a significant decline from baseline to 18 months after injury ($p = .02$) that was maintained at the long-term follow-up ($p = .05$). Mothers reported consistent levels of distress during the initial 18 months after injury with a nonsignificant trend for increased distress from this follow-up to the long-term follow-up ($p = .06$). Although fathers reported greater distress than mothers during the initial 18 months following injury (baseline: $p < .01$, 6 months: $p < .01$, 12 months: $p < .01$, 18 months: $p = .01$), the later decline in paternal distress coupled with the nonsignificant increase in maternal distress resulted in similar levels of parental distress at the long-term follow-up.

Clinical Elevations
Results of the logistic regression revealed that injury severity was related to the likelihood of parents reporting clinically significant levels of GSI ($\chi^2(2) = 8.41$, $p = .01$) and DEP ($\chi^2(2) = 7.90$, $p = .02$) regardless of parent sex and time since injury. Parents of children with severe TBI were more likely to report elevated levels of general distress ($p = .01$) and depression ($p = .07$). Specifically, 34% of parental reports of general distress were in the elevated range for the severe TBI group throughout the study period, while only 17% of those in the moderate TBI group and 18% of those in the OI group reported clinically elevated levels of GSI throughout the study period. Similarly, within the severe TBI group, 27% of parental reports of depression were in the clinically elevated range, while 13% of those in the moderate TBI group and 17% of those in the OI group fell into the clinically elevated range throughout the study period.

Coping Strategies
Table IV presents means and standard errors for the three coping strategies by rater and injury group over time. No significant main effects or interactions were noted for active or acceptance coping strategies. Significant findings related to denial-based coping are presented below.

Denial/Disengagement Coping
Significant main effects of SES, $F(1,199) = 14.97$, $p < .01$, and rater, $F(1,153) = 15.22$, $p < .01$. Parents of higher SES (as determined by median split) reported lower levels of denial (high SES: $M = 16.43$, $SD = 3.90$; low SES: $M = 18.0$, $SD = 5.16$). The rater effect is best understood through examination of the significant group × rater × time interaction,

Table IV. Means, Standard Errors, and ns for Mother- and Father-Reported Coping Styles for All Injury Groups at All Time Points

Assessment	Orthopedic injuries				Moderate				Severe			
	Mother	n	Father	n	Mother	n	Father	n	Mother	n	Father	n
Active coping												
Baseline	33.63 (1.32)	116	30.19 (0.87)	86	32.95 (1.07)	60	31.69 (1.32)	36	30.94 (1.81)	21	32.12 (2.35)	11
6 months	30.85 (0.83)	98	30.92 (0.94)	73	32.22 (1.10)	55	29.08 (1.36)	33	29.41 (1.92)	18	33.58 (2.45)	10
12 months	30.21 (0.87)	87	31.41 (0.96)	67	30.45 (1.13)	52	30.49 (1.36)	33	29.10 (1.80)	21	27.67 (2.56)	9
18 months	29.99 (0.87)	87	30.38 (0.98)	64	31.28 (1.14)	51	29.07 (1.48)	27	29.50 (1.81)	21	29.02 (2.35)	11
Long term	30.59 (0.96)	67	31.46 (1.07)	52	30.39 (1.28)	38	26.90 (1.62)	22	32.18 (2.13)	14	29.08 (2.45)	10
Acceptance coping												
Baseline	35.62 (0.64)	116	33.09 (0.73)	87	35.08 (0.89)	60	34.41 (1.11)	36	33.41 (1.51)	21	33.00 (1.51)	11
6 months	33.89 (0.69)	98	33.19 (0.79)	72	35.56 (0.93)	55	31.86 (1.16)	32	34.04 (1.61)	18	34.33 (2.07)	10
12 months	33.67 (0.73)	87	33.77 (0.81)	67	34.70 (0.95)	52	33.99 (1.15)	33	33.66 (1.51)	21	31.09 (2.16)	9
18 months	33.16 (0.73)	87	34.19 (0.83)	64	34.57 (0.96)	51	32.03 (1.25)	27	33.40 (1.52)	21	31.15 (1.98)	11
Long term	33.55 (0.81)	67	34.22 (0.90)	52	33.22 (1.08)	38	29.65 (1.37)	22	35.60 (1.79)	14	31.10 (2.06)	10
Denial coping												
Baseline	17.53 (0.42)	116	17.35 (0.47)	86	17.01 (0.59)	60	18.05 (0.71)	36	17.20 (1.00)	21	18.78 (1.26)	11
6 months	17.51 (0.45)	98	17.66 (0.50)	72	17.79 (0.61)	55	18.07 (0.73)	33	17.85 (1.05)	18	18.80 (1.30)	10
12 months	16.67 (0.47)	87	17.56 (0.52)	67	17.13 (0.62)	52	18.05 (0.73)	33	17.07 (0.99)	21	18.73 (1.35)	9
18 months	16.39 (0.47)	87	17.03 (0.53)	64	16.82 (0.62)	51	16.24 (0.79)	27	15.81 (1.00)	21	20.55 (1.25)	11
Long term	17.59 (0.52)	67	17.93 (0.57)	52	17.21 (0.69)	38	16.10 (0.85)	22	19.02 (1.15)	14	14.54 (1.30)	10

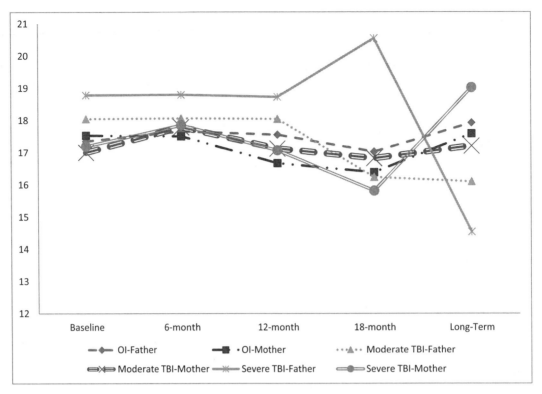

Figure 1. Depicts the mean level of denial coping reported by mothers and fathers of children with OI, moderate TBI, and severe TBI over time.

$F(2, 1137) = 5.98$, $p = .003$; see Figure 1), as parent sex moderated the relationship between injury group and use of denial/disengagement coping over time. During the first 12 months after injury, both mothers and fathers reported equivalent levels of denial across all injury groups; however, differential effects of injury were noted at the 18-month and long-term follow up.

Although mothers and fathers of children with OI and moderate TBI did not differ in reported denial across the study period, differences between maternal and paternal ratings were observed in parents of children with severe TBI at 18-month and long-term follow-ups. Specifically, by 18 months after injury, fathers reported significantly more denial than mothers ($t(362) = 3.63$, $p = .0003$). This was followed by a decrease in paternal denial (18 months to long-term: $p < .01$) and increase in maternal denial (18 months to long-term: $p = .01$), which resulted in a reversal of the pattern seen at 18 months after injury, with fathers reporting significantly less denial than mothers at the long-term follow-up ($t(362) = -3.10$, $p = .002$).

Overall, the effect of injury type and severity was more pronounced for fathers over time. Specifically, at 18 months after injury, fathers of children with severe TBI reported greater levels of denial than fathers of children with OI ($t(362) = -2.59$, $p = .01$) and fathers of children with moderate TBI ($t(362) = -2.92$, $p < .01$). Interestingly, by the long-term follow-up, fathers of children with OI reported greater denial than fathers of children with severe TBI ($t(362) = 2.38$, $p = .03$). Injury characteristics did not predict maternal ratings of denial at any time point.

Discussion

The present study is one of the first to examine long-term differences in how mothers and fathers respond to TBI in their preschool children, and extends our knowledge regarding parental response following TBI. Analyses that included a long-term follow-up (~7 years) indicate that mothers and fathers experience differing levels of psychological distress, which vary as a function of time since injury. Additionally, while coping strategies that involved denial varied as a function of time since injury, injury type, and rater sex, this was not observed for strategies that involved active coping or acceptance.

When examining parental distress, we found that fathers reported greater levels of depression and general distress during the initial 18 months after injury, regardless of injury type; however, an increase in maternal distress over time resulted in mothers and fathers experiencing similar levels of depression and distress many years after injury. The elevated levels of paternal distress are consistent with previous findings (Wade et al., 2010). The increase in maternal distress at the long-term follow-up was unexpected. Stancin et al. (2010) reported that parents of preschool-age children may not be acutely distressed following injury because the impact of the child's impairment may not be immediately clear. The present study examines distress at a long-term follow-up, approximately 7 years after injury. At this point, children are between the ages of 9 and 14 years, and the increased distress reported by mothers may be related to increasing awareness of the subtle deficits associated with the TBI that were not apparent earlier. The increase in distress may also be related to developmental factors. Parents often perceive adolescence as the most difficult period of their child's development, and report the highest level of parenting stress during this period (Buchanan et al., 1990; Pasley & Gecas, 1984; Pearlin & Liebermann, 1979; Small, Cornelius, & Eastman, 1983). Early adolescence is accompanied by an increase in parent–child conflict along with the development of autonomy, both of which are significantly related to parental stress (Kohn, Lafreniere, & Gurevich, 1991; Laursen, Coy, & Collins, 1998; Small, Eastman, & Cornelius, 1988; Taylor, 1991). Depending on the long-term deficits experienced by their child (i.e., externalizing behavior, poor executive functioning, impaired social competence), this period may be associated with even greater stress for parents of children with TBI. Further, while mothers are reporting an increase in distress, fathers are reporting a decrease in distress over time. One potential explanation is that fathers may be less involved in the educational planning and behavioral management than mothers, and therefore may not experience the stress associated with emerging deficits and parent–child conflicts in the same way as mothers. While injury severity was not associated with overall levels of parental distress or depression, it was significantly associated with an increased likelihood of clinically elevated levels of parental distress, with a greater proportion of parents of children with severe TBI reporting clinically elevated distress. This was true regardless of parent sex or time since injury, suggesting that these parents remain more distressed than others, even many years after injury. Changes in the source of parental distress time (i.e., concern for survival and physical recovery initially to managing externalizing behaviors, academic impairments, and independent living years after injury) were not evaluated in the current study. Future studies of parental distress after TBI would benefit from identifying specific sources of distress over time. This would allow for professionals to proactively discuss future potential stressors, and target interventions appropriately.

Consistent with hypotheses, the coping strategies reported by mothers and fathers following OI were fairly stable over time following the acute injury. This is likely related to the nature of the injury. OI are typically accompanied by a clear trajectory for recovery, with a timeline related to cast removal and completion of physical therapy. Further, the sequelae of the injury are unlikely to become more prominent or impairing as the child ages. Additionally, mothers and fathers of kids with OI report more denial/disengagement at the extended follow-up assessment, perhaps because their children have likely been fully recovered for a number of years, making the injury-related stressors a distant memory for these families.

With regards to denial, only parents in the severe TBI group demonstrated significant differences between mothers and fathers, with fathers reporting greater denial 18 months after injury and mothers reported greater denial in the long term after injury. Fathers reporting greater denial 18 months after injury is consistent with the previous report by Wade et al. (2010) on the same cohort. However, the decline in denial reported by fathers and increase in denial reported by mothers, resulting in higher levels reported by mothers than fathers at the long-term follow up, was unexpected. These findings suggest that mothers and fathers may experiencing changing perceptions of the injury and its consequences. Mothers may be attributing residual and emerging problems to adolescence; whereas fathers may finally be accepting that the injury has resulted in changes for the child and family. As reported by Stancin et al. (2010), injury-related stress is likely to increase as the child is faced with additional social and academic stressors outside of school. Additionally, increased maternal distress may be associated with concerns mothers have related to long-term independence in light of the long-term impairments associated with the injury coupled with ineffective active coping strategies. However, given that denial is strongly associated with distress (Aldwin & Revenson, 1987; Billings & Moos, 1984; Felton & Revenson, 1984; Felton et al., 1984; Holahan & Moos, 1987; Wade et al., 2001), increasing maternal denial may contribute to higher levels of distress over time. Similarly, the decline in denial reported by fathers may be associated with the decline in distress reported by fathers. As discussed above, it is possible that fathers are further removed from the processes of obtaining services for their child or more distanced from their child's emerging deficits giving fathers fewer opportunities to use denial as a coping strategy. These findings highlight the complexity of parental response to early childhood injury and underscore the importance of addressing the impact of TBI on families even years after injury.

Overall, mothers and fathers are reporting similar levels of distress many years after injury; however, mothers and fathers of children with a history of severe TBI reported different levels of denial coping at 18-month and long-term follow up. While this increased discrepancy in coping style does not appear to be accompanied by increased distress at the long-term follow up, previous studies have reported that conflicting, or complimentary, coping styles may be related to parental stress or conflict (Benn & McColl, 2004; Wade et al., 2010). Further, while findings suggest that not all families of children with a history of TBI are in need to treatment, differences in response to injury and emerging deficits may contribute to family strain over time.

Although the present study provides valuable new information, it is not without limitations. Although the study is unique in being prospective in nature and collecting both mother and father ratings, the sample size of children with severe TBI was small, possibly limiting statistical power in some of the injury group comparisons. Additionally, to assess differences in coping between mothers and fathers, regardless of parental relationship, we used all parent ratings rather than only including dyadic relationships. This did increase our sample size, but limited our ability to compare mothers and fathers within a family, or whether parents use complementary or conflicting strategies.

While these findings should be considered preliminary given the small number of fathers in some groups (i.e., severe TBI), they do provide some insight for future intervention development and research. First, assessing the sources of distress over time is important for understanding the stressors families of children with TBI face overtime, and is information that would improve care for children with TBI and their families. This is particularly true for parents of children with severe TBI, as they were more likely to report clinically elevated levels of distress throughout recovery. Parents may report similar levels of distress from acute recovery through years postinjury, but the sources of the stress may be qualitatively different. For example, managing stressors of acute recovery (i.e., concern for survival, hospital stay, numerous medical appointments) are different than those that are often reported years after injury (i.e., externalizing behaviors, academic and social difficulties, concerns for independent living). Interestingly, fathers report declining levels of distress over time after injury. Future studies should seek to better understand the mechanisms underlying this reduction in distress to inform intervention and determine how and when to best support both mothers and fathers.

Likewise, understanding of how mothers and fathers within a family cope with stressors and how this relates to levels of distress is important in working with families following injury. Different coping styles may be more effective for managing different sources of stress at different points throughout recovery. This knowledge is key to creating interventions that are developmentally and environmentally (i.e., individual treatment, family treatment, school based treatment, etc.) appropriate. Further, a better understanding of how discrepant coping styles impact distress and the role of the marital relationship throughout long-term recovery is required. Under some circumstances, it may be beneficial for parents to adopt different/complimentary coping styles to manage the variety of stressors; however, significant discrepancies may make parents feel that they are not on the same page as their partner, further contributing to levels of distress. Interestingly, mothers and fathers of children with severe TBI reported increasingly discrepant levels of denial coping over time, again highlighting the need to understand these phenomena in this at-risk group. Examining how these factors operate in married parents, separated co-parenting parents, and single parents is also crucial to identifying and developing interventions. Given the confound of marital status within the TBI group, we were not able to examine this question. Future projects should attempt to recruit families who report clinically significant levels of distress to examine these factors in a population most at need for intervention. Additionally, future research would benefit from recruiting children with a range of family structures, to gain insight into how risk factors vary within this environmental context. Knowledge gleaned will be crucial to identifying patients and families who are most likely to experience significant distress after TBI, and fuel development of interventions targeting specific areas of stress and less effective coping.

Funding

This publication was supported by grant R01 HD42729 from the National Institute of Child Health and Human Development and Trauma Research grants from the State of Ohio Emergency Medical Services. Additional support was provided through Grant 8 UL1 TR000077 from the National Center for Advancing Translational Sciences of the National Institutes of Health. Its contents are solely the responsibility of the authors and do not necessarily represent the official views of National Institutes of Health.

Conflicts of interest: None declared.

References

Aitken, M. E., McCarthy, M. L., Slomine, B. S., Ding, R., Durbin, D. R., Jaffe, K. M., ... Mackenzie, E. J.; CHAT Study Group. (2009). Family burden after traumatic brain injury in children. *Pediatrics*, 123, 199–206. doi: 10.1542/peds.2008-0607

Aldwin, C. M., & Revenson, T. A. (1987). Does coping help? A reexamination of the relation between coping and mental health. *Journal of Personality and Social Psychology*, 53, 337–348.

Anderson, V. A., Catroppa, C., Dudgeon, P., Morse, S. A., Haritou, F., & Rosenfeld, J. V. (2006). Understanding predictors of functional recovery and outcome 30 months following early childhood head injury. *Neuropsychology*, 20, 42–57. doi: 10.1037/0894-4105.20.1.42

Anderson, V. A., Morse, S. A., Klug, G., Catroppa, C., Haritou, F., Rosenfeld, J., & Pentland, L. (1997). Predicting recovery from head injury in young children: A prospective analysis. *Journal of International Neuropsychological Society*, 3, 568–580.

Babikian, T., Merkley, T., Savage, R. C., Giza, C. C., & Levin, H. (2015). Chronic aspects of pediatric traumatic brain injury: Review of the literature. *Journal of Neurotrauma*, 32, 1849–1860. doi: 10.1089/neu.2015.3971

Baker, J. P., & Berenbaum, H. (2007). Emotional approach and problem-focused coping: A comparison of potentially adaptive strategies. *Cognition & Emotion*, 21, 95–118. doi: 10.1080/02699930600562276

Benn, K. M., & McColl, M. A. (2004). Parental coping following childhood acquired brain injury. *Brain Injury*, 18, 239–255. doi: 10.1080/02699050310001617343

Billings, A. G., & Moos, R. H. (1984). Coping, stress, and social resources among adults with unipolar depression. *Journal of Personality and Social Psychology*, 46, 877–891.

Buchanan, C. M., Eccles, J. S., Flanagan, C., Midgley, C., Feldlaufer, H., & Harold, R. D. (1990). Parents' and teachers' beliegs about adolescents: Effects of sex and experience. *Jounral of Youth & Adolescence*, 19, 363–394.

Carver, C. S., Scheier, M. F., & Weintraub, J. K. (1989). Assessing coping strategies: A theoretically based approach. *Journal of Personality and Social Psychology*, 56, 267–283.

Catroppa, C., Anderson, V. A., Morse, S. A., Haritou, F., & Rosenfeld, J. V. (2008). Outcome and predictors of functional recovery 5 years following pediatric traumatic brain injury (TBI). *Journal of Pediatric Psychology*, 33, 707–718. doi: 10.1093/jpepsy/jsn006

Compas, B. E., & Boyer, M. C. (2001). Coping and attention: Implications for child health and pediatric conditions. *Journal of Developmental and Behavioral Pediatrics*, 22, 323–333.

Derogatis, L., & Melilsaratos, N. (1983). The brief symptom inventory: An introductory report. *Psychological Medicine*, 13, 595–605.

Derogatis, L. R. (1993a). *The Brief Symptom Inventory (BSI) administration, scoring, and procedures manual*. Minneapolis, MN: National Computer Systems.

Derogatis, L. R. (1993b). *SCL-90-R: Administration, scoring, and procedures manual* (3rd ed.). Minneapolis, MN: National Computer Systems.

Ewing-Cobbs, L., Prasad, M. R., Kramer, L., Cox, C. S., Baumgartner, J., Fletcher, S., ... Swank, P. (2006). Late intellectual and academic outcomes following traumatic brain injury sustained during early childhood. *Journal of Neurosurgery*, 105, 287–296. doi: doi:10.3171/ped.2006.105.4.287

Fay, T. B., Yeates, K. O., Wade, S. L., Drotar, D., Stancin, T., & Taylor, H. G. (2009). Predicting longitudinal patterns of functional deficits in children with traumatic brain injury. *Neuropsychology*, 23, 271–282. doi: 10.1037/a0014936

Felton, B. J., & Revenson, T. A. (1984). Coping with chronic illness: A study of illness controllability and the influence of coping strategies on psychological adjustment. *Journal of Consulting and Clinical Psychology*, 52, 343–353.

Felton, B. J., Revenson, T. A., & Hinrichsen, G. A. (1984). Stress and coping in the explanation of psychological adjustment among chronically ill adults. *Social Sciences and Medicine*, 18, 889–898.

Ganesalingam, K., Yeates, K. O., Ginn, M. S., Taylor, H. G., Dietrich, A., Nuss, K., & Wright, M. (2008). Family burden and parental distress following mild traumatic brain injury in children and its relationship to post-concussive symptoms. *Journal of Pediatric Psychology*, 33, 621–629. doi: 10.1093/jpepsy/jsm133

Hawley, C. A., Ward, A. B., Magnay, A. R., & Long, J. (2003). Parental stress and burden following traumatic brain injury amongst children and adolescents. *Brain Injury*, 17, 1–23. doi: doi:10.1080/0269905021000010096

Holahan, C. J., & Moos, R. H. (1987). Personal and contextual determinants of coping strategies. *Journal of Personality and Social Psychology*, 52, 946–955.

Holmbeck, G. N., Gorey-Ferguson, L., Hudson, T., Seefeldt, T., Shapera, W., Turner, T., & Uhler, J. (1997). Maternal, paternal, and marital functioning in families of preadolescents with spina bifida. *Journal of Pediatric Psychology*, 22, 167–181.

Kohn, P. M., Lafreniere, K., & Gurevich, M. (1991). Hassles, health, and personality. *Journal of Personality and Social Psychology*, 61, 478–482.

Lamb, M. E. (2013). *The father's role: Cross cultural perspectives*. Hillsdale, NJ: Lawrence Erlbaum Associates.

Laursen, B., Coy, K. C., & Collins, W. A. (1998). Reconsidering changes in parent-child conflict across adolescence: A meta-analysis. *Child Development*, 69, 817–832.

Lazarus, R. S., & Folkman, S. (1984). *Stress, appraisal, and coping*. New York: Springer.

Macias, M. M., Saylor, C. F., Haire, K. B., & Bell, N. L. (2007). Predictors of paternal versus maternal stress in families of children with neural tube defects. *Children's Health Care*, 36, 99–115. doi: 10.1080/02739610701334558

Narad, M. E., Treble-Barna, A., Peugh, J., Yeates, K. O., Taylor, H. G., Stancin, T., & Wade, S. L. (2016). Recovery trajectories of executive functioning after pediatric TBI: Latent class growth modeling analysis. *Journal of Head Trauma Rehabilitation*. doi: 10.1097/htr.0000000000000247.

Pasley, K., & Gecas, V. (1984). Adolescent development. *Annual Review of Psychology*, 39, 583–607.

Pearlin, L., & Liebermann, M. (1979). Sources of emotional distress. *Research in Community and Mental Health*, 1, 217–248.

Perlesz, A., & O'loughlan, M. (1998). Changes in stress and burden in families seeking therapy following traumatic brain injury: A follow-up study. *International Journal of Rehabilitation Research*, 21, 339–354.

Petranovich, C., et al. The longitudinal association of maternal psychological distress and child behavior following early childhood traumatic brain injury (TBI): An autoregressive cross-lagged panel analysis. Under Review.

Phares, V., Lopez, E., Fields, S., Kamboukos, D., & Duhig, A. M. (2005). Are fathers involved in pediatric psychology research and treatment? *Journal of Pediatric Psychology*, *30*, 631–643.

Raj, S. P., Wade, S. L., Cassedy, A., Taylor, H. G., Stancin, T., Brown, T. M., & Kirkwood, M. W. (2014). Parent psychological functioning and communication predict externalizing behavior problems after pediatric traumatic brain injury. *Journal of Pediatric Psychology*, *39*, 84–95. doi: 10.1093/jpepsy/jsto75

Rivara, J. B., Fay, G. C., Jaffe, K. M., Polissar, N. L., Shurtleff, H. A., & Martin, K. M. (1992). Predictors of family functioning one year following traumatic brain injury in children. *Archives of Physical Medicine and Rehabilitation*, *73*, 899–910.

Rivara, J. B., Jaffe, K. M., Polissar, N. L., Fay, G. C., Liao, S. Q., & Martin, K. M. (1996). Predictors of family functioning and change 3 years after traumatic brain injury in children. *Archives of Physical Medicine and Rehabilitation*, *77*, 754–764.

Shudy, M., de Almeida, M. L., Ly, S., Landon, C., Groft, S., Jenkins, T. L., & Nicholson, C. E. (2006). Impact of pediatric critical illness and injury on families: A systematic literature review. *Pediatrics*, *118*, S203–S218. doi: 10.1542/peds.2006-0951B

Sloper, P. (2000). Predictors of distress in parents of children with cancer: A prospective study. *Journal of Pediatric Psychology*, *25*, 79–91.

Small, S. A., Cornelius, S., & Eastman, G. (1983). *Parenting adoelscent children: A period of adult storm and stress?* Paper presented at the 91st Annual Meeting of the American Psychological Association, Anaheim, CA.

Small, S. A., Eastman, G., & Cornelius, S. (1988). Adolescent autonomy and parental stress. *Journal of Youth and Adolescence*, *17*, 377–391. doi: 10.1007/BF01537880

Stancin, T., Wade, S. L., Walz, N. C., Yeates, K. O., & Taylor, H. G. (2010). Family adaptation 18 months after traumatic brain injury in early childhood. *Journal of Developmental and Behavioral Pediatrics*, *31*, 317–325. doi: 10.1097/DBP.0b013e3181dbaf32

Taylor, H. G., Yeates, K. O., Wade, S. L., Drotar, D., Stancin, T., & Burant, C. (2001). Bidirectional child-family influences on outcomes of traumatic brain injury in children. *Journal of International Neuropsychological Society*, *7*, 755–767.

Taylor, S. E. (1991). *Health psychology* (2nd ed.). New York: McGraw-Hill.

Thurman, D. J. (2016). The epidemiology of traumatic brain injury in children and youths: A review of research since 1990. *Journal of Child Neurology*, *31*, 20–7. doi: 10.1177/0883073814544363

Verhaeghe, S., Defloor, T., & Grypdonck, M. (2005). Stress and coping among families of patients with traumatic brain injury: A review of the literature. *Journal of Clinical Nursing*, *14*, 1004–1012. doi: DOI 10.1111/j.1365-2702.2005.01126.x

Wade, S. L., Borawski, E. A., Taylor, H. G., Drotar, D., Yeates, K. O., & Stancin, T. (2001). The relationship of caregiver coping to family outcomes during the initial year following pediatric traumatic injury. *Journal of Consulting and Clinical Psychology*, *69*, 406–415.

Wade, S. L., Taylor, H. G., Drotar, D., Stancin, T., & Yeates, K. O. (1998). Family burden and adaptation during the initial year after traumatic brain injury in children. *Pediatrics*, *102*, 110–116.

Wade, S. L., Taylor, H. G., Drotar, D., Stancin, T., Yeates, K. O., & Minich, N. M. (2002). A prospective study of long-term caregiver and family adaptation following brain injury in children. *Journal of Head Trauma Rehabilitation*, *17*, 96–111.

Wade, S. L., Walz, N. C., Cassedy, A., Taylor, H. G., Stancin, T., & Yeates, K. O. (2010). Caregiver functioning following early childhood TBI: Do moms and dads respond differently? *NeuroRehabilitation*, *27*, 63–72. doi: 10.3233/NRE-2010-0581

Weinraub, M., & Wolf, B. M. (1983). Effects of stress and social supports on mother-child interactions in single- and two-parent families. *Child Development*, *54*, 1297–1311.

Bidirectional Associations Between Disordered Eating and Health-Related Quality of Life in Elementary School-Age Youth

Tarrah B. Mitchell, M.A and Ric G. Steele, PhD

Clinical Child Psychology Program, University of Kansas

All correspondence concerning this article should be addressed to Ric G. Steele, PhD, ABPP Clinical Child Psychology Program, University of Kansas, 2010 Dole Human Development Center 1000 Sunnyside Avenue, Lawrence, KS 66049, USA. E-mail: rsteele@ku.edu

Received March 24, 2016; revisions received August 23, 2016; accepted August 30, 2016

Abstract

Objective To examine longitudinal, bidirectional associations between disordered eating and physical/psychosocial health-related quality of life (HRQOL) in a nonclinical community sample of elementary school-age youth. **Methods** Participants included 130 children between the ages of 7 and 10 years (M age $= 8.62$). Disordered eating and physical/psychosocial HRQOL were assessed using self-report measures at three time points. The potential bidirectional associations were examined using a longitudinal panel model. **Results** Higher disordered eating predicted lower psychosocial HRQOL during a 6-month period within the same academic year, and lower HRQOL predicted higher disordered eating during a 6-month period across academic years. **Conclusion** The current study found longitudinal, bidirectional associations between disordered eating and psychosocial, but not physical, HRQOL. The results provide evidence for psychosocial HRQOL as a potential predictor and consequence of disordered eating attitudes. Limitations, future directions, and implications of this research are discussed.

Key words: children; disordered eating; longitudinal; quality of life.

Disordered eating attitudes and behaviors, which can be defined as a "range of abnormal eating behaviors with different severity that involve ... fear of fatness, unhealthy weight control behaviors and preoccupation thinking about food" (Khodabakhsh & Kiani, 2014, p. 400), have traditionally been understood to develop during adolescence. However, there is evidence of a childhood development model of disordered eating (Wertheim, Paxton, & Blaney, 2009), which suggests that disordered eating may develop in elementary school-age boys and girls. For example, Lowes and Tiggemann (2003) found that body ideals and concerns developed around 5–6 years of age and that the concept of dieting was understood by 7–8 years of age. Furthermore, Combs, Pearson, Zapolski, and Smith (2013) found that in the previous 2 weeks, 12.1% of elementary school-age youth reported binge eating, 4.8% reported purging, and 9.7% reported restricting food intake; the results also indicated that the disordered eating attitudes and behaviors were similar for girls and boys. This childhood development model is further highlighted by a 119% increase in hospitalizations for disordered eating in children <12 years of age between the years of 1999 and 2006 (Agency for Healthcare Research and Quality, 2009), which may be because there has been an increase in the attitudes and behaviors or because there has been an increase in awareness and screening. Because there is evidence to suggest that disordered eating attitudes and behaviors are present in elementary school-age youth, the context of the development of the attitudes and behaviors and the consequences that result from them must be studied to identify children at risk and areas for intervention.

Many studies that examine the consequences of disordered eating attitudes and behaviors in youth focus on physical health-related consequences such as weight cycling, malnutrition, full-syndrome eating disorders, and obesity (e.g., Johnson, Cohen, Kasen, & Brook, 2002; Neumark-Sztainer et al., 2006). In addition to the physical consequences of disordered eating, there are also psychosocial consequences including increased risk for depression, low self-esteem, substance use, missed classes in school, and suicidal ideation (e.g., Ackard, Fulkerson, & Neumark-Sztainer, 2011; Brausch & Gutierrez, 2009; Yanover & Thompson, 2008). Because the negative consequences of disordered eating attitudes and behaviors range across various domains (i.e., physical, psychological, and social), current researchers and clinicians rely on a biopsychosocial framework to understand the negative impact of the attitudes and behaviors on youth (see Smolak & Thompson, 2009).

Although numerous studies have examined the effects of disordered eating attitudes and behaviors on individual physical or psychosocial factors within the biopsychosocial framework, studies rarely examine the impact of such attitudes and behaviors on youth across multiple domains. To measure the burden of a health condition on a person's overall functioning, the Center for Disease Control (2011b) recommends examining health-related quality of life (HRQOL), a multidimensional concept of a person's perceptions of his or her physical and psychosocial health (Spieth & Harris, 1996). Public health researchers are widely incorporating measures of HRQOL into their research studies as a "patient reported outcome" (Acquadro et al., 2003) because information is collected directly from the individual without being filtered by another person (i.e., researcher or clinician; Centers for Disease Control and Prevention [CDC], 2011b). Such patient-reported outcomes can help researchers and clinicians understand how health conditions influence symptoms and functioning. Therefore, assessing the associations among physical and psychosocial HRQOL and disordered eating attitudes and behaviors may be important to understanding the overall burden of disordered eating on individuals.

In addition to examinations of the consequences of disordered eating attitudes and behaviors in youth, a robust literature has examined various predictors of disordered eating. A biopsychosocial framework can also be used to conceptualize the risk factors for disordered eating attitudes and behaviors (e.g., Ricciardelli, McCabe, Holt, & Finemore, 2003; Rodgers, Paxton, & McLean, 2014). Biological or physical risk factors include higher weight status and alterations in serotonin levels (e.g., Ricciardelli et al., 2003; Rodgers et al. 2014; Stice, 2002). Psychological factors that contribute to the development of disordered eating attitudes and behaviors include negative emotionality and low self-esteem, and social factors that contribute include peer influence such as teasing and social status (Croll, Neumark-Sztainer, Story, & Ireland, 2002; Littleton & Ollendick, 2003; Ricciardelli & McCabe, 2004; Stice, 2002). Of note, these psychological and social factors are incorporated into, and are domains of, the multidimensional concept of HRQOL. For example, items on the psychosocial health subscale of the Pediatric Quality of Life Inventory (PedsQL™ 4.0; Varni, Seid, & Kurtin, 2001), a common pediatric HRQOL measure, inquire whether the individual feels sad, blue, or angry, which are all indicators of negative emotionality. Other items on the psychosocial health subscale of the PedsQL inquire about self-esteem (e.g., "I cannot do things that other kids my age can do."), teasing (e.g., "Other kids tease me."), and social status (e.g., "Other kids do not want to be my friend."). A broad, multidimensional concept like HRQOL may be measuring multiple risk factors of disordered eating; therefore, HRQOL represents a potentially important predictor, in addition to a consequence, of disordered eating attitudes and behaviors.

Although the literature on disordered eating attitudes and behaviors in youth has established an association with HRQOL, a methodological limitation in the extant literature is that all identified studies examining the associations were cross-sectional, which precludes conclusions about causality and directionality among variables. For example, cross-sectional methodologies were used in each of the four recent studies that found an association between disordered eating attitudes and behaviors and HRQOL in adolescents (e.g., Doyle, Le Grange, Goldschmidt, & Wilfley, 2007; Herpertz-Dahlmann, Wille, Hölling, Vloet, & Ravens-Sieberer, 2008; Jalali-Farahani, Chin, Nasir, & Amiri, 2015; Jenkins et al., 2014), and in both studies that found an association between the variables in elementary school-age youth (e.g., Gowey, Lim, Clifford, & Janicke, 2014; Mitchell & Steele, 2016).[1] Of note, the cross-sectional evidence suggests that disordered eating attitudes and behaviors may be particularly associated with psychosocial HRQOL, rather than physical HRQOL (e.g., Baiano et al., 2014; Doll, Petersen, & Stewert-Brown, 2005; Gowey et al., 2014; Jalali-Farahani et al., 2015). Although the authors of these studies had hypotheses about the directionality of the variables (i.e., HRQOL as a consequence of disordered eating attitudes and behaviors), they mentioned the limitations of their cross-sectional methodologies and

---

[1] Four of the six identified articles used the PedsQL (Varni et al., 2001) as the measure of HRQOL (Doyle et al., 2007; Jalali-Farahani et al., 2015; Gowey et al., 2014; Mitchell & Steele, in press). The other two studies (Herpertz-Dahlmann et al., 2008; Jenkins et al., 2014) used other validated measures of HRQOL with similar subscales.

called for future research to examine the variables longitudinally to further elucidate causality and directionality.

Only one study was identified that has examined the longitudinal associations between disordered eating attitudes and behaviors and HRQOL. In a 9-year study of adult women, Wade and colleagues (2012) reported that women with higher levels of disordered eating reported lower HRQOL. However, Wade et al. (2012) did not examine HRQOL as a predictor of disordered eating over time, limiting the conclusions regarding the directionality of effects. The current study aims to fill the gap in the literature by examining the longitudinal, bidirectional associations between disordered eating attitudes and HRQOL in elementary school-age youth to elucidate whether HRQOL is a risk factor or consequence (or both) of disordered eating. Understanding the directionality and causality of the associations among the variables could inform prevention and intervention efforts for elementary school-age youth.

The primary goal of the current study was to address gaps in the extant literature by examining potential longitudinal, bidirectional associations between disordered eating attitudes and behaviors and HRQOL. A nonclinical, community sample of elementary school-age boys and girls was chosen because many studies that have examined the association between disordered eating attitudes and behaviors and HRQOL have included clinical samples of youth (mostly adolescents) with clinical eating disorders or with overweight/obesity (e.g., Doyle et al., 2007; Gowey et al., 2014; Jenkins et al., 2014). Although examining the associations in clinical samples provides useful information, the samples often represent youth who are exhibiting extreme disordered eating and significant impairment in HRQOL. Wade and colleagues (2012) posited that even subclinical levels of symptomatology significantly affect well-being. Therefore, a longitudinal investigation in a community sample allows the findings to be generalized to a wider range of the population.

Based on the existing literature, it was first hypothesized that higher levels of disordered eating attitudes and behaviors would predict lower levels of psychosocial HRQOL. Second, it was hypothesized that lower levels of psychosocial HRQOL would be associated with higher levels of disordered eating over time. It was not hypothesized that physical HRQOL would be a predictor or consequence of disordered eating attitudes and behaviors in this sample for three reasons. First, there is previous evidence to suggest that psychosocial HRQOL, but not physical HRQOL, is associated with disordered eating (e.g., Baiano et al, 2014; Doll et al., 2005; Gowey et al., 2014; Jalali-Farahani et al, 2015). Second, the physical risk factors (e.g., weight status and serotonin levels) and consequences (e.g., weight cycling and malnutrition) of disordered eating are not fully captured in measures of HRQOL (e.g., the PedsQL). Third, physical functioning may not be affected when disordered eating is emerging in childhood because of reduced severity and/or chronicity. Because of the lack of available literature on the suggested time lag necessary to see effects, the current study examined the variables every 6 months, across a 1-year period, as a starting point to examine causality and directionality. Owing to the dearth of literature examining longitudinal associations at varying time intervals, specific hypotheses regarding the time intervals required to see desired effects were not speculated.

Method

Participants

Participants included 130 youth who were enrolled in second to fourth grades at two public elementary schools in the Midwest United States. Students were considered eligible for the current study if (a) they were enrolled in second, third, or fourth grade at the two designated elementary schools at Time 1, (b) they read and spoke English, and (c) their parents or guardians provided written consent. Census data indicated that the schools were located in a middle-class community with a median household income of $46,929 (United States Census Bureau, 2015), and school records indicated that 38.61% of children in the district were from economically disadvantaged homes (Kansas State Department of Education, 2014).

Procedure

The measures included in the current study were a part of a larger survey packet for a project that evaluated the associations among psychosocial variables, physical activity, and weight status.[2] Students were recruited from two public elementary schools in a Midwestern community; the two schools were chosen to allow for a sample of participants that would be representative of the community (e.g., race, ethnicity, socioeconomic status). Information about the study and consent forms were distributed to parents during school events and via weekly folders sent home by homeroom teachers. Parents were asked to return the consent form, regardless of whether they granted or denied consent. According to the State Department of Education, 297 students were eligible for the study at the time of recruitment, yielding an estimated participation rate of approximately 44%. However, only 59 parents indicated that they denied consent, leaving >100 eligible students without parental response;

---

2 Time 1 data of the current study overlapped with the data analyzed in Mitchell and Steele (2016).

therefore, it could not be confirmed that all parents of eligible students received study information.

Assent was collected before data collection from the students whose parents granted consent. The research team collected self-report data in group format during the school day at a time that was convenient for the schools to minimize the disruption to the school schedule. Trained research staff read measures aloud to the participants and were available to answer questions as needed. Objective measures of height and weight were also collected in private locations in the school. Time 1 occurred approximately 3 months after the beginning of the spring semester, Time 2 occurred 6 months later in the fall semester, and Time 3 occurred 6 months later (1 year from Time 1) in the spring semester. Participants received gift cards to incentivize participation and to compensate students for their time and effort. The procedures described above were approved by the authors' institutional review board, the local public school district office of research and assessment, and the participating schools' administrators.

Measures

Disordered Eating Attitudes and Behaviors

Self-reported disordered eating attitudes and behaviors were assessed at all time points using the Children's Eating Attitudes Test (ChEAT; Maloney, McGuire, & Daniels, 1988). Anton and colleagues (2006) validated a scoring procedure of the ChEAT in a community sample of youth between the ages of 7 and 13 using 20 items on a 6-point Likert scale from *Never* (1) to *Always* (6). Example questions include *I eat diet foods* and *I stay away from foods with sugar in them*. Anton and colleagues (2006) found a six-factor structure including overconcern with body size, food preoccupation, calorie awareness and control, dieting, vomiting, and social pressure to gain weight. The total score was used for analyses in the current study. The measure had good internal consistency in the current sample (Time 1 $\alpha = 0.85$; Time 2 $\alpha = 0.79$; Time 3 $\alpha = 0.83$).

Health-related Quality of Life

Self-reported HRQOL was assessed at all time points using the PedsQL™ 4.0 (Varni et al., 2001). The PedsQL is a 23-item measure that has been validated in community samples of youth between the ages of 5 and 18. The measure has four subscales (i.e., physical, emotional, social, and academic functioning), two summary scores (i.e., physical HRQOL and psychosocial HRQOL), and an aggregate total scale score; the physical HRQOL summary score is simply the physical subscale, and the psychosocial HRQOL summary score is the average of the emotional, social, and academic subscales. Participants indicated how much of a problem they had on each item in the past month on a 4-point Likert scale from *Never* to *Always*. The physical and psychosocial summary scores have been shown to differentiate between healthy and patient populations, to correlate with measures of illness burden, and to have good internal consistency ($\alpha = 0.77$–0.85; Varni et al., 2001). Both summary scores had good internal consistency in the current sample across time points ($\alpha = 0.75$–0.89).

Weight Status

Research staff collected height and weight to the nearest 0.1 cm and kg, respectively, while the participants wore light clothing and no shoes. To ensure reliability, triple measurements were collected and averaged, and body mass index z-score (BMIz) was calculated using a SAS script as recommended by the Centers for Disease Control (CDC, 2011a). BMIz at Time 1 was used as a control variable in analyses.

Demographics

Participants self-reported on demographic information such as their age, date of birth, grade, sex, and race/ethnicity. Because the current sample had low percentages of participants in racial/ethnic minority groups, a dichotomized variable was used in analyses, with Caucasian coded as 0 and any racial/ethnic minority coded as 1.

Data Analytic Plan

Descriptive statistics for study variables were conducted using IBM SPSS Statistics Version 22. Additionally, logistic regression analyses were conducted using SPSS to determine whether there were differences in participants who completed all waves of data collection in comparison with those dropped out of the study.

The potential bidirectional associations between disordered eating attitudes and behaviors and physical/psychosocial HRQOL across three time points were examined simultaneously by estimating a longitudinal panel model using Mplus statistical software (Version 7; Muthén & Muthén, 1998–2015). All analyses included standardized continuous variables to aid in interpretation. Initial inspection of the data at the three time points indicated that the variables met the assumptions of normality (see Table I; Kline, 2011), so nonnormality did not have to be accounted for in analyses. Percent missing values for study variables ranged from 0% to 25%. To account for the missing data, full information maximum likelihood estimation (FIML) was used; compared with other methods of handling missing data (e.g., listwise and pairwise deletion), FIML has been shown to provide

Table I. Descriptive Statistics and Correlations Among Study Variables

	1	2	3	4	5	6	7	8	9	10	11	12	13
1. Child sex	–												
2. Grade level	.02	–											
3. Race/ethnicity	−.02	.00	–										
4. T1 BMIz	.21*	−.04	.13	–									
5. T1 disordered eating	−.02	−.04	−.09	.37**	–								
6. T1 physical HRQOL	.13	.14	−.02	−.12	−.46**	–							
7. T1 psychosocial HRQOL	.17	.05	.01	−.20	−.39**	.66**	–						
8. T2 disordered eating	−.12	−.08	−.19	.19	.52**	−.33**	−.49**	–					
9. T2 physical HRQOL	.20*	.27**	−.01	−.39**	−.28**	.57**	.60**	−.31**	–				
10. T2 psychosocial HRQOL	.11	.12	.04	−.31**	−.29**	.47**	.68**	−.42**	.70**	–			
11. T3 disordered eating	−.08	−.11	.01	.36**	.48**	−.15	−.31**	.57**	−.40**	−.39**	–		
12. T3 physical HRQOL	.17	.15	.16	−.09	.25*	.08	.16	−.16	.15	.25*	−.09	–	
13. T3 psychosocial HRQOL	.20	.09	.14	−.06	−.35**	.19	.19	−.48**	.15	.40**	−.42**	.51**	–
Mean	–	–	–	0.22	2.07	80.86	73.03	1.92	80.52	76.61	1.72	86.06	82.82
SD	–	–	–	1.06	0.61	16.51	17.44	0.48	15.60	15.26	0.52	11.11	10.71
Minimum	–	–	–	−2.51	1.12	10.71	17.86	1.00	0.00	26.67	1.00	50.00	55.00
Maximum	–	–	–	2.60	4.46	100.00	100.00	4.16	100.00	98.33	3.55	100.00	100.00
Skewness	–	–	–	0.18	1.47	−1.48	−0.71	1.36	−1.67	−0.90	1.16	−1.07	−0.38
Kurtosis	–	–	–	−0.24	3.21	3.14	0.27	4.04	5.10	0.71	1.35	0.93	−0.51

Note. $*p < .05$; $**p < .01$; child sex (0 = female, 1 = male); grade (0 = second grade, 1 = third grade, 2 = fourth grade); race/ethnicity (0 = Caucasian; 1 = minority); BMIz = body mass index z-score; HRQOL = health-related quality of life.

parameter estimates that are less biased (Arbuckle, 1996).

The path model was estimated to explore the possible reciprocal influences while taking into account the stability of the constructs and controlling for child sex, grade level (a proxy for age), race/ethnicity, and BMIz; these variables were selected as covariates because levels of disordered eating attitudes and behaviors and HRQOL have been shown to differ based on these factors (e.g., Evans, Tovée, Boothroyd, & Drewett, 2013; Franko & Edwards George, 2009; Mitchell & Steele, 2016; Ricciardelli, McCabe, Mussap, & Holt, 2009; Wertheim et al., 2009). The initial model allowed each predictor variable and the residuals of the outcome variables to covary. Thus, this model was fully saturated and fit the data perfectly, so model fit statistics were not relevant.

To determine the likelihood of finding a significant result if the effect exists in the population, a power analysis was conducted using G*Power 3.1.9.2. Time 2 and Time 3 dependent variables in the model were predicted by seven predictors (four covariates and three primary variables). For example, Time 2 physical HRQOL was predicted by grade, sex, race/ethnicity, BMIz, Time 1 physical HRQOL, Time 1 psychosocial HRQOL, and Time 1 disordered eating. The power analysis revealed that there would be 80% power to detect medium effects with a sample size of 103, seven predictors, and an alpha coefficient of 0.05. Given that medium to large effects exist in the population, the sample size of the current study provided sufficient power to test hypotheses; however, the current study is underpowered to detect small effects.

Results

Participants at Time 1 included 130 students between the ages of 7 and 10 ($M = 8.62$, $SD = 1.11$; 46% boys). The racial/ethnic composition of the sample was 65.2% Caucasian, 7.4% African American, 5.4% Asian, 1.8% Hispanic, 1.8% American Indian, and 17.9% biracial/other (i.e., either reported multiple racial/ethnic groups or indicated a group that was not listed as an option); this racial/ethnic composition was representative of the overall demographic makeup of the school district (Kansas State Department of Education, 2014). The mean BMIz for participants was 0.22 ($SD = 1.06$); 78.15% of children were of healthy weight, 12.61% were overweight, and 9.24% were obese. In total, 33 participants dropped out of the study before Time 3. Regression analyses revealed that there were no differences on demographic characteristics (i.e., grade, sex, race/ethnicity, and BMIz) and Time 1 primary variables (i.e., disordered eating attitudes and behaviors, physical HRQOL, and psychosocial HRQOL) in these participants and those who completed all waves of data collection (all $p > .05$).

Preliminary Analyses

Means, *SD*s, and correlations among all study variables are presented in Table I. The average scores for disordered eating attitudes and behaviors at all time points indicated that on average, children reported rarely engaging in the attitudes and behaviors (Anton et al., 2006), and the average scores for physical and psychosocial HRQOL for children in the current sample across all time points were similar to other 8–12-year-olds in a validation of the HRQOL measure (physical HRQOL: $M = 85.57$, $SD = 13.42$; psychosocial HRQOL: $M = 78.68$, $SD = 14.59$; Varni, Burwinkle, & Seid, 2006). Boys had higher levels of physical and psychosocial HRQOL and BMIz. In addition, older participants reported higher levels of both types of HRQOL. Higher BMIz was also associated with higher disordered eating at Time 1 and Time 3 and with lower physical and psychosocial HRQOL at Time 2.

As shown, disordered eating attitudes and behaviors were positively associated across each wave of data. Similarly, physical and psychosocial HRQOL were positively correlated across each wave of data. Disordered eating was negatively correlated with both physical and psychosocial HRQOL at Time 1 and at Time 2; however, disordered eating was only negatively associated with psychosocial HRQOL at Time 3.

Path Analysis Models
Disordered Eating Attitudes and Behaviors

Results indicated that disordered eating attitudes and behaviors were stable across both 6-month intervals (see Table II or Figure 1). Lower psychosocial HRQOL predicted higher disordered eating attitudes and behaviors across the 6-month period between Time 1 and Time 2 (across academic years; β = −0.37, standard error [SE] = 0.13, $p = 0.00$), but not across the 6-month period from Time 2 to Time 3 (within the same academic year) or the 1-year period from Time 1 to Time 3. Physical HRQOL did not predict disordered eating attitudes and behaviors across any time point.

Health-related Quality of Life

Results indicated that psychosocial HRQOL was stable across both 6-month intervals; however, physical HRQOL was only stable from Time 1 to Time 2 (across academic years; see Table II or Figure 1). Higher disordered eating attitudes and behaviors predicted lower psychosocial HRQOL across the 6-month period between Time 2 and Time 3 (within the same academic year; β = −0.33, SE = 0.12, $p = .01$), but not during the 6-month period from Time 1 to Time 2 (across academic years) or across the 1-year period from Time 1 to Time 3. Disordered eating attitudes and behaviors did not predict physical HRQOL across any time point.

Discussion

The current study was designed to examine potential longitudinal, bidirectional associations between disordered eating attitudes and behaviors and physical/psychosocial HRQOL in a community sample of elementary school-age youth. Previous research has examined the associations using cross-sectional analyses, often with clinical samples of adolescent females. The current study addressed gaps in the literature because it examined the possible longitudinal, bidirectional associations between disordered eating attitudes and physical/psychosocial HRQOL in elementary school-age youth to elucidate whether HRQOL is a risk factor or consequence (or both) of disordered eating attitudes and behaviors.

The first hypothesis, that higher levels of disordered eating attitudes and behaviors would predict lower levels of psychosocial HRQOL, was partially supported. Higher disordered eating attitude and behavior scores predicted subsequent lower psychosocial HRQOL scores only across a period from Time 2 to Time 3. Higher disordered eating did not predict lower psychosocial HRQOL across academic years from Time 1 to Time 2 or from Time 1 to Time 3. The second hypothesis, that lower psychosocial HRQOL scores would predict subsequent higher disordered eating attitudes and behaviors scores, was also partially supported. Lower psychosocial HRQOL predicted higher disordered eating attitudes and behaviors across the 6-month period across academic years (Time 1–Time 2), but not across a 6-month period within the same academic year (Time 2–Time 3) or during a 1-year period (Time 1–Time 3).

The current study is the first to provide evidence that psychosocial HRQOL can be viewed as a potential risk factor and a consequence of disordered eating attitudes and behaviors in elementary school-age youth. Based on the findings, it could be suggested that researchers and health care providers monitor disordered eating at the beginning of the school year and implement prevention efforts to protect against potential impairment in psychosocial functioning. It could also be suggested that researchers and health care providers implement prevention efforts at the end of the school year or during the summer for youth with lower psychosocial HRQOL (more negative emotionality, lower self-esteem, more teasing, lower social status) to protect against disordered eating attitudes and behaviors in the coming year. With these suggestions, it should be noted that children like those in the current sample might never be seen in a clinical setting

Disordered Eating and Quality of Life

Table II. Path Models Predicting Disordered Eating Attitudes and Behaviors and Health-Related Quality of Life

	Time 2									Time 3								
	Disordered eating			Physical HRQOL			Psychosocial HRQOL			Disordered eating			Physical HRQOL			Psychosocial HRQOL		
	β	SE	p	β	SE	p	β	SE	p	β	SE	p	β	SE	p	β	SE	p
Child sex	0.13	0.15	.40	−0.18	0.14	.19	−0.09	0.14	.55	−0.05	0.15	.76	−0.38	0.20	.06	**−0.42**	**0.17**	**.01**
Grade level	0.06	0.12	.61	0.23	0.11	.12	0.12	0.12	.30	0.04	0.11	.74	0.07	0.14	.62	−0.01	0.12	.93
Race/ethnicity	**−0.32**	**0.16**	**.04**	0.17	0.14	.24	0.17	0.15	.26	0.20	0.16	.21	0.28	0.21	.20	0.07	0.18	.69
T1 BMIz	−0.14	0.10	.16	**−0.27**	**0.09**	**.00**	−0.12	0.09	.17	**0.21**	**0.11**	**.04**	0.02	0.14	.89	0.03	0.11	.78
T1 disordered eating	**0.54**	**0.09**	**.00**	0.14	0.09	.11	−0.03	0.09	.74	0.18	0.13	.14	−0.27	0.17	.11	−0.23	0.14	.10
T1 physical HRQOL	0.11	0.13	.41	**0.45**	**0.11**	**.00**	0.19	0.11	.10	0.04	0.15	.82	−0.31	0.19	.11	−0.04	0.16	.82
T1 psychosocial HRQOL	**−0.37**	**0.13**	**.00**	0.16	0.12	.17	**0.49**	**0.11**	**.00**	0.19	0.15	.21	0.02	0.19	.91	−0.27	0.15	.08
T2 disordered eating	–	–	–	–	–	–	–	–	–	**0.46**	**0.12**	**.00**	0.03	0.15	.86	**−0.33**	**0.12**	**.01**
T2 physical HRQOL	–	–	–	–	–	–	–	–	–	−0.19	0.16	.23	0.15	0.20	.45	−0.15	0.16	.34
T2 psychosocial HRQOL	–	–	–	–	–	–	–	–	–	−0.08	0.13	.56	0.26	0.16	.11	**0.50**	**0.13**	**.00**

Note. Child sex (0 = female, 1 = male); grade (0 = second grade, 1 = third grade, 2 = fourth grade); race/ethnicity (0 = Caucasian; 1 = minority); bold estimates represent statistically significant paths; BMIz = body mass index z-score; HRQOL = health-related quality of life; SE = standard error.

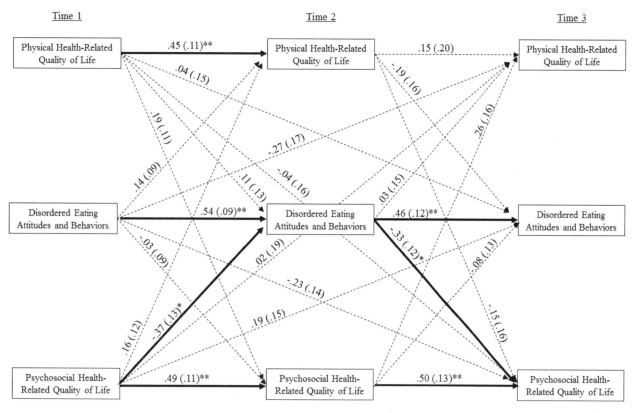

Figure 1. Path analysis model of the longitudinal associations among disordered eating attitudes and behaviors and physical/psychosocial health-related quality of life across three time points.
Note. Standardized estimates and standard errors are reported along paths between variables. Solid lines and asterisks (*$p < .05$; **$p < .01$; ***$p < .001$) indicate statistically significant paths, and dotted lines indicate nonsignificant paths. Child sex, grade level, race/ethnicity, and BMIz were included as control variables, but were not included in the figure for ease of interpretation. Additionally, each predictor variable and the residuals of the outcome variables were allowed to covary, but were not included in the figure for ease of interpretation.

because of their overall limited symptomatology and impairment in functioning. Therefore, it may be appropriate for assessment of eating attitudes and behaviors and psychosocial HRQOL to occur in the school setting. However, because the current study is the first of its nature, more research is needed before conclusions or recommendations about prevention/intervention efforts can be definitively made.

As hypothesized, physical HRQOL did not predict disordered eating, and disordered eating did not predict physical HRQOL in this nonclinical sample of elementary school-age youth across any time point. As previously posited, it could be that physical functioning is not impacted when disordered eating is just emerging in childhood, and so it may be important to examine the longitudinal association between physical HRQOL and disordered eating in older adolescents or adults. Alternatively, it could be that the physical risk factors (e.g., weight status and serotonin levels) and consequences (e.g., weight cycling and malnutrition) of disordered eating are not fully captured in measures of HRQOL (e.g., the PedsQL). This limitation of the current study could be addressed in future research by considering alternate measures of physical functioning in relation to disordered eating attitudes and behaviors. Although the current study suggests that it may not be appropriate to consider physical HRQOL as a predictor or consequence of disordered eating, more evidence is needed.

Additional limitations of the current study must be taken into account when interpreting the study findings. First, the large majority of the sample was Caucasian and middle class, which limits generalizability; future studies should examine the longitudinal, bidirectional associations in more diverse samples. Another limitation was that, on average, the participants in the study reported "rarely engaging" in disordered eating attitudes and behaviors and reported relatively high levels of HRQOL. It is suggested that future research should examine the bidirectional, longitudinal relationships in samples with more severe symptomatology and impairment. The current study was also limited in the power to examine child sex as a moderator of the bidirectional associations between disordered eating attitudes and behaviors and HRQOL. However, there is research to suggest that there are no differences in elementary school-age boys and girls on variables such as body dissatisfaction, importance of weight, weight-loss strategies, or pressure to lose weight (e.g., Combs et al., 2013; Gowey et al., 2014; Ricciardelli, McCabe, Holt, & Finemore, 2003). On the other hand, it appears that sex differences in disordered eating attitudes and behaviors may only become apparent after 10 years of age (Ricciardelli & McCabe, 2001), and so future studies could include child sex as a moderator in older samples.

Because the current study used only included self-report data (with the exception of objectively measured BMIz), common method variance may have biased the direction or strength of the associations between variables, so future studies should incorporate multiple informants. Further, the current study was limited by the absence of literature, suggesting an appropriate time lag to examine the association between the variables. Ideally, time points in longitudinal studies should be theoretically sound, based on the length of time it would take to see effects; however, as the current study was the first identified study to examine these variables longitudinally in youth, the current time lag of 6 months was as a convenient marker. Future studies should include varying time points to continue to explore the appropriate time lag between the variables.

Notwithstanding these limitations, the current study is the first to examine the associations between disordered eating attitudes and behaviors and physical/psychosocial HRQOL longitudinally and bidirectionally in a community sample of elementary school-age boys and girls, providing information about directionality and causality. Results suggested that there are longitudinal, bidirectional associations between disordered eating attitudes and behaviors and psychosocial HRQOL in elementary school-age youth. Further, results indicate that the time interval used between assessments is critical to understanding the observed effects. Higher disordered eating attitudes and behaviors predicted lower psychosocial HRQOL only during a 6-month period within the same school year, and lower psychosocial HRQOL predicted higher levels of disordered eating during a 6-month period across academic years. Physical HRQOL did not predict disordered eating, and disordered eating did not predict physical HRQOL, across any time point. The findings indicate that future studies should consider psychosocial HRQOL as both a predictor and consequence of disordered eating attitudes and behaviors.

Funding

No conflicts of interest or funding declared.

Conflicts of interest: None declared.

References

Ackard, D. M., Fulkerson, J. A., & Neumark-Sztainer, D. (2011). Psychological and behavioral risk profiles as they relate to eating disorder diagnoses and symptomatology among a school-based sample of youth. *International Journal of Eating Disorders*, 44, 440–446. doi:10.1002/eat.20846

Acquadro, C., Berzon, R., Dubois, D., Leidy, N. K., Marquis, P., Revicki, D., & Rothman, M. (2003). Incorporating the patient's perspective into drug development and communication: An ad hoc task force report of the patient-reported outcomes (PRO) harmonization group meeting at the Food and Drug Administration, February 16, 2001. *Value Health*, 6, 522–531. doi:10.1046/j.1524-4733.2003.65309.x

Agency for Healthcare Research and Quality. (2009). Eating disorders are sending more Americans to the hospital.

Retrieved from http://archive.ahrq.gov/news/newsletters/research-activities/may09/0509RA30.html

Anton, S. D., Han, H., Newton, R. L. J., Martin, C. K., York-Crowe, E., Stewart, T. M., & Williamson, D. A. (2006). Reformulation of the children's eating attitudes test (ChEAT): Factor structure and scoring method in a non-clinical population. *Eating and Weight Disorders*, 11, 201–210. doi:10.1007/BF03327572

Arbuckle, J. L. (1996). Full information estimation in the presence of incomplete data. In G. A. Marcoulides & R. E. Shumaker (Eds.), *Advanced structural equation modeling: Issues and techniques* (pp. 243–277). Mahwah, NW: Lawrence Erlbaum Associates, Inc.

Baiano, M., Salvo, P., Righetti, P., Cereser, L., Baldissera, E., Camponogara, I., & Balestrieri, M. (2014). Exploring health-related quality of life in eating disorders by a cross-sectional study and a comprehensive review. *BMC Psychiatry*, 14, 165. doi: 10.1186/1471-244X-14-165.

Brausch, A. M., & Gutierrez, P. M. (2009). The role of body image and disordered eating as risk factors for depression and suicidal ideation in adolescents. *Suicide and Life-Threatening Behavior*, 39, 58–71. doi:10.1521/suli.2009.39.1.58

Centers for Disease Control and Prevention. (2011a). About BMI for children and teens. Retrieved from http://www.cdc.gov/healthyweight/assessing/bmi/childrens_bmi\

Centers for Disease Control and Prevention. (2011b). Health-related quality of life. Retrieved from http://www.cdc.gov/hrqol/concept.htm

Combs, J. L., Pearson, C. M., Zapolski, T. C. B., & Smith, G. T. (2013). Preadolescent disordered eating predicts subsequent eating dysfunction. *Journal of Pediatric Psychology*, 38, 41–49. doi:10.1093/jpepsy/jss094

Croll, J. K., Neumark-Sztainer, D., Story, M., & Ireland, M. (2002). Prevalence and risk and protective factors related to disordered eating behaviors among adolescents: Relationship to gender and ethnicity. *Journal of Adolescent Health*, 31, 166–175. doi:10.1016/S1054-139X(02)00368-3

Doll, H. A., Petersen, S. E., & Stewart-Brown, S. L. (2005). Eating disorders and emotional and physical well-being: Associations between student self-reports of eating disorders and quality of life as measured by the SF-36. *Quality of Life Research*, 14, 705–717. doi:10.1007/s11136-004-0792-0

Doyle, A. C., Le Grange, D., Goldschmidt, A., & Wilfley, D. E. (2007). Psychosocial and physical impairment in overweight adolescents at high risk for eating disorders. *Obesity*, 15, 145–154. doi:10.1038/oby.2007.515

Evans, E. H., Tovée, M. J., Boothroyd, L. G., & Drewett, R. F. (2013). Body dissatisfaction and disordered eating attitudes in 7- to 11-year-old girls: Testing a sociocultural model. *Body Image*, 10, 8–15. doi:10.1016/j.bodyim.2012.10.001

Edwards, George, J. B., & Franko, D. L. (2009). Cultural issues in eating pathology and body image among children and adolescents. *Journal of Pediatric Psychology*, 35(3), 231–242.

Gowey, M. A., Lim, C. S., Clifford, L. M., & Janicke, D. M. (2014). Disordered eating and health-related quality of life in overweight and obese children. *Journal of Pediatric Psychology*, 39, 552–561. doi:10.1093/jpepsy/jsu012

Herpertz-Dahlmann, B., Wille, N., Hölling, H., Vloet, T. D., & Ravens-Sieberer, U. (2008). Disordered eating behaviour and attitudes, associated psychopathology and health-related quality of life: Results of the BELLA study. *European Child & Adolescent Psychiatry*, 17, 82–91. doi:10.1007/s00787-008-1009-9

Jalali-Farahani, S., Chin, Y. S., Nasir, M. T. M., & Amiri, P. (2015). Disordered eating and its association with overweight and health-related quality of life among adolescents in selected high schools of Tehran. *Child Psychiatry and Human Development*, 46, 485–492. doi:10.1007/s10578-014-0489-8

Jenkins, P. E., Hoste, R. R., Doyle, A. C., Eddy, K., Crosby, R. D., Hill, L., ... Le Grange, D. (2014). Health-related quality of life among adolescents with eating disorders. *Journal of Psychosomatic Research*, 76, 1–5. doi:10.1016/j.jpsychores.2013.11.006

Johnson, J. G., Cohen, P., Kasen, S., & Brook, J. S. (2002). Childhood adversities associated with risk for eating disorders or weight problems during adolescence or early adulthood. *The American Journal of Psychiatry*, 159, 394–400. doi:10.1176/appi.ajp.159.3.394

Kansas State Department of Education. (2014). Report card 2013-2014. Retrieved from http://online.ksde.org/rcard/district.aspx?org_no=D0497

Khodabakhsh, M. R., & Kiani, F. (2014). Body image disturbance and perfectionism as predictor's factors of disordered eating behavior among female students. *International Journal of Pediatrics*, 2, 399–406.

Kline, R. B. (2011). *Principles and practice of structural equation modeling* (3rd edn.). New York, NY: Guilford Press.

Littleton, H. L., & Ollendick, T. (2003). Negative body image and disordered eating behavior in children and adolescents: What places youth at risk and how can these problems be prevented? *Clinical Child and Family Psychology Review*, 6, 51–66. doi:10.1023/A:1022266017046

Lowes, J., & Tiggemann, M. (2003). Body dissatisfaction, dieting awareness and the impact of parental influence in young children. *British Journal of Health Psychology*, 8, 135–147. doi:10.1348/135910703321649123

Maloney, M. J., McGuire, J. B., & Daniels, S. R. (1988). Reliability testing of a children's version of the eating attitude test. *Journal of the American Academy of Child & Adolescent Psychiatry*, 27, 541–543.

Mitchell, T. B., & Steele, R. G. (2016). The effect of body mass index, negative affect, and disordered eating on health-related quality of life in preadolescent youth: A moderated mediation analysis. *Journal of Pediatric Psychology*, 41(7), 768–776. doi:10.1093/jpepsy/jsv163

Muthén, L. K., Muthén, B. O. (1998–2015). *Mplus User's Guide* (7th edn.). Los Angeles, CA: Muthén & Muthén.

Neumark-Sztainer, D., Wall, M., Guo, J., Story, M., Haines, J., & Eisenberg, M. (2006). Obesity, disordered eating, and eating disorders in a longitudinal study of adolescents: How do dieters fare 5 years later? *Journal of the American Dietetic Association*, 106, 559–568. doi:10.1016/j.jada.2006.01.003

Ricciardelli, L. A., & McCabe, M. P. (2001). Children's body image concerns and eating disturbance: A review of the literature. *Clinical Psychology Review*, 21, 325–344. doi:10.1016/S0272-7358(99)00051-3

Ricciardelli, L. A., & McCabe, M. P. (2004). A biopsychosocial model of disordered eating and the pursuit of muscularity in adolescent boys. *Psychological Bulletin*, 130, 179–205. doi:10.1037/0033-2909.130.2.179

Ricciardelli, L. A., McCabe, M. P., Holt, K. E., & Finemore, J. (2003). A biopsychosocial model for understanding body image and body change strategies among children. *Journal of Applied Developmental Psychology*, 24, 475–495. doi:10.1016/S0193-3973(03)00070-4

Ricciardelli, L. A., McCabe, M. P., Mussap, A. J., & Holt, K. E. (2009). A Body image in preadolescent boys. In L. Smolak & K.L. Thompson (Eds.), Body image, eating disorders, and obesity in youth: Assessment, prevention, and treatment (2nd edn.; pp. 77–96). Washington, DC: American Psychological Association.

Rodgers, R. F., Paxton, S. J., & McLean, S. A. (2014). A biopsychosocial model of body image concerns and disordered eating in early adolescent girls. *Journal of Youth and Adolescence*, 43, 814–823. doi:10.1016/S0193-3973(03)00070-4

Smolak, L., Thompson, K. J. (2009). *Body image, eating disorders, and obesity in youth: Assessment, prevention, and treatment* (2nd edn.). Washington, DC: American Psychological Association.

Spieth, L. E., & Harris, C. V. (1996). Assessment of health-related quality of life in children and adolescents: An integrative review. *Journal of Pediatric Psychology*, 21, 175–193. doi:10.1093/jpepsy/21.2.175

Stice, E. (2002). Risk and maintenance factors for eating pathology: A meta-analytic review. *Psychological Bulletin*, 128, 825–848. doi:10.1037/0033-2909.128.5.825

United States Census Bureau. (2015). QuickFacts: Lawrence, Kansas. Retrieved from http://www.census.gov/quickfacts/table/PST045215/2038900.

Varni, J. W., Burwinkle, T. M., & Seid, M. (2006). The PedsQL™ 4.0 as a school population health measure: Feasibility, reliability, and validity. *Quality of Life Research*, 15, 203–215. doi:10.1007/s11136-005-1388-z

Varni, J. W., Seid, M., & Kurtin, P. S. (2001). PedsQL™ 4.0: Reliability and validity of the Pediatric Quality of Life Inventory (TM) version 4.0 generic core scales in healthy and patient populations. *Medical Care*, 39, 800–812. doi:10.1097/00005650-200108000-00006

Wade, T. D., Wilksch, S. M., & Lee, C. (2012). A longitudinal investigation of the impact of disordered eating on young women's quality of life. *Health Psychology*, 31, 352–359. doi:10.1037/a0025956

Wertheim, E. H., Paxton, S. J., Blaney, S. (2009). Body image in girls. In L. Smolak & K. J. Thompson (Eds.), *Body image, eating disorders, and obesity in youth: Assessment, prevention, and treatment* (2nd edn., pp. 47–76). Washington, DC: American Psychological Association.

Yanover, T., & Thompson, J. K. (2008). Self-reported interference with academic functioning and eating disordered symptoms: Associations with multiple dimensions of body image. *Body Image*, 5, 326–328. doi:10.1016/j.bodyim.2008.03.008

Empirically Derived Patterns of Pain, Stooling, and Incontinence and Their Relations to Health-Related Quality of Life Among Youth With Chronic Constipation

Kimberly L. Klages,[1] BS, Kristoffer S. Berlin,[1,2] PhD, Alan H. Silverman,[3,4] PhD, Suzanne Mugie,[5] MD, Carlo Di Lorenzo,[5] MD, Samuel Nurko,[6] MD, Ananthasekar Ponnambalam,[7] MD, Rina Sanghavi,[8] MD, and Manu R. Sood,[4] MD

[1]Department of Psychology, The University of Memphis, [2]University of Tennessee Health Sciences Center, [3]Department of Gastroenterology, Children's Hospital of Wisconsin, [4]Department of Gastroenterology, Medical College of Wisconsin, [5]Department of Gastroenterology, Nationwide Children's Hospital, [6]Department of Gastroenterology, Boston Children's Hospital, [7]Department of Gastroenterology, Children's and Women's Hospital at University of South Alabama, [8]Department of Gastroenterology, University of Texas Southwest Medical Center

All correspondence concerning this article should be addressed to Kimberly L. Klages, BS, Department of Psychology, Room 202, The University of Memphis, Memphis, TN 38152, USA. E-mail: klklages@memphis.edu

Received February 28, 2016; revisions received June 29, 2016; accepted June 30, 2016

Abstract

Objective Chronic constipation is associated with pain, stress, and fecal incontinence, which negatively impact health-related quality of life (HRQoL); however, it is unclear if patterns of pain, stool frequency, and incontinence are differentially associated with HRQoL in youth with chronic constipation. **Methods** 410 caregivers completed a demographics and symptoms form, the Parental Opinions of Pediatric Constipation, Pediatric Symptom Checklist, and the Functional Disability Inventory. **Results** Stooling patterns were derived using Latent Variable Mixture Modeling. A three-class model emerged: *withholding/avoiding* (*WA*), *pain*, and *fecal incontinence* (*FI*). The *pain* class reported the greatest amount of disease burden/distress, greatest impairments in illness-related activity limitations, more psychosocial problems, and, along with the *FI* class, elevated levels of family conflict. The *FI* class reported the greatest amount of parental worry of social impact. **Conclusions** Youth with chronic constipation who experience pain or fecal incontinence may be at a greater risk for specific HRQoL problems such as illness-related activity limitations, psychosocial issues, disease burden and worry, and family conflict.

Key words: elimination disorders; gastroenterology; pain; quality of life.

Chronic constipation is a common pediatric gastrointestinal disorder with a prevalence up to 29.6% in the general population and is often associated with infrequent defecation, hard and large stools, pain while stooling, abdominal pain, and distress (Bongers, van Dijk, Benninga, & Grootenhuis, 2009). In the United States alone, constipation is responsible for more than 2.5 million physician consultations, 92,000 hospitalizations, and several hundred million dollars per year for medication costs (Lembo & Camilleri, 2003). Although several definitions of constipation exist, the Rome III criterion is most widely used in medical settings (Kaugars et al., 2010). According to Rome III criteria, the diagnosis for functional constipation requires at least two or more of the following for one month or more in infants and children under 4 years of age and at least once per week for two months or more in children 4 and up prior to diagnosis: two or fewer defecations per week, at least one period of fecal incontinence per week after acquiring toileting skills, history of retentive posturing or excessive volitional stool retention, history of painful or hard bowel movements, presence of a large fecal mass in the rectum, and/or a history of large-diameter stools that may obstruct the toilet ("Guidelines–Rome III Diagnostic Criteria for Functional Gastrointestinal Disorders," 2006). Up to 84% of children with chronic constipation experience frequent episodes of fecal incontinence, or the passage of whole bowel movements in their underwear (Cunningham & Banez, 2006). Although most children with chronic constipation respond to medical treatment within one year, approximately one-third of patients experience symptoms into adulthood (Bongers, Benninga, Maurice-Stam, & Grootenhuis, 2009).

Biopsychobehavioral Model of Chronic Constipation

Cox, Sutphen, Borowitz, Kovatchev, and Ling (1998) proposed a biopsychobehavioral model of chronic constipation with fecal incontinence in which constipating events lead to fecal impaction and the buildup of large and hard bowel movements that are difficult to pass. Children with chronic constipation may cope with these painful defecations by withholding stools or avoiding stooling, eventually releasing the bowel movement via overflow incontinence. Avoiding stooling or withholding bowel movements exacerbates constipation, and, in turn, leads to greater fecal incontinence, thus maintaining a maladaptive pattern of stooling (Luxem, Christophersen, Purvis, & Baer, 1997). Subsequent fecal incontinence episodes may lead to peer and family conflict, which may culminate in poor self-esteem and poor self-worth (Cox et al., 1998). Furthermore, parents may use punishment to reduce fecal incontinence accidents; however, punitive techniques are likely to cause more guilt, poor self-esteem, and anxiety in a child and thus significantly impacting health-related quality of life (HRQoL) in youth with chronic constipation experiencing fecal incontinence (Landmark, Rappaport, Fenton, & Levine, 1986; Nolan & Oberklaid, 1993; Owens-Stively, 1987).

Pain and Health-Related Quality of Life Among Youth With Chronic Constipation

Past research has shown that youth with chronic constipation experiencing increased symptomatology, such as abdominal pain and pain while stooling, reported lower levels of HRQoL when compared with youth experiencing fewer symptoms (Rajindrajith et al., 2013). Furthermore, Rajindrajith and colleagues (2013) found a negative correlation between HRQoL and general somatic symptoms (such as aches, pains, and altered body functioning) in youth with chronic constipation. The severity of these somatic symptoms significantly impacted the youth's ability to perform daily activities, thus contributing to lower perceived HRQoL (Rajindrajith et al., 2013). It is currently unclear exactly which somatic symptom patterns exist among youth with chronic constipation and how these symptoms contribute to HRQoL. Youssef, Langseder, Verga, Mones, and Rosh (2005) assessed HRQoL in children with chronic constipation and compared them to children with other chronic gastroenterology conditions and healthy controls. The impact of chronic constipation on HRQoL of affected children was similar to children with inflammatory bowel disease (IBD), a chronic health condition associated with inflammation of the gastrointestinal tract (Youssef et al., 2005). Similar to IBD, youth with chronic constipation often experience bloating, abdominal pain, and pain while stooling that significantly impacts HRQoL (Benninga, Voskuijl, & Taminiau, 2004). In youth with very infrequent stooling, the evacuation of large stools is usually preceded by complaints of abdominal pain, and this pain has been reported as the most distressing consequence of constipation (Benninga et al., 2004; Freeman, Riley, Duke, & Fu, 2014).

Internalizing and Externalizing Behaviors Among Youth With Chronic Constipation

Youth with chronic constipation and fecal incontinence may be at an increased risk for more problematic externalizing and internalizing behaviors that negatively impact child and family HRQoL (Kaugars et al, 2010; Bongers, van Dijik, Benninga, & Grootenhuis, 2009; Joinson, Heron, Butler, & von Gontard, 2006; Youssef et al., 2005). Regarding behavioral difficulties, Cox et al. (2002) found both mothers and teachers of children with fecal incontinence reported higher rates of aggressiveness, attention problems, and withdrawn behaviors when compared with a sample of children without fecal incontinence. Furthermore, Joinson and colleagues (2006) also noted that parents of children with frequent fecal incontinence reported increased attention and activity problems, obsessions and compulsions, and oppositional behaviors when compared with children who soil occasionally or not at all. Children with chronic constipation are also to be perceived by their parents as more stubborn, defiant, disobedient, and resistant to following instructions than children without (Burket et al., 2006). Khan et al. (2006) found that children with higher levels of fecal incontinence (more episodes and longer duration) also had poorer long-term outcomes such as increased family conflict and difficulties with peer relationships as adults. These internalizing and externalizing behaviors that are often associated with chronic constipation and fecal incontinence have been shown to contribute to poorer HRQoL (Bongers, van Dijik, Benninga, & Grootenhuis, 2009).

Peer Relations Among Youth With Chronic Constipation

The troublesome nature of constipation may cause social embarrassment and rejection by peers. Peers often develop negative stereotypes about youth with fecal incontinence, often labeling them as "dirty" or "stinky" and therefore reject these individuals (Campbell, Cox, & Borowitz, 2009). Bongers, van Dijik, Benninga, and Grootenhuis (2009) reported that youth with constipation-associated fecal incontinence reported worrying about experiencing unnoticed fecal incontinence during school and believed that their defecation caused problems at school. These beliefs may lead to feelings of shame, which can heighten feelings of peer rejection (Joinson et al., 2006; Nolan & Oberklaid, 1993). Individuals with fecal incontinence may respond to peer rejection with poor self-esteem, hostility, or learned helplessness, which, in turn, negatively impact HRQoL (Campbell, Cox, & Borowitz, 2009).

While previous research focused on the individual impact of fecal incontinence, symptom duration, or overall symptom severity on HRQoL (Bongers, Benninga, Maurice-Stam, & Grootenhuis, 2009; Clarke et al., 2008; Youssef et al., 2005), the present study takes a person-centered approach to determine if specific patterns (i.e., latent profiles) of symptoms of constipation, such as stooling (stool size, consistency, frequency, presence of blood in stool, and incontinence), pain (abdominal and while stooling), age, and holding/avoiding stooling exist among youth with chronic constipation. If these latent profiles exist, a second aim of the current study is to determine whether these patterns differentially impact parent report of functional disability, psychosocial functioning, and constipation-specific HRQoL (parental burden/distress, family conflict, and parental worry of social impact) in youth with chronic constipation. It was anticipated that three to four distinct patterns would emerge, and the two profiles that were characterized by youth experiencing either pain or fecal incontinence would report the greatest psychosocial issues, increased functional disability, and decreased HRQoL.

Methods

Participants and Procedure

This study was part of a larger, multisite study investigating quality of life in youth with chronic constipation and fecal incontinence. Caregivers of youth with chronic constipation were recruited from pediatric gastrointestinal clinics at five participating academic medical centers across the United States. A total of 468 caregivers were initially enrolled in the study and 410 had sufficient data and met inclusion criteria (Silverman et al., 2015). The total sample consisted of 122 participants from Children's Hospital of Wisconsin, 154 participants from Nationwide Children's Hospital, 73 participants from Boston Children's Hospital, 39 participants from the University of Texas Southwestern Medical Center, and 22 participants from Children's and Women's Hospital from South Alabama. The study was approved by the respective institutional review board committees at each participating institution. Written informed consent for participation was obtained from adult caregivers, and data were collected in pediatric gastrointestinal clinics at each medical center. To be included in the study, families needed to be fluent in English and their child had to meet the Rome III criteria for functional constipation or functional constipation with fecal incontinence. Exclusion criteria for the present study included (1) children with a diagnosis of fecal incontinence (without constipation), (2) children with moderate to severe developmental delays, (3) children with associated chronic disease that may have had an impact on quality of life (e.g., cerebral palsy, spine deformity or malformations, severe psychiatric illness, etc.), and (4) children with a diagnosis of irritable bowel syndrome.

Measures
Demographics and Constipation Symptoms Questionnaire

Caregivers of children aged 2–18 completed a demographic questionnaire to report on youth gender, ethnicity/race, age, and diagnosis. Caregivers also reported youth's condition type according to Rome III criteria (i.e., constipation or constipation with fecal incontinence), typical stool size (i.e., small marble, golf ball, tennis ball, or larger than tennis ball), frequency (free response of the number of bowel movements per week), and stool consistency following the Bristol Stool Chart (Type 1, hard lumps to 7, entirely liquid; Heaton & Lewis, 1997). Caregivers rated relevant clinical information regarding abdominal pain, pain while stooling (0 = Never, 1 = Sometimes, 3 = Often 4 = Always), and fecal incontinence using a 4-point Likert scale (0 = Never, 1 = Small amount, 2 = Moderate amount, 3 = Large amount). The mean (SD) age of youth in the sample was 7.8 (3.5) years and 52% of the sample were male. In all, 78% of the participants were Caucasian, 9% African American, 5% Hispanic/Latino, 3.1% Asian/Asian American, and 4% identified as other. A total of 45% of the subjects were categorized as having functional constipation alone and 55% of the subjects were categorized as having functional constipation with fecal incontinence.

Parental Opinions of Pediatric Constipation

The Parental Opinions of Pediatric Constipation (POOPC; Silverman et al., 2015) is a 24-item parent report scale that used 5 point anchors (1 = strongly disagree to 5 = strongly agree). The POOPC consists of a total score and 4 subscales (Burden/Distress, Family Conflict, Difficulties with the Medical Team, and Worry about Social Impact) that assess the effects of pediatric constipation and constipation with fecal incontinence on HRQoL. This measure was developed using qualitative findings, and series of exploratory and confirmatory factor analyses among families seeking constipation treatment in a multidisciplinary clinic (Kaugars et al., 2010). The POOPC has been found to have internally consistent scales ($\alpha = .79–.90$); good convergent, discriminant, and construct validity; and good measurement invariance across ages ranging from 2 to 18 years (Silverman et al., 2015). The Burden/Distress subscale assesses a pattern of caregiver concerns that focus on their child's negative experiences of having constipation (e.g., pain, lack of improvement of symptoms, duration of symptoms, and embarrassment). The Family Conflict subscale assesses a pattern of caregiver concerns focusing on conflicts between family members related to following the constipation treatment regimen (e.g., asking the child to use the toilet, child resisting treatment, worry that the relationship with the child is damaged due to treatment). The Difficulties with the Medical Team subscale measures patterns of caregiver concerns with their child's healthcare provider. The Worry of Social Impact subscale assesses parent concerns related to peer relationships (e.g., child is not asked to play, others finding out about the problem).

Functional Disability Inventory

Caregivers completed the Functional Disability Inventory (FDI; Walker & Greene, 1991; $\alpha = .93$, current study), which is a 15-item parent report measure that assesses the child's difficulty in completing daily activities in four domains: home, school, recreational, and social. Each item is rated on a 5-point Likert scale (0 = no trouble to 4 = impossible). A total score is computed, 0–60, with higher scores indicating greater illness-related disability. Internal consistency reliability of the validation sample ranged from .86 to .91 (Walker & Greene, 1991). Validity was supported by significant correlations between child- and parent-report FDI scores with measures of school-related disability, pain, and somatic symptoms.

Pediatric Symptom Checklist

The Pediatric Symptom Checklist (PSC; Gardner et al., 1999) assesses parent report screening measure to identify children and adolescents who may be in need of further evaluation, or as an indicator of psychosocial well-being prior to and following intervention or treatment. The PSC consists of 35 items. Each item is rated as Never = 0, Sometimes = 1, or Often = 2. Higher scores indicate greater psychological impairment in children. The authors report evidence of good sensitivity and specificity, minimal concurrent validity, and moderate convergent validity (Gardner et al., 1999; $\alpha = .93$ for the current study).

Analytic Plan

Latent Variable Mixture Modeling (LVMM) was used to empirically derive patterns of pain, incontinence, and stooling (frequency, consistency, and size) in youth with chronic constipation. LVMM is a person-centered statistical approach (similar to cluster analyses) that classifies individuals into unobserved subgroupings (latent classes) with similar patterns to determine the extent to which these patterns may relate to the variables of interest (Berlin, Karazsia, & Klages, In Press; Berlin, Williams, & Parra, 2014; Berlin, Parra, & Williams, 2014). Person-centered approaches are useful when complex interactions may exist between variables of interest (Bergman, von Eye, & Magnusson, 2006; Berlin, Karazsia, & Klages, In Press). Person-centered approaches use individuals as the standard unit of the analyses rather than variables (Bauer & Shanahan, 2007; Berlin, Parra, & Williams, 2014; Berlin, Williams, et al., 2014), allowing for intricate patterns among the variables to be identified, thus providing useful descriptive information about the complex patterns among variables. A mix of ordinal (abdominal pain, pain while stooling, typical stool size, stool consistency, and age), binary (condition type, blood in stool, holding/avoiding stooling), and count (stool frequency) indicators were used in LVMM. A zero-inflated negative binomial model was chosen for count data because a sizeable minority of the sample (20%) reported zero bowel movements per week, leading to overly dispersed data ($M = 4.56$, $SD = 6.24$). Zero-inflated models result in two variables: (1) a binary variable reflecting membership in a group that is "always zero" versus a group that can take on values of zero and greater, and (2) the count of bowel movements per week leading among those not always at zero. An exploratory approach was used to establish our model (i.e., additional classes were estimated until a statistically proper and/or practical solution is no longer obtained), and the best fitting model for describing varying classes was selected based on clinical relevance and goodness-of-fit statistics. The model was compared on various forms of fit-statistics, including the Bayesian Information Criterion (BIC; Schwarz, 1978) and the Akaike Information Criterion (AIC; Akaike, 1974), where lower values on these indicate a better model fit, and the Lo–Mendell–Rubin test (LMR; Lo, Mendell, & Rubin, 2001), which statistically compares the improvement of adjacent models (e.g., 1 vs. 2, 2 vs. 3, etc.) where a p-value less than 0.05 indicates the best model fit. The entropy statistic was calculated to indicate classification precision, higher values reflecting better accuracy (Berlin, Williams, et al., 2014). Robust full information maximum likelihood was used to account for missing data and for adjustments to the standard errors for non-normality and non-independence across sites (for all models tested, see Table I).

To determine class differences in HRQoL (POOPC subscales, FDI, and PSC) while controlling for age, a manual BCH procedure was used (Asparouhuv & Muthén, 2014). The BCH method can be used to evaluate measurement error weighted intercepts/means across classes and allows for covariates. BCH weighted class intercepts (which reflect the predicted values of the outcome at the average participant age which was mean-centered) were compared using the scaled log-likelihood difference test (Muthén & Muthén, 2012). All estimates (intercepts, regression coefficients, variances, etc.) were allowed to vary across classes.

Results

Youth with chronic constipation were empirically assigned to groups, or classes, based on patterns of pain, incontinence, and stooling. The patterns of fit statistics (Table I) were mixed, suggesting that one-class (LMR), two-class (BIC), and three-plus-class (AIC) models were potentially viable. As such, the class characteristics (uniqueness vs. similarity to each other) and size were considered next. The three-class model provided three profile patterns with clearly differentiated indicator values and distinct characteristics (i.e., distinction of youth experiencing predominately pain and youth experiencing predominately fecal incontinence), while the two-class model provided less of a distinction between class important clinical characteristics (i.e., high/low pain classes with no distinct fecal incontinence class). The four-class model only provided a slight variation of the three-class model in which the pain class was divided into two classes (youth experiencing predominately abdominal pain and youth experiencing predominately pain while stooling; see Table I for goodness-of-fit statistics). When considering possible targets of intervention and typical presenting problems, the three-class model was reasoned to be optimal (latent classes are depicted in Figure 1). Univariate entropy indicated that the ordinal variables that contributed most to class formation consisted of pain while stooling (.221) and stool consistency (0.199), followed by age (0.121), stool size (0.087), and abdominal pain (0.082).

Class Characteristics

The largest profile of this three-class model, the *fecal incontinence* (FI; $n = 177$, 43.3%) class, was characterized by slightly younger youth ($M = 6.24$, $SD = 0.24$ years of age) experiencing fecal incontinence and loose stools. The *FI* class had relatively low (log) odds ($est. = -3.04$, $SE = 0.62$, $p < .01$) of having zero weekly bowel movements ($\sim 4.6\%$ of *FI* class). Among those not always experiencing zero bowel movement per week in the *FI* class, youth experienced an average of 1.8 ($SE = 0.622$, $p < .01$) bowel movements per week. The second largest profile, the *withholding/avoiding* (WA; $n = 154$, 37.6%) class, was characterized by youth ($M = 7.72$, $SD = 0.31$ years of age) experiencing stool greater stool withholding and stooling avoidance. The *WA* class had the highest (log) odds ($est. = -1.81$, $SE = 0.57$, $p < .001$, 14% of *LFS* class) of having zero weekly bowel movements; however, among those not always at zero bowel movements per week in the *WA* class, youth experienced an average of 1.81 ($SE = 0.06$, $p < .001$) bowel movements per week. The smallest profile that emerged, the *pain* ($n = 78$, 19.1%) class, was characterized by youth ($M = 7.62$, $SD = 0.26$ years of age) experiencing large, hard, painful, bloody stools, abdominal pain, and infrequent stooling, and a relatively low (log) odds of zero bowel movements per week ($est. = -3.45$, $SE = 1.94$, $p = .076$, $\sim 3.1\%$ of *pain* class). Among those not always experiencing zero bowel movements per week in the *pain* class, youth experienced an average of 0.98 ($SE = 0.114$, $p < .001$) weekly bowel movements.

Constipation-Specific HRQoL

Significant differences were found between classes for the POOPC subscales when controlling for age

Table I. Goodness-of-Fit Statistics for 1, 2, 3, and 4 Classes: Information Criteria, Entropy, Likelihood Ratio Tests for LVMMs of Youth With Chronic Constipation

Number of classes	Log-likelihood	AIC	BIC	Entropy	LMR	LMR-p
1	−4096.636	8255.273	8379.774	NA	NA	NA
2	−3987.978	8099.956	8348.958	0.754	216.158	0.8878
3	−3903.044	7992.089	8365.591	0.770	168.960	1.00
4	−3824.447	7896.894	8394.898	0.798	160.210	1.00

Note. AIC = Akaike Information Criterion; BIC = Bayesian Information Criterion; LMR = Lo–Mendell–Rubin test; LMR p = Lo–Mendell–Rubin test p-value.

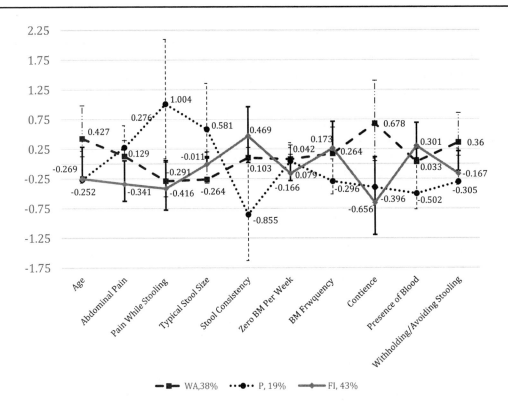

Figure 1. Three-class models of pain, incontinence, and stooling patterns z-scores.

differences across classes. Caregivers of youth in the *pain* class reported significantly more disease burden and distress than youth in the *FI* (est. = 4.02 vs. est. = 3.77; $p < .001$; $d = 0.61$) and *WA* (est. = 3.62, $p < .001$; $d = 1.01$) classes. Caregivers of youth in the *FI* class reported significantly more burden/distress than youth in the *WA* class (est. = 3.77 vs. est. = 3.62; $p < .001$; $d = 0.45$). Caregivers of youth in the *WA* class reported significantly less family conflict than the *FI* (est. = 2.47 vs. est. = 2.95, $p < .001$; $d = 0.97$) and *pain* (est. = 2.84; $p < .001$; $d = .50$) classes. Caregivers of youth in the *FI* reported significantly more worry of social impact on the POOPC than both *WA* (est. = 2.77 vs. est. = 2.14, $p < .001$; $d = 0.43$) and *pain* (est. = 2.46, $p = .04$; $d = 0.31$) youth. Caregivers of youth in the *pain* class reported significantly more worry of social impact than caregivers of youth in the *WA* class (est. = 2.46 vs. est. = 2.14, $p < .001$; $d = 0.23$). Regarding caregivers' difficulty with the medical treatment team, caregivers of youth in the *WA* class reported significantly less difficulty with the medical team than youth in the *pain* class (est. = 2.10 vs. est. = 2.22, $p < .001$; $d = 0.17$).

Functional Disability and Psychosocial Problems

Significant differences (controlling for age) were also found between classes for the PSC and FDI. Caregivers of youth in the *WA* class reported significantly less functional disability when compared with youth in the *pain* class (est. = 1.53 vs. est. = 1.68, $p = .02$; $d = 0.29$). FI caregivers reported significantly less, albeit small differences in functional disability than *WA* (est. = 1.49 vs. est. = 1.53, $p < .001$; $d = 0.07$). Caregivers of youth in the *WA* class reported significantly less psychosocial problems when compared with the *pain* class (est. = 1.48 vs. est. = 1.58, $p < .001$; $d = 0.36$). Caregivers of youth in the *FI* class also reported significantly less psychosocial problems when compared with youth in the *pain* class (est. = 1.49 vs. est. = 1.58, $p < .001$; $d = 0.38$). An overview of all class comparisons and details of the regression model can be found in Table II and the online Supplemental Materials, respectively.

Discussion

Using a relatively novel person-centered approach, the present study identified patterns of stooling and examined the how these patterns were differentially associated with HRQoL in youth with chronic constipation. Three unique profiles emerged: first, the largest profile, the *fecal incontinence* class, was characterized by youth experiencing symptoms of more frequent stooling and fecal incontinence. The second largest profile, the *withholding/avoiding* class, was characterized by youth experiencing increased withholding stool and stooling avoidance. The smallest profile that emerged, the *pain* class, was characterized by youth presenting with

Table II. Intercepts, Standard Errors, and Comparisons Across HRQoL Measures for Each Latent Class

Measures	Withholding/avoiding, estimate (SE)	Pain, estimate (SE)	Fecal incontinence, estimate (SE)	Class comparisons
POOPC burden/worry	3.62 (0.028)	4.02 (0.047)	3.77 (0.031)	$P > WA** \& FI** \& FI > WA**$
POOPC family conflict	2.47 (0.034)	2.84 (0.112)	2.96 (0.042)	$P > WA** \& FI > WA**$
POOPC social worry	2.14 (0.142)	2.46 (0.101)	2.77 (0.083)	$FI > P* \& WA** \& P > WA**$
POOPC treatment team	2.10 (0.075)	2.22 (0.058)	2.18 (0.114)	$WA < P**$
FDI	1.53 (0.042)	1.68 (0.058)	1.49 (0.042)	$P > WA* \& WA > FI**$
PSC	1.49 (0.013)	1.58 (0.041)	1.49 (0.006)	$P > WA** \& P > FI**$

Note. WA = withholding/avoiding class; P = pain class; FI = fecal Incontinence class.
*$p < .05$, **$p < .01$.

symptoms of abdominal pain, hard, large, and painful stools; and infrequent stooling. Overall, caregivers of youth in the *pain* class reported the greatest amount of disease burden and distress, greatest impairments in illness-related activity limitations, more psychosocial problems, and, along with the *fecal incontinence* group, elevated levels of family conflict. Caregivers of youth in the *fecal incontinence* class reported the greatest amount of parental worry of social impact. Furthermore, caregivers of youth in the *withholding/avoiding* class reported the least amount of difficulty with the medical treatment team than caregivers of youth in the *pain* and *fecal incontinence* classes.

Pain and HRQoL

These findings are consistent with previous variable-centered reports that youth with chronic constipation who experience abdominal pain and fecal incontinence may be at risk for poorer HRQoL relative to affected youth not experiencing these symptoms. Similar to previous variable-centered studies, we found in our person-centered analyses that caregivers in classes with youth with chronic constipation experiencing abdominal pain and infrequent stooling reported greater illness-related activity limitations, and more psychosocial problems, suggesting that the negative symptoms of constipation (i.e. pain, duration of symptoms) significantly impact HRQoL (Cox et al., 1998; Rajindrajith et al., 2013; Youssef et al., 2005). The present study extends this past research by demonstrating distinct symptom patterns are differentially associated with disease-specific aspects of HRQoL. More specifically, rather than demonstrating broad problems in HRQoL, this study allowed for a more nuanced examination of the associations between symptom patterns and various facets of HRQoL.

In our person-centered analyses, caregivers in classes of youth experiencing both abdominal and stooling pain reported greater functional disability and more disease burden, distress, and psychosocial problems, suggesting that the negative symptoms of constipation may significantly impact how parents perceive their child's HRQoL. Consistent with previous findings, pain, specifically chronic pain, strongly impacts parent-perceived HRQoL (Hunfeld et al., 2001). Furthermore, chronic pain is positively associated with psychological distress and disability (Andrasik et al., 1988; Balagué, Skovron, Nordin, Dutoit, & Waldburger, 1995; Brattberg, 1994). Similarly, Mano, Khan, Ladwig, and Weisman (2011) found that mothers of youth with chronic pain reported low levels of HRQoL and suggested that the type of pain (whether it is abdominal pain or headaches) may have less of an impact on HRQoL than other factors, such as functional disability. Additionally, Warschburger and colleagues (2014) found comparable results in a sample of children with abdominal pain due to functional or organic gastrointestinal disorders, in which abdominal pain greatly contributed to increased levels of psychosocial strain, and, in turn, adversely impacted HRQoL.

Fecal Incontinence and HRQoL

Unlike Youssef et al. (2005), we found a significant (medium-sized) difference in HRQoL between classes of children with and without a preponderance of fecal incontinence, suggesting that frequent fecal incontinence may differentially impact HRQoL in children with chronic constipation. As the current study used a disease-specific measure of HRQoL, it is possible that non-disease-specific measures lack sensitivity to assess the impact of fecal incontinence on HRQoL (Bongers, Benninga, Maurice-Stam, & Grootenhuis, 2009). Furthermore, our findings may differ from Youssef and colleagues (2005) because parents of youth with constipation tend to report lower levels of HRQoL for their children when compared with parents of typically developing youth, those with other chronic gastrointestinal diseases, and when compared with child self-report. Bongers, van Dijik, Benninga, and Grootenhuis (2009) noted that parents of youth with constipation and fecal incontinence tend to be more concerned of the social consequences than their child, as their child may be unaware of the social consequences of their defecation problem.

Peer Relationships

Caregivers of youth in the *fecal incontinence* class also reported greater concerns for peer relationships. Due to the embarrassing nature of the disease, parents of children with fecal incontinence may worry about their child experiencing greater deficits in social functioning, such as peer victimization and engaging in antisocial behavior, than parents of children without fecal incontinence (Kaugars et al., 2010). Parents may view their child as unable to adequately clean themselves after experiencing severe fecal incontinence and, therefore, become easy targets for social ridicule and bullying (Clarke et al, 2008). Bongers, van Dijik, Benninga, and Grootenhuis (2009) found that 23% of children with fecal incontinence reported regular bullying due to their defecation problem. In contrast, Cox et al (2003) reported that neither parent nor child indicated peer rejection as an outcome of fecal incontinence. Further research is needed in this area to assess if youth with fecal incontinence experience greater social functioning deficits in comparison with youth with chronic constipation without fecal incontinence.

Withholding/Avoiding Symptoms and HRQoL

Interestingly, caregivers of the *withholding/avoiding* class reported low levels of difficulties with the medical treatment team, functional disability, and psychosocial problems in comparison with the *pain* class and low levels of family conflict in comparison with both the *pain* and *fecal incontinence* classes. Youth in the *withholding/avoiding* class of the current study tended to be older in age (which was controlled for statistically) and their caregivers reported intermediate levels of abdominal pain, pain while stooling, stool consistency, bowel movement frequency per week, and high levels of continence relative to the *pain* and *fecal incontinence* classes. It may be possible that caregivers of youth experiencing high pain who are dissatisfied with their medical treatment team are less likely to adhere to laxative regimens, thus maintaining their child's maladaptive stooling pattern. These findings further suggest that pain and fecal incontinence may have a larger impact on perceived HRQoL, functional disability, and psychosocial well-being than other symptoms; however, more research in this area is needed to establish if pain and incontinence account for these outcomes across the classes.

Clinical Implications of the Current Study

There are several important clinical implications to these findings. The present study provides convergent and discriminant validity (social worry higher in those in the fecal incontinence class, etc.) for the POOPC as a measure of parent-perceived HRQoL in youth with chronic constipation. As such, the POOPC may be an invaluable clinical tool for pediatric psychologists to detect specific domains for treatment among youth with chronic constipation and their families (Silverman et al., 2015). Specifically, the POOPC may be potentially sensitive to disease-specific processes and may serve as a helpful tool for determining how to tailor existing interventions or determine whether additional treatment modules are needed in efforts to improve HRQoL in youth with chronic constipation. For example, tailored interventions for youth with similar presenting concerns to those in the pain class might be aimed at enhancing how families cope with the distressing/burdensome nature of functional constipation and improving psychosocial functioning and family conflict. Youth experiencing predominately fecal incontinence may benefit from interventions aimed at targeting interpersonal relationships (i.e. peers and family). In contrast, youth experiencing withholding/avoidance may need minimal tailoring of existing evidence-based treatments given these patterns of results. The current study also highlights the need for medical providers to be aware of caregiver or patient dissatisfaction with the medical team, as it may impact HRQoL. Assessments of family–medical team interactions may be potentially helpful for implementation of interventions focused on improving family treatment satisfaction, such as active listening and negotiation of behavior change to improve family treatment satisfaction, (Kinmonth et al. 1998), and, thus, increasing overall HRQoL among patients and caregivers.

Limitations of the Current Study

This study has several limitations that should be acknowledged. First, this sample draws from specialty clinics and participants are likely to have longstanding difficulties with constipation and may present with the most severe of the clinical cases. This may have biased the response pattern to more severe symptoms and may thus have more negative reporting of HRQoL, psychosocial functioning, and functional disability. Additionally, this study does not have a healthy control group, which may be useful in comparing parent-perceived HRQoL between typically developing youth and youth with chronic constipation. Furthermore, given the broad range of youth with chronic constipation in the current study, we relied on parent report, which may impact the current results. In addition, the POOPC was developed for caregiver responses only, and there is no, at this time, child self-report version. It is important to also note that medication use was not included as an indicator in our LVMM analyses. For example, stool softeners, and osmotic, stimulant laxatives and lubricant laxatives may have potentially impacted youth's symptomology and, thus, class membership. Future research is needed to examine the association between medication use, pain, fecal incontinence, and avoidance.

In summary, the current study examined how specific symptom patterns of pain, stool frequency, and incontinence impact parent-perceived psychosocial issues, illness-related activity limitations, and disease-specific aspects of HRQoL, including disease burden and distress, family conflict, parental worry of social impact, and satisfaction with the treatment team, among youth with chronic constipation. Overall, we found that caregivers of youth in pain class reported greater levels of illness-related activity limitations, more psychosocial issues, increased disease burden and worry, and, along with the fecal incontinence class, more family conflict, suggesting that youth with chronic constipation associated with pain or fecal incontinence may be at risk for poorer disease-specific HRQoL. Furthermore, varying HRQoL across classes suggests that the POOPC may be more sensitive to differential levels of family conflict, peer relationships, and disease burden and distress relative to measures of functional disability and psychosocial problems. In addition to addressing gastrointestinal symptoms, targeting family conflict, peer relationships, and coping with the burden and distress of constipation may be helpful to improve HRQoL in youth with chronic constipation. Future research is needed to assess how these patterns of pain, stool frequency, and incontinence associated with HRQoL differentially in youth with chronic constipation using youth self-report and how these initial patterns may predict treatment response.

Supplementary Data

Supplementary data can be found at: http://www.jpepsy.oxfordjournals.org/.

Acknowledgments

The authors would like to thank the staff of the constipation clinics at Children's Hospital of Wisconsin, Nationwide Children's Hospital, Boston Children's Hospital, University of Texas Southwestern Medical Center, and the Children's and Women's Hospital at University of South Alabama. Finally, the authors would like to thank the parents and children who participated in this study.

Conflicts of interest: None declared.

References

Akaike, H. (1974). A new look at the statistical model identification. *IEEE transactions on automatic control*, 19(6), 716–723.

Andrasik, F., Kabela, E., Quinn, S., Attanasio, V., Blanchard, E. B., & Rosenblum, E. L. (1988). Psychological functioning of children who have recurrent migraine. *Pain*, 34, 43–52.

Asparouhuv, T., & Muthén, B. (2014). Auxiliary variables in mixture modeling: Using the BCH method in Mplus to estimate distal outcome model and an arbitrary secondary model. *Mplus Web Notes*, 21, 1–22.

Balagué, F., Skovron, M. L., Nordin, M., Dutoit, G., & Waldburger, M. (1995). Low back pain in schoolchildren: A study of familial and psychological factors. *Spine*, 20, 1265–1270.

Bauer, D. J., & Shanahan, M. J. (2007). Modeling complex interactions: Person-centered and variable-centered approaches. *Modeling contextual effects in longitudinal studies*, 255–283.

Benninga, M. A., Voskuijl, W. P., & Taminiau, J. A. (2004). Childhood constipation: Is there new light at the end of the tunnel? *Journal of Pediatric Gastroenterology and Nutrition*, 39, 448–464.

Bergman, L. R., Von Eye, A., & Magnusson, D. (2006). Person-oriented research strategies in developmental psychopathology.

Berlin, K. S., Karazsia, B. T., & Klages, K. L. (In Press). Research design in pediatric psychology: The state of our science, recommendations, and future considerations. In M. Roberts, & R. Steele (Eds.), *Handbook of pediatric psychology* (5th ed.). New York, NY: Guilford Press.

Berlin, K. S., Parra, G. R., & Williams, N. A. (2014). An introduction to latent variable mixture modeling (part 2): Longitudinal latent class growth analysis and growth mixture models. *Journal of Pediatric Psychology*, 39, 188–203. doi:10.1093/jpepsy/jsto84

Berlin, K. S., Williams, N. A., & Parra, G. R. (2014). An introduction to latent variable mixture modeling (part 1): Overview and cross-sectional latent class and latent profile analyses. *Journal of Pediatric Psychology*, 39, 174–187. doi:10.1093/jpepsy/jsto84

Bongers, M., Benninga, M., Maurice-Stam, H., & Grootenhuis, M. (2009). Health-related quality of life in young adults with symptoms of constipation continuing from childhood into adulthood. *Health and Quality of Life Outcomes*, 7, 20. doi:10.1186/1477-7525-7-20

Bongers, M. E., van Dijk, M., Benninga, M. A., & Grootenhuis, M. A. (2009). Health related quality of life in children with constipation-associated fecal incontinence. *Journal of Pediatrics*, 154, 749–753. doi:10.1016/j.jpeds.2008.11.029

Brattberg, G. (1994). The incidence of back pain and headache among Swedish school children. *Quality of Life Research*, 3, 27–31.

Burket, R. C., Cox, D. J., Tam, A. P., Ritterband, L., Borowitz, S., Sutphen, J. ... , & Kovatchev, B. (2006). Does" stubbornness" have a role in pediatric constipation? *Journal of Developmental and Behavioral Pediatrics*, 27, 106–111.

Campbell, L. K., Cox, D. J., & Borowitz, S. M. (2009). Elimination disorders. In M. C. Roberts, & R. G. Steele (Eds.), *The Handbook of Pediatric Psychology* (pp. 481–490). New York, NY: Gilford Press.

Clarke, M., Chow, C., Chase, J., Gibb, S., Hutson, J., & Southwell, B. (2008). Quality of life in children with slow transit constipation. *Journal of Pediatric Surgery*, 43, 320–324. doi:10.1016/j.jpedsurg.2007.10.020

Cunningham, C., & Banez, G. (2006). *Inflammatory bowel disease and pediatric gastrointestinal disorders: Biopsychosocial assessment and treatment* (pp. 31–54). New York, NY: Springer Science Business Media, LLC.

Cox, D., Ritterband, L., Quillian, W., Kovatchev, B., Morris, J., Sutphen, J., & Borowitz, S. (2003). Assessment of behavioral mechanisms maintaining encopresis: Virginia encopresis-constipation appreciation test. *Journal of Pediatric Psychology*, 28, 375–382. doi:10.1093/jpepsy/jsgo27

Cox, D. J., Morris, J. B., Borowitz, S. M., & Sutphen, J. L. (2002). Psychological differences between children with and without chronic encopresis. *Journal of Pediatric Psychology, 27,* 585–591.

Cox, D. J., Sutphen, J. L., Borowitz, S. M., Kovatchev, B., & Ling, W. (1998). Contribution of behavior therapy and biofeedback to laxative therapy in the treatment of pediatric encopresis. *Annals of Behavioral Medicine, 20,* 70–76.

Freeman, K. A., Riley, A., Duke, D. C., & Fu, R. (2014). Systematic review and meta-analysis of behavioral interventions for fecal incontinence with constipation. *Journal of Pediatric Psychology, 39,* 887–902.

Gardner, W., Murphy, J. M., Childs, G., Kelleher, K., Pagano, M. E., Jellinek, M. S. . . . , & Chiapetta, L. (1999). The PSC-17: A brief pediatric symptom checklist with psychosocial problem subscales. A report from PROS and ASPN. *Ambulatory Child Health, 5,* 225–236.

Rome Foundation. (2006). Guidelines–Rome III Diagnostic Criteria for Functional Gastrointestinal Disorders. *J Gastrointestinal Liver Disease, 15,* 307–312. Retrieved from http://www.ncbi.nlm.nih.gov/pubmed/17203570

Heaton, K. W., & Lewis, S. J. (1997). Stool form scale as a useful guide to intestinal transit time'. *Scandinavian Journal of Gastroenterology, 2,* 920–924.

Hunfeld, J. A. M., Perquin, C. W., Duivenvoorden, H. J., Hazebroek-Kampschreur, A. A. J. M., Passchier, J., van Suijlekom-Smit, L. W. A., & Wouden, J. C. (2001). Chronic pain and its impact on quality of life in adolescents and their families. *Journal of Pediatric Psychology, 26,* 145–153.

Joinson, C., Heron, J., Butler, U., & von Gontard, A. (2006). Psychological differences between children with and without soiling problems. *Pediatrics, 117,* 1575–1584. doi:10.1542/peds.2005-1773 16651311

Kaugars, A. S., Silverman, A., Kinservik, M., Heinze, S., Reinemann, L., Sander, M., & Sood, M. (2010). Families' perspectives on the effect of constipation and fecal incontinence on quality of life. *Journal of Pediatric Gastroenterology and Nutrition, 51,* 747–752. doi:10.1097/MPG.0b013e3181de0651

Khan, S., Campo, J., Bridge, J., Chiappetta, L., Wald, A., & di Lorenzo, C. (2006). Long-term outcome of functional childhood constipation. *Digestive Diseases and Sciences, 52,* 54–69. doi:10.1007/s10620-006-9308-9.

Kinmonth, A. L., Woodcock, A., Griffin, S., Spiegal, N., & Campbell, M. J. (1998). Randomised controlled trial of patient centred care of diabetes in general practice: Impact on current wellbeing and future disease risk. *BMJ, 317,* 1202–1208.

Landmark, G. B., Rappaport, L., Fenton, T., & Levine, M.D. (1986). Locus of control and self-esteem in children with encopresis. *Journal of Developmental and Behavioral Pediatrics, 7,* 111–113.

Lembo, A., & Camilleri, M. (2003). Chronic constipation. *New England Journal of Medicine, 349,* 1360–1368.

Lo, Y., Mendell, N. R., & Rubin, D. B. (2001). Testing the number of components in a normal mixture. *Biometrika, 88*(3), 767–778.

Luxem, M., Christophersen, E., Purvis, P., & Baer, D. (1997). Behavioral-medical treatment of pediatric toileting refusal. *Journal of Developmental and Behavioral Pediatrics, 18,* 34–41.

Mano, K. E., Khan, K. A., Ladwig, R. J., & Weisman, S. J. (2011). The impact of pediatric chronic pain on parents' health-related quality of life and family functioning: Reliability and validity of the PedsQL 4.0 Family Impact Module. *Journal of Pediatric Psychology, 36,* 517–527. doi:10.1093/jpepsy/jsp099.

Muthén, L. K., & Muthén, B. O. (1998). Mplus User's Guide (7th edn). *Muthén & Muthén: Los Angeles, CA, USA, 2012.*

Nolan, T., & Oberklaid, F. (1993). New concepts in the management of encopresis. *Pediatric in Review, 14,* 447–451. Retrieved from http://www.ncbi.nlm.nih.gov/pubmed/8284284

Owens-Stively, J. A. (1987). Self-esteem and compliance in encopretic children. *Child Psychiatry and Human Development, 18,* 13–21.

Rajindrajith, S., Devanarayana, N. M., & Benninga, M. A. (2013). Review article: Fecal incontinence in children: Epidemiology, pathophysiology, clinical evaluation and management. *Alimentary Pharmacology and Therapeutics, 37,* 37–48.

Schwarz, G. (1978). Estimating the dimension of a model. *The annals of statistics, 6*(2), 461–464.

Silverman, A. H., Berlin, K., Di Lorenzo, C., Nurko, S., Kamody, R., Ponnambalam, A. . . . , Sood, M. (2015). Measuring health related quality of life with the parental opinions of pediatric constipation questionnaire. *Journal of Pediatric Psychology, 40,* 814–824. doi:10.1093/jpepsy/jsv028

Walker, L. S., & Greene, J. W. (1991). The functional disability inventory: Measuring a neglected dimension of child health status. *Journal of Pediatric Psychology, 16,* 39–58. Retrieved from http://www.ncbi.nlm.nih.gov/pubmed/1826329

Warschburger, P., Hänig, J., Friedt, M., Posovszky, C., Schier, M., & Calvano, C. (2014). Health-related quality of life in children with abdominal pain due to functional or organic gastrointestinal disorders. *Journal of Pediatric Psychology, 39,* 45–54.

Youssef, N. N., Langseder, A. L., Verga, B. J., Mones, R. L., & Rosh, J. R. (2005). Chronic childhood constipation is associated with impaired quality of life: A case-controlled study. *Journal of Pediatric Gastroenterology and Nutrition, 41,* 56–60.

Daily Pain, Physical Activity, and Home Fluid Intake in Pediatric Sickle Cell Disease

Cynthia W. Karlson,[1,2] PhD, Anna M. Baker,[3] PhD, Maggie H. Bromberg,[4] PhD, Thomas David Elkin,[1,2] PhD, Suvankar Majumdar,[1] MD, and Tonya M. Palermo,[4,5] PhD

[1]Division of Hematology-Oncology, Department of Pediatrics, University of Mississippi Medical Center, [2]Department of Psychiatry and Human Behavior, University of Mississippi Medical Center, [3]Adherence Research Center, Johns Hopkins School of Medicine, [4]Center for Child Health, Behavior, and Development, Seattle Children's Research Institute, and [5]Department of Anesthesiology and Pain Medicine, University of Washington School of Medicine

All correspondence concerning this article should be addressed to Cynthia W. Karlson, PhD, University of Mississippi Medical Center, 2500 North State Street, Jackson, MS 39216, USA. E-mail: ckarlson@umc.edu

Received January 13, 2016; revisions received May 27, 2016; accepted June 7, 2016

Abstract

Objectives This study examined the temporal relationship between physical activity, fluid intake, and daily pain in children with sickle cell disease (SCD) with frequent pain. **Methods** A total of 30 African American children (M age = 13.9; 53% female; 76.3% type SS) who reported pain more than or equal to once every 2 weeks and their parents completed measures of pain and anxiety/depressive symptoms. Children then completed a daily pain diary and wore a physical activity Actiwatch for 14 days at home. **Results** Contrary to physiological theory-based hypotheses, lower physical activity was associated with greater pain during the same day and the next day. Less pain was associated with greater physical activity the next day. There was no relationship between self-reported home fluid intake and daily pain (p's < .05). **Conclusions** Results lend support for a complex bidirectional relationship between physical activity and daily pain in pediatric SCD, and identify physical activity as a target for future research.

Key words: adolescents; children; hematology; pain; physical activity; rehydration.

Sickle cell disease (SCD) results from a single genetic mutation, leading to sickling of red blood cells from local hypoxia and vaso-occlusive pain episodes (Davis, Mashegu, & Majumdar, 2015). Pain is a hallmark symptom that occurs frequently in children with SCD and often leads to psychosocial disruption or hospitalization (Barakat, Lash, Lutz, & Nicolaou, 2006; Palermo, Schwartz, Drotar, & McGowan, 2002). Children with SCD who experience frequent pain tend to have increased anxiety and depression, decreased physical mobility, and greater functional disability (Peterson & Palermo, 2004; Unal, Toros, Kütük, & Uyaniker, 2011; Zempsky et al., 2013). Two nonpharmacological strategies traditionally recommended to help manage SCD pain at home and minimize the likelihood of vaso-occlusive pain complications include limiting physical activity to prevent hypoxia and rehydration/staying well hydrated to prevent dehydration (National Health Institute [NIH], Division of Blood Diseases and Resources, 2002; Okomo & Meremikwu, 2015; Tewari, Brousse, Piel, Menzel, & Rees, 2015). Physical activity and dehydration are theorized to increase the likelihood of a vaso-occlusive pain crisis through a series of metabolic changes that occur with these physiological states (Connes, Machado, Hue, & Reid, 2011; Tewari, et al., 2015). Therefore, a more thorough understanding of the temporal relationship between frequent pain, physical activity, and fluid intake may have meaningful clinical implications and help guide nonpharmacological pain management recommendations for children with SCD. Home-based assessment is particularly important in this population, given that most pediatric SCD pain episodes are managed at home (Dampier et al., 2004). However, thus far, there has been minimal evaluation of nonpharmacological pain management strategies in the home setting.

Past research on physical activity (defined as any type of body movement) and pain in children with SCD has principally examined increased pain as predicting impairments in physical (e.g., sports, walking), social (e.g., activities), and academic (e.g., homework) functioning (Gil et al., 2000; Lewandowski, Palermo, Kirchner, & Drotar, 2009). More recent investigation into the biological effects of physical activity and exercise (defined as planned and/or sustained physical activity) has produced somewhat mixed results. For instance, Alvarado et al. (2015) demonstrated that heart rate recovery after maximum exercise was impaired in 60 children with SCD compared with 15 healthy controls. Another study examined the effect of moderate to vigorous exercise on hypoxia in 32 children with SCD and found that 42% experienced postexercise hypoxia but that hypoxia was not correlated with pain crises (Halphen et al., 2014). Similar to existing physical activity research, investigators have focused on the use of intravenous fluids in the acute pain setting during hospitalization (Reagan, DeBaun, & Frei-Jones, 2011), while minimal research has investigated the effect of hydration on pain in the home setting. Specifically, a recent Cochrane review concluded that although extra fluids are routinely administered during acute pain crises there have been no controlled trials to evaluate its efficacy for treating acute pain (Okomo & Meremikwu, 2015). Although these data are limited, such studies advocate further examination of these relationships in pediatric SCD.

Objective laboratory experiments of the relationship between physical activity and theorized mechanisms for SCD pain is useful; however, laboratory experiments do not capture routine daily functioning nor capture typical levels of physical activity (Long, Palermo, & Manees, 2008). Actigraphy offers a noninvasive means of objectively and continuously capturing physical activity levels during normal daily routines (Long et al., 2008; Puyau, Adolph, Vohra, & Butte, 2002). Mean and peak physical activity levels have been examined in studies of youth with other chronic pain conditions (e.g., migraines, musculoskeletal pain, abdominal pain) and found to relate to self-reported pain frequency and pain intensity (Kashikar-Zuck et al., 2010; Rabbitts, Holley, Karlson, & Palermo, 2014; Wilson & Palermo, 2012). Actigraphy measured mean physical activity and peak physical activity levels are furthermore documented to be lower in youth with chronic pain ($M_{\text{mean physical activity}}$ = 415 counts/min, SD = 112; $M_{\text{peak physical activity}}$ = 2,430 counts/min, SD = 575) compared with healthy controls ($M_{\text{mean physical activity}}$ = 515 counts/min, SD = 111; $M_{\text{peak physical activity}}$ = 3,561, SD = 921; Long et al., 2008). Some research supports a bidirectional association between pain and physical activity levels. In a study of youth 12–18 years with chronic pain, greater pain intensity was related to lower peak levels of activity the next day (Rabbitts et al., 2014). Higher mean activity levels during the day also predicted lower end-of-day pain intensity ratings. It remains to be determined whether a similar bidirectional association is present in children with SCD.

The aim of this study was to examine the temporal and potentially bidirectional relationships between daily physical activity measured by actigraphy, self-report fluid intake, and self-report pain in children with SCD who experience frequent pain in the home setting. Given that anxiety and depression are often associated with increased pain in pediatric SCD, anxiety/depression was examined and controlled for in this study. In concordance with clinical recommendations to limit physical activity and increase fluid intake to prevent vaso-occlusive pain episodes (Okomo & Meremikwu, 2015; Tewari et al., 2015), we hypothesized that (1) lower physical activity and higher fluid intake would be associated with less pain reported during the *same* day, (2) lower physical activity and higher fluid intake today would be associated with less pain reported during the *following/next* day (next day), and (3) less pain today would be associated with lower physical activity levels during the next day.

Method

Participants
Institutional review board ethics committee approval was granted for this study. Informed consent was obtained from legal guardian participants (parent) and assent from child participants in accordance with state and institutional statutes. A single center, prospective daily diary methodology was used. Study inclusion criteria for child participants were (a) 8–18 years of age, (b) SCD types hemoglobin SS, SC, Sβ+ thalassemia, or Sβ⁰ thalassemia, and (c) frequent pain occurring at least once every 2 weeks (to capture the experience of pain during the 2-week study period and provide adequate variability for statistical analyses; Connelly, Rapoff, Thompson, & Connelly, 2006; Wilson & Palermo, 2012). Children were excluded if the child had developmental delay or cognitive impairment documented in his/her medical chart.

Participation Rate
One hundred twenty-six African American children with SCD were screened for eligibility between January 2012 and July 2013. Thirty-six children

(29%) with frequent pain agreed to participate and were enrolled. Eighty-six children (68%) did not meet inclusion criteria owing to infrequent pain. Other reasons for nonenrollment included: not interested ($n = 1$), parent not present ($n = 1$), child with cognitive impairment ($n = 1$), and child deemed ineligible owing to medical noncompliance ($n = 1$). Of those enrolled, six participants (5%) were excluded owing to having >60% missing data, not providing any daily diary data, and/or not providing any actigraphy data. This pattern of missing data is likely nonrandom and introduces biased statistical estimations (Dong & Peng, 2013). There was no significant difference between those excluded owing to missing data and those who completed the study in regard to age, gender, or SCD type (p's > .05). The final sample consisted of 30 child participants and their parent.

Procedures

Potential child participants were identified by a clinic nurse at routine hematology outpatient appointments. Research assistants conducted a brief screening interview and obtained informed consent. Parents and children completed questionnaires listed below. Children were then provided with a 14-day paper daily diary and fitted with a wrist-mounted actigraphy device. A 21-day study period was initially pilot tested with three children with SCD. However, owing to poor adherence, the study period was modified to 14 days. A 14-day study period is shown to provide a large enough measurement window for pain episodes while minimizing adherence concerns observed in longer daily diary studies (Burkhart, Dunbar-Jacob, & Rohay, 2001). Children were instructed to complete one diary entry before going to bed (Connelly et al., 2006; Karlson et al., 2013). Research assistants called families each week to remind children to complete the pain diary and continue wearing the Actiwatch. If families could not be reached, a voice message was left and/or a letter sent as a reminder of study procedures. Daily diaries and Actiwatches were returned in person or via mail at the end of 14 days. No child was hospitalized for pain during the study period. Families received $30 compensation for completing questionnaires and $\geq 50\%$ of diary and actigraphy days.

Descriptive and Co-Variate Measures
Demographics and Medications
Child age, gender, grade in school, parent marital status, parent education, and family income were collected on a parent demographics questionnaire. Parents also reported their child's prescription and over-the-counter medications (NIH, 2002).

Pain Questionnaire
The Pain Questionnaire (Wilson & Palermo, 2012) was completed by parents and children to screen for frequency of pain and to assess typical pain during the past 3 months. Several individual domains of physical pain were reported: (1) frequency (0 = *Not at all* to 6 = *Daily*), (2) number of locations of bodily pain, (3) duration (0 = *Less than 1 hour* to 3 = *All day*), and (4) pain intensity on an 11-point numeric rating scale (0 = *No pain* to 10 = *Worst pain possible*) (von Baeyer, 2009).

Revised Child Anxiety and Depression Scale
The Revised Child Anxiety and Depression Scale (RCADS) is a 47-item child self-report and parent proxy report measure of anxiety and depressive symptoms on a 4-point scale (0 = *never* to 3 = *always*; Chorpita, Yim, Moffitt, Umemoto, & Francis, 2000). Scores are based on gender and grade. The RCADS demonstrates excellent internal consistency in children with SCD ($\alpha = .94$; Carpentier, Elkin, & Starnes, 2009). The RCADS total anxiety and depression score was used in this study ($\alpha = .95$).

Daily Outcome Measures
Pain
Pain duration was calculated in minutes based on child report of when their pain started and stopped. Children were asked to rate pain intensity, "How much hurt did you have from your sickle cell pain [today]?" using a visual analog scale ranging from 0 (*no pain*) to 6 (*worst pain*; Connelly et al., 2006; von Baeyer & Spagrud, 2007).

Fluid Intake
Children reported the number of glasses of water, fruit juice, soda, tea, coffee, and other beverages (e.g., milk, sports drink) consumed each day (De Keyzer et al., 2011; Garipağaoğlu et al., 2008). Children were oriented to one "glass" and corresponding fluid ounces through a series of pictures (soda can, drinking glass, water bottle) located at the back of each diary (Bolland, Ward, & Bolland, 1990), with 1 glass = 12 fluid ounces.

Physical Activity
Objective recordings of daily physical activity were assessed using an Actiwatch 2 (Phillips Respironics, Bend, OR). The watch-like device was worn by children on their nondominant wrist for the 14-day study period. A minimum of 7 actiwatch days was used in this study (Ekblom, Nyberg, Bak, Ekelund, & Marcus, 2012). Wrist actigraphy has been validated in both healthy adolescents (Ekblom et al., 2012; Puyau et al., 2002) and children with chronic pain (Rabbitts et al., 2014; Wilson & Palermo, 2012). Movement

counts were stored on the device in 1-min epochs. If participants had <7 hr of continuous data in the activity interval, that day's data were excluded owing to high likelihood that the device was removed during the day. Periods of no activity for ≥30 contiguous minutes were also excluded.

Two actigraphic activity variables were computed using the Actiware 5.59 software package: (1) mean physical activity = mean number of activity counts per 1-min epoch during each daytime wake period and (2) peak physical activity = the highest number of activity counts in a 1-min epoch achieved per daytime wake period. Light physical activity was defined as 50–699 counts/min, moderate physical activity was 700–2,499 counts/min, and vigorous physical activity was ≥2,500 counts/min (Puyau, Adolph, Vohra, Zakeri, & Butte, 2004). Daily physical activity levels tended to decrease in older children ($r = -.47$, $p < .01$); therefore, age was controlled for in analyses.

Statistical Analyses

Demographic characteristics of the final sample were summarized using descriptive statistics in SPSS 22.0 (Tabachnick & Fidell, 2007). Random missing child and parent questionnaire items (5.0%) and random missing child daily diary items (pain duration, pain intensity, and fluid intake; 8.9%) were imputed using LISREL 8.71 (Scientific Software International, Inc., Lincolnwood, IL) mean estimate multiple imputation strategy with five iterations. Between-group differences (completers vs. noncompleters and pain days vs. nonpain days) were examined using independent sample t tests for continuous data and chi-squared (χ^2) test for categorical data. Pearson correlations examined predictor and outcome variables.

Analyses of within-subject changes over time were conducted using maximum likelihood estimation multilevel modeling (MLM) in LISREL 8.71 for continuous outcome variables (Goldstein, 1986). The date of diary entries was compared with and matched with objective actiwatch dates to maximize integrity of self-report data. Unconditional means models in SPSS 22.0 indicated adequate interindividual variance in primary outcomes for MLM analyses (intraclass correlation coefficients = .39–.78; Sheck & Ma, 2011). Additionally, unconditional growth models indicated significant individual variance across time for physical activity and fluid intake variables (t's ≥ 2.07, p's < .05). Missing daily diary and actigraphy days (range: 0–7 days; 3.6%) were handled in MLM analyses, which uses full information maximum likelihood estimation to account for differences in the number of observations (i.e., full days) owing to missing data (Goldstein, 1986; Longford, 1987). MLM analyses were modeled with 14 days nested within 30 participants. *Level 1* variables were those measured on a repeated basis (pain, physical activity, and fluid intake). Variables that were measured once (child age, child gender, and anxiety/depression) contained only between-person variance and were modeled as *Level 2* variables. Post hoc power analyses using the two-sided ratio formula of true parameter value to standard error (Snijders, 2005) revealed that the available 394 study days provided >0.80 power for primary Level 1 MLM analyses examining the effects of physical activity and fluid intake on pain severity. The variables of child age, gender, and anxiety/depression symptoms were controlled for in MLM analyses. χ^2 assessed model fit and effect size (ES) was calculated as the square root of $[t^2/(df + t^2)]$. A significance of $p < .05$ was used.

Two general models were computed. The first model was computed to estimate concurrent effects (same-day associations) and the second to estimate lagged effects (next-day associations). Concurrent models were those in which child physical activity or fluid intake (independent variable) was related to pain (dependent variable) during the same day. β_{0j} represents the conditional mean outcome score (pain). β_{1j} represents the slop of the predictor criterion variable. The Level 1 and Level 2 equations are as follows:

Level 1: $(Pain)_{ij} = \beta_{0j} + \beta_{1j}(Physical\ Activity)_{ij} + \beta_{2j}(Time)_{ij} + e_{ij}$

Level 2: $\beta_{0j} = \gamma 00 + \gamma 01(Covariate\ Age)_j + \gamma 02(Covariate\ Gender)_j + \gamma 03(Covariate\ Anxiety/Depression)_j + u_{0j}$

The lagged effects model was the same as the concurrent effects model except that all of the independent variables were measured at the previous time point the day before ($d-1$). Lagged models tested whether physical activity or fluid intake predicted pain the next day while controlling for the previous value of pain. Thus, the general lagged Level 1 model of pain and physical activity is:

Level 1: $(Pain)_{ij} = \beta_{0j} + \beta_{1j}(Physical\ Activity\ d-1)_{ij} + \beta_{2j}(Pain\ d-1)_{ij} + \beta_{3j}(Time)_{ij} + e_{ij}$

Level 2: $\beta_{0j} = \gamma 00 + \gamma 01(Covariate\ Age)_j + \gamma 02(Covariate\ Gender)_j + \gamma 03(Covariate\ Anxiety/Depression)_j + u_{0j}$

Cross-lagged associations were also tested where the independent variables and dependent variables were reversed. In the cross-lagged analyses, we tested if pain predicted physical activity the next day while controlling for the previous value of physical activity. This model is:

Level 1: $(Physical\ Activity)_{ij} = \beta_{0j} + \beta_{1j}(Pain\ d-1)_{ij} + \beta_{2j}(Physical\ Activity\ d-1)_{ij} + \beta_{3j}(Time)_{ij} + e_{ij}$

Level 2: $\beta_{0j} = \gamma 00 + \gamma 01(Covariate\ Age)_j + \gamma 02(Covariate\ Gender)_j + \gamma 03(Covariate\ Anxiety/Depression)_j + u_{0j}$

Results

Participant Characteristics

Participant characteristics are shown in Table I. Children reported pain primarily in the legs (27%), head (23%), and back (23%). Daily pain frequency, intensity, and duration were not significantly different for calendar season (winter, spring, summer, fall) or weekend versus weekday (p's > .05). More frequent pain was associated with greater anxiety/depression ($r = .31, p < .001$). Parent report of pain on the Pain Questionnaire and RCADS-measured anxiety/depression symptoms was highly correlated with child report (r's = .44–.76, p's ≤ .02).

Child medications included Folic Acid (100%), Hydroxycarbamide (24%), Deferasirox (24%), narcotic/opiod pain medication (83%; e.g., Acetaminophen and Codeine, Oxycodone), over-the-counter pain medication (62%; e.g., Ibuprofen, Acetaminophen), antidepressant (7%; Amitriptyline), and other prescription medication (59%; e.g., Fluticasone Propionate [Advair]). Use of Hydroxycarbamide was associated with less daily pain intensity ($r = -.11, p = .03$). Nine children (30%) were on chronic transfusion therapy owing to stroke or other SCD complication. Chronic transfusion was correlated with less frequent daily pain ($r = -.10, p = .04$) and less daily pain intensity ($r = -.14, p < .01$). Annual family income was <$20,000 (Median = $10,000–$19,999), which is below the U.S. 2014 poverty guideline (U.S. Department of Health and Human Services, 2014).

Daily Pain, Physical Activity, and Fluid Intake: Diary and Actigraphy Data

A total of 394 days of diary and actigraphy data were used for analysis, with an average of 13 days (SD = 1.5; range: 7–14 days) per child.

Daily Pain

Table II shows pain days compared with nonpain days. Children reported pain occurring, on average, on 43% of the 14 study days. Eight children (37%) reported 0–2 pain days, 13 children (43%) had 3–6 pain days, 4 children (13%) had 7–10 pain days, and 5 children (17%) had 11–14 pain days. When pain occurred, children reported moderate pain durations (M = 4 hr, 5 min, SD = 168 min) and moderate pain intensity (M = 3.8, SD = 1.5).

Daily Physical Activity

Overall, mean physical activity was of light intensity (M = 386 counts/min, SD = 143; 97.7% of days). Overall peak physical activity (M = 2,820 counts/min, SD = 1,118) was of moderate (42.4% of days) to vigorous intensity (57.4% of days). Children exhibited significantly decreased peak physical activity on pain days compared with nonpain days.

Daily Fluid Intake

On average, children reported drinking seven glasses (SD = 4.4) of fluid a day, with four glasses (SD = 3.6) being water. Children did not report a difference in water or total fluid intake on pain days compared with nonpain days. Post hoc analyses revealed no differences in pain duration, $t(145) = -0.04, p = .97$, or pain intensity, $t(145) = -0.85, p = 0.40$, for children who reported low fluid intake (≤ 3 glasses/day = 1 SD below mean) compared with children who reported high fluid intake (≥ 11 glasses/day = 1 SD above mean).

Table I. Child Descriptive Statistics on Baseline Questionnaires

Characteristics	N = 30 M	(SD)
Age	13.9	(2.9)
Female n (%)	16	(53.3)
Hemoglobin (Hb) SS n (%)	23	(76.3)
Hemoglobin (Hb) SC n (%)	4	(13.3)
Hemoglobin (Hb) other n (%)	3	(10.0)
Chronic transfusion	9	(30.0)
Typical number of painful areas	4.5	(2.9)
Typical pain intensity (0–10)	6.4	(2.2)
Typical pain limit activity (0–10)	5.5	(2.6)
RCADS anxiety/depression (T-score)	48.7	(14.3)
RCADS clinical anxiety/depression n (%)	5	(16.7)

Note. Baseline Pain Questionnaire values are reported here and assess typical pain during the past 3 months.

Table II. Descriptive Statistics for Child Pain Diary and Actiwatch Variables

Outcome variable	Nonpain days N = 226 M (SD)		Pain days N = 168 M (SD)		t	p
Mean physical activity	397.65	(139.38)	370.74	(147.27)	1.85	.07
Peak physical activity	2,936.40	(1,138.99)	2,664.55	(1,044.13)	2.40	.02
Water intake glasses	4.67	(3.96)	4.10	(3.10)	1.55	.12
Total fluid intake glasses	7.25	(4.73)	6.74	(3.96)	1.12	.26

Note. Nonpain days versus pain days between group comparisons were conducted using independent t tests.

Table III. MLM Linear Regressions Examining Physical Activity and Fluid Intake as Associated With Same-Day Pain

Model variable	Pain duration				Pain intensity			
	β	SE	z	p	β	SE	z	p
Covariates								
Age	−0.01	0.04	−0.37	.71	0.05	0.04	1.14	.26
Gender	−0.34	0.23	−1.48	.14	−0.11	0.24	−0.44	.66
Anxiety/depression	0.06	0.12	0.49	.63	0.17	0.12	1.36	.17
Predictor variables[a]								
Peak physical activity	−0.10	0.05	−2.00	<.05	−0.17	0.04	−3.67	<.001
Mean physical activity	−0.09	0.06	−1.62	.10	−0.09	0.06	−1.63	.10
Water intake	−0.00	0.06	−0.03	.97	−0.04	0.06	−0.70	.49
Total fluid intake	−0.04	0.06	−0.67	.50	−0.05	0.06	−0.91	.37

Note. [a]Predictor variables were run in separate regression models. Covariates included child age, gender, and RCADS child anxiety/depression. β values for pain duration represent how many standard deviations pain duration will change per standard deviation change in the predictor variable (physical activity, fluid intake); β values for pain intensity represent how many standard deviations pain intensity will change per standard deviation change in the predictor variable.

Table IV. MLM Linear Regressions Examining Physical Activity and Fluid Intake as Associated With Next-Day Pain

Model variable	Next-day pain duration				Next-day pain intensity			
	β	SE	z	p	β	SE	z	p
Covariates								
Age	−0.01	0.04	−0.25	.81	0.04	0.03	1.21	.23
Gender	−0.26	0.19	−1.34	.18	−0.04	0.17	−0.24	.81
Anxiety/depression	0.05	0.10	0.47	.64	0.13	0.09	1.38	.17
Pain today	0.19	0.05	3.71	<.001	0.32	0.05	6.42	<.001
Predictor variables[a]								
Peak physical activity	0.00	0.05	0.02	.98	−0.03	0.05	−0.73	.47
Mean physical activity	−0.14	0.06	−2.43	.02	−0.15	0.05	−2.73	.01
Water intake	−0.05	0.07	−0.72	.47	0.04	0.06	0.61	.54
Total fluid intake	−0.07	0.06	−1.17	.24	0.04	0.06	0.62	.53

Note. [a]Predictor variables were run in separate regression models. Covariates included child age, gender, and RCADS child anxiety/depression. β values for pain duration represent how many standard deviations pain duration will change per standard deviation change in the predictor variable (physical activity, fluid intake); β values for pain intensity represent how many standard deviations pain intensity will change per standard deviation change in the predictor variable.

Same Day Associations: Physical Activity, Fluid Intake, and Pain

Results of MLM analyses examining same-day associations (see Table III) were all contrary to hypotheses. Lower peak physical activity was associated with more intense pain [$z(390) = -3.67, p < .001$, ES = 0.18, $\chi^2(7) = 974.03$] and longer pain duration [$z(390) = -2.00, p < .05$, ES = 0.10, $\chi^2(7) = 1,005.44$] during the same day. Mean physical activity was not associated with pain during the same day (p's > .05). Self-report water and total fluid intake were also not associated with pain during the same day (p's > .05).

Physical Activity and Fluid Intake Predicting Next-Day Pain

Results of physical activity and fluid intake predicting next-day pain were also contrary to clinically based hypotheses and are shown in Table IV. Lower mean physical activity was associated with greater pain intensity the next day [$z(362) = -2.73, p = 0.01$, ES = 0.14, $\chi^2(8) = 877.73$] and longer pain duration the next day [$z(362) = -2.43, p = 0.02$, ES = 0.13, $\chi^2(8) = 931.36$]. Peak physical activity was not associated with pain the next day. Neither self-report water nor total fluid intake was associated with pain the next day.

Pain Predicting Next-Day Physical Activity

Pain predicting next-day physical activity level results are shown in Table V. Similar to above and contrary to hypotheses, shorter pain duration [$z(362) = -2.15, p = .03$, ES = 0.11, $\chi^2(8) = 951.88$] and less pain intensity [$z(362) = -2.54, p = .01$, ES = 0.13, $\chi^2(8) = 950.09$] were associated with higher peak physical activity levels the next day. Pain was not associated with mean physical activity levels the next day.

Discussion

The current study examined the daily temporal relationships between physical activity, self-report fluid

Table V. MLM Linear Regressions Examining Pain as Associated With Next-Day Physical Activity

Model variable	Next-day mean physical activity				Next-day peak physical activity			
	β	SE	z	p	β	SE	z	p
Covariates								
Age	−0.17	0.03	−5.07	<.001	−0.11	0.03	−3.81	<.001
Gender	−0.02	0.16	−0.11	.91	−0.07	0.15	−0.46	.64
Anxiety/depression	−0.10	0.09	−1.19	.23	0.05	0.08	0.65	.51
Physical activity today	0.19	0.05	3.81	<.001	0.11	0.05	2.26	.02
Predictor variables[a]								
Pain duration	0.03	0.04	0.67	.50	−0.11	0.05	−2.15	.03
Pain intensity	−0.07	0.04	−1.59	.11	−0.14	0.05	−2.54	.01

Note. [a]Predictor variables were run in separate regression models. Covariates included child age, gender, RCADS child anxiety/depression scores, and same-day physical activity level. β values for average physical activity represent how many standard deviations physical activity will change per standard deviation change the expected change in the predictor variable (pain occurrence, pain duration, pain intensity).

intake, and self-report pain in children with SCD. We controlled for child age, gender, anxiety/depression symptoms, and autoregressive same-day variables in analyses. Overall results indicated that lower levels of physical activity were associated with more pain in this sample, demonstrating small ESs (ES range 0.10–0.18). Specifically, we found that lower peak physical activity was associated with longer pain duration and more intense pain within the same day. Regarding physical activity predicting pain the next day, we found that lower mean physical activity today was associated with longer pain duration and more intense pain the next day. For pain today predicting physical activity the next day, we found that shorter pain duration and less intense pain today was associated with greater peak physical activity levels the next day. Self-report fluid intake was not associated with pain in any regression models. Overall, results are contrary to previous pediatric SCD clinical recommendations (NIH, 2002) but are consistent with more recent literature in pediatric chronic pain populations.

These results provide preliminary support for a bidirectional relationship between pain and physical activity in children with SCD; however, it is important to note that these results are correlational and do not suggest a causal relationship. It may be the case that children who experience more frequent pain are less likely to be physically active in general, which would explain study findings. This would be consistent with previous research that children with SCD may restrict their activity on days they experience higher pain intensity (Gil et al., 2000; Lewandowski et al., 2009). On the other hand, findings are consistent with recent laboratory research demonstrating that exercise-induced hypoxia (Halphen et al., 2014) is not associated with pain in children with SCD. Burgeoning research in pediatric SCD points toward components of central sensitization, pain hypersensitivity, and vulnerable phenotypes (e.g., female gender, pain catastrophizing, emotional stress) maintaining persistent pain in pediatric SCD (Darbari et al., 2014). As such, frequent or persistent pain (nonvaso-occlusive pain) in children with SCD may be similar to other pediatric chronic pain conditions (Kashikar-Zuck et al., 2010; Rabbitts et al., 2014) and have similar mechanisms of action. Research in non-SCD pediatric pain populations (e.g., abdominal pain, juvenile arthritis, musculoskeletal pain, and migraine headache) demonstrates that modulated muscle strength training and moderate aerobic exercise are effective in reducing pain in children and adolescents (Busch et al., 2013; Cunningham & Kashikar-Zuck, 2013; Varkey, Cider, Carlsson, & Linde, 2011). Although we cannot infer cause for the observed association between less physical activity and greater pain, current results identify physical activity as a target for future research in pediatric SCD (Bromberg, Schechter, Nurko, Zempsky, & Schanberg, 2014).

This is the first study to examine the relationship between self-report fluid intake and daily pain in the home setting. Although rehydration is clinically indicated for acute vaso-occlusive pain crisis (Meremikwu, 2009; Yawn et al., 2014), we found no relationship between self-report fluid intake at home and same-day or next-day pain, even at low levels of daily fluid intake. Participants in this study reported an average fluid intake of seven glasses per day, which approximates daily recommendations for males and female youth (U.S. Institute of Medicine, Food and Nutrition Board, 2004), and may indicate that moderate daily fluid intake is sufficient for most SCD home-based management. Study results may alternatively suggest that the known pathophysiology of vaso-occlusive pain (sickling of red blood cells and local deoxygenation/hypoxia) may not be immediately or directly impacted by daily fluid levels. Research is needed that uses a more objective measure of hydration to examine probable complex physiological processes involving hydration levels and pain in the home setting.

Although there are several strengths to this study such as the use of a repeated measures daily diary and objective actigraphy to measure physical activity, there are several limitations that warrant discussion. Foremost is that pain and fluid intake were recorded once at the end of the day using self-report paper diaries. Paper diaries are not time-stamped so children could have completed diary entries at a later time, making diaries subject to reporting bias and possible inaccurate data. The relatively short measurement period (14 days) may also have provided limited power and limited ability to fully capture complex relationships and potential interactions between physical activity, fluid intake, and pain in this population. Future studies would benefit from longer measurement periods, use of electronic with-in day repeated assessment, objective hydration measurement, and examining potential interactions of these variables. In addition, 68% of children approached for this study were not eligible owing to infrequent pain. This study's focus on frequent pain limits the generalizability of results to the broader pediatric SCD population. Finally, despite having a large number of data points and adequate power through the use of daily diary ($n = 394$), the small sample size ($n = 30$) and wide age range may further limit generalizability of study findings. Future research would benefit from examining these relationships in developmental subgroups, as well as children with SCD who do not report frequent pain.

In conclusion, current results suggest a complex bidirectional relationship between pain and physical activity levels in children with SCD. Although we cannot draw a causal or temporal relationship from these results, this is the first study to demonstrate that greater physical activity levels do not directly relate to greater pain in pediatric SCD, but may instead relate to less pain. Further research appears warranted to further elucidate these relationships and guide future clinical recommendations for pediatric SCD home-based management.

Acknowledgments

The authors thank the families at the University of Mississippi Medical Center Sickle Cell Clinic for their participation in this project.

Funding

This work was supported by a grant from the American Psychological Association (Division 54) Society of Pediatric Psychology Diversity Research Grant awarded to Cynthia W. Karlson, Ph.D.

Conflicts of interest: None declared.

References

Alvarado, A. M., Ward, K. M., Muntz, D. S., Thompson, A. A., Rodeghier, M., Fernhall, B., & Liem, R. I. (2015). Heart rate recovery is impaired after maximal exercise testing in children with sickle cell anemia. *Journal of Pediatrics, 166,* 389–393.e1. doi: 10.1016/j.jpeds.2014.10.064.

Barakat, L. P., Lash, L., Lutz, M. J., & Nicolaou, D. C. (2006). Psychosocial adaptation of children and adolescents with sickle cell disease. In R. Brown (Ed.), *Comprehensive Handbook of Childhood Cancer and Sickle Cell Disease: A Biopsychosocial Approach* (pp. 471–495). New York, NY: Oxford University Press.

Bolland, J. E., Ward, J. Y., & Bolland, T. W. (1990). Improved accuracy of estimating food quantities up to 4 weeks after training. *Journal of the American Dietetic Association, 90,* 1402–1404, 1407.

Bromberg, M. H., Schechter, N. L., Nurko, S., Zempsky, W. T., & Schanberg, L. E. (2014). Persistent pain in chronically ill children without detectable disease activity. *Pain Management, 4,* 211–219. doi: 10.2217/pmt.14.6

Busch, A. J., Webber, S. C., Richards, R. S., Bidonde, J., Schachter, C. L., Schafer, L. A. . . . , Overend, T. J. (2013). Resistance exercise training for fibromyalgia. *The Cochrane Database of Systematic Reviews, 12,* CD010884. doi: 10.1002/14651858.CD010884

Burkhart, P. V., Dunbar-Jacob, J. M., & Rohay, J. M. (2001). Accuracy of children's self-reported adherence to treatment. *Journal of Nursing Scholarship, 33,* 27–32. doi: 10.1111/j.1547-5069.2001.00027

Carpentier, M. Y., Elkin, T. D., & Starnes, S. E. (2009). Behavioral inhibition and its relation to anxiety and depression symptoms in adolescents with sickle cell disease: A preliminary study. *Journal of Pediatric Oncology Nursing, 26,* 158–166. doi: 10.1177/1043454

Chorpita, B. F., Yim, L., Moffitt, C., Umemoto, L. A., & Francis, S. E. (2000). Assessment of symptoms of DSM-IV anxiety and depression in children: A revised child and depression scale. *Behaviour Research and Therapy, 38,* 835–855.

Connelly, M., Rapoff, M. A., Thompson, N., & Connelly, W. (2006). Headstrong: A pilot study of a CD-ROM intervention for recurrent pediatric headache. *Journal of Pediatric Psychology, 31,* 737–747.

Connes, P., Machado, R., Hue, O., & Reid, H. (2011). Exercise limitation, exercise testing and exercise recommendations in sickle cell anemia. *Clinical Hemorheology and Microcirculation, 49,* 151–163. doi: 10.3233/CH-2011-1465.

Cunningham, N. R., & Kashikar-Zuck, S. (2013). Nonpharmacological treatment of pain in rheumatic diseases and other musculoskeletal pain conditions. *Current Rheumatology Reports, 15,* 306. doi: 10.1007/s11926-012-0306-y

Dampier, C., Setty, B. N., Eggleston, B., Brodecki, D., O'neal, P., & Stuart, M. (2004). Vaso-occlusion in children with sickle cell disease: Clinical characteristics and biologic correlates. *Journal of Pediatric Hematology/Oncology, 26,* 785–790.

Davis, D., Mashegu, H., & Majumdar, S. (2015). An update on sickle cell anemia in children and adolescents. *Journal of the Mississippi State Medical Association, 56,* 268–271.

De Keyzer, W., Huybrechts, I., De Vriendt, V., Vandevijvere, S., Slimani, N., Van Oyen, H., & De Henauw, S. (2011). Repeated 24-hour recalls versus dietary records for estimating nutrient intakes in a national food consumption survey. *Food and Nutrition Research*, 55, 7307. doi: 10.3402/fnr.v55i0.7307

Dong, Y., & Peng, C.Y.J. (2013). Principled missing data methods for researchers. *SpringerPlus*, 2, 222–239. doi: 10.1186/2193-1801-2-222.

Darbari, D. S., Ballas, S. K., & Clauw, D. J. (2014). Thinking beyond sickling to better understand pain in sickle cell disease. *European Journal of Haematology*, 93, 89–95. doi:10.1111/ejh.12340.

Ekblom, O., Nyberg, G., Bak, E. E., Ekelund, U., & Marcus, C. (2012). Validity and comparability of a wrist-worn accelerometer in children. *Journal of Physical Activity and Health*, 9, 389–393.

Garipağaoğlu, M., Sahip, Y., Budak, N., Akdikmen, Ö., Altan, T., & Baban, M. (2008). Food types in the diet and the nutrient intake of obese and non–obese children. *Journal of Clinical Research in Pediatric Endocrinology*, 1, 21–29. doi: 10.4008/jcrpe.v1i1.5

Gil, K. M., Porter, L., Ready, J., Workman, E., Sedway, J., & Anthony, K. K. (2000). Pain in children and adolescents with sickle cell disease: An analysis of daily pain diaries. *Children's Health Care*, 29, 225–241. doi: 10.1207/S15326888CHC2904_1

Goldstein, H. (1986). Multilevel mixed linear model analysis using interative generalized least squares. *Biometrika*, 73, 43–56. doi: 10.2307/2336270

Halphen, I., Elie, C., Brousse, V., Le Bourgeois, M., Allali, S., Bonnet, D., & de Montalembert, M. (2014). Severe nocturnal and postexercise hypoxia in children and adolescents with sickle cell disease. *PLos One*, 9, e97462. doi: 10.1371/journal.pone.0097462.

Institute of Medicine (U.S.), Panel on Dietary Reference Intakes for Electrolytes and Water, Standing Committee on the Scientific Evaluation of Dietary Reference Intakes, Food and Nutrition Board. (2004). *Dietary Reference Intakes for Water, Potassium, Sodium, Chloride, and Sulfate*. Washington, D.C.: The National Academies Press. doi: 10.17226/10925

Karlson, C. W., Litzenburg, C. C., Sampilo, M. L., Rapoff, M. A., Connelly, M., Bickel, J. L. ... , Powers, S. W. (2013). Relationship between daily mood and migraine in children. *Headache*, 53, 1624–1634. doi: 10.1111/head.12215

Kashikar-Zuck, S., Flowers, S. R., Verkamp, E., Ting, T. V., Lynch-Jordan, A. M., Graham, T. B., ... ,Lovell, D. (2010). Actigraphy-based physical activity monitoring in adolescents with juvenile primary fibromyalgia syndrome. *Journal of Pain*, 11, 885–893. doi: 10.1016/j.jpain.2009.12.009

Lewandowski, A. S., Palermo, T. M., Kirchner, H. L., & Drotar, D. (2009). Comparing diary and retrospective reports of pain and activity restriction in children and adolescents with chronic pain conditions. *Clinical Journal of Pain*, 25, 299–306. doi: 10.1097/AJP.0b013e3181965578

Long, A. C., Palermo, T. M., & Manees, A. M. (2008). Using actigraphy to compare physical activity levels in adolescents with chronic pain and healthy adolescents. *Journal of Pediatric Psychology*, 33, 660–665. doi: 10.1093/jpepsy/jsm136

Longford, N. T. (1987). A fast scoring algorithm for maximum likelihood estimation in unbalances mixed models with nested random effects. *Biometrika*, 74, 817–827. doi: 10.2307/2336476

Meremikwu, M. M. (2009). Sickle cell disease. *Clinical Evidence*, pii: 2402.

National Institutes of Health, National Heart, Lung, and Blood Institute, Division of Blood Diseases and Resources. (2002). *The Management of Sickle Cell Disease* (NIH Publication No. 02-2117). Retrieved from http://www.nhlbi.nih.gov/files/docs/ guidelines/sc_mngt.pdf

Okomo, U., & Meremikwu, M. M. (2015). Fluid replacement therapy for acute episodes of pain in people with sickle cell disease. *Cochrane Database of Systematic Reviews*, 3, CD005406. doi: 10.1002/14651858.CD005406.pub4

Palermo, T. M., Schwartz, L., Drotar, D., & McGowan, K. (2002). Parental report of health-related quality of life in children with sickle cell disease. *Journal of Behavioral Medicine*, 25, 269–283.

Puyau, M. R., Adolph, A. L., Vohra, F. A., & Butte, N. F. (2002). Validation and calibration of physical activity monitors in children. *Obesity Research*, 10, 150–157. PubMed PMID: 11886937

Peterson, C. C., & Palermo, T. M. (2004). Parental reinforcement of recurrent pain: the moderating impact of child depression and anxiety on functional disability. *J Pediatr Psychol*, 29(5), 331–341. doi: 10.1093/jpepsy/jsh037.

Puyau, M. R., Adolph, A., Vohra, F., Zakeri, I., & Butte, N. (2004). Prediction of Activity Energy Expenditure Using Accelerometers in Children. *Medicine and Science in Sports and Exercise*, 36, 1625–1631.

Rabbitts, J. A., Holley, A. L., Karlson, C. W., & Palermo, T. M. (2014). Bidirectional associations between pain and physical activity in adolescents. *Clinical Journal of Pain*, 30, 251–258. doi: 10.1097/AJP.0b013e31829550c6

Reagan, M. M., DeBaun, M. R., & Frei-Jones, M. J. (2011). Multi-modal intervention for the inpatient management of sickle cell pain significantly decreases the rate of acute chest syndrome. *Pediatric Blood and Cancer*, 56, 262–266. doi: 10.1002/pbc.22808

Sheck, D. T. L., & Ma, C. M. S. (2011). Longitudinal data analyses using linear mixed models in SPSS: Concepts, procedures and illustrations. *TheScientificWorldJournal*, 11, 42–76. doi: 10.1100/tsw.2011.2.

Snijders, T. A. B. (2005). Power and sample size in multilevel linear models. In B. S. Everitt& D. C. Howell (Eds.), *Encyclopedia of statistics in behavioral science* (Vol. 3, pp. 1570–1573). Chicester: Wiley.

Tabachnick, B. G., & Fidell, L. S. (2007). *Using multivariate statistics* (5th ed.). Boston, MA: Allyn and Bacon.

Tewari, S., Brousse, V., Piel, F. B., Menzel, S., & Rees, D. C. (2015). Environmental determinants of severity in sickle cell disease. *Haematologica*, 100, 1108–1116. doi: 10.3324/haematol. 2014.120030

U.S. Department of Health and Human Services, Office of the Assistant Secretary for Planning and Evaluation. (2014). *2014 poverty guidelines*. Retrieved from http://aspe.hhs.gov/ poverty/14poverty.cfm

Unal, S., Toros, F., Kütük, M. Ö., & Uyaniker, M. G. (2011). Evaluation of the psychological problems in children with sickle cell anemia and their families. *Pediatric Hematology and Oncology*, *28*, 321–328. doi: 10.3109/08880018.2010.540735

Varkey, E., Cider, A., Carlsson, J., & Linde, M. (2011). Exercise as migraine prophylaxis: A randomized study using relaxation and topiramate as controls. *Cephalalgia*, *31*, 1428–1438. doi: 10.1177/0333102411419681

von Baeyer, C. L. (2009). Numerical rating scale for self-report of pain intensity in children and adolescents: Recent progress and further questions. *European Journal of Pain*, *13*, 1005–1007. DOI: 10.1016/j.ejpain.2009.08.006

von Baeyer, C. L., & Spagrud, L. J. (2007). Systematic review of observational (behavioral) measures of pain for children and adolescents aged 3 to 18 years. *Pain*, *127*, 140. doi: 10.1016/j.pain.2006.08.014

Wilson, A. C., & Palermo, T. M. (2012). Physical activity and function in adolescents with chronic pain: A controlled study using actigraphy. *Journal of Pain*, *13*, 121–130. doi: 10.1016/j.jpain.2011.08.008

Yawn, B. P., Buchanan, G. R., Afenyi-Annan, A. N., Ballas, S. K., Hassell, K. L., James, A. H., . . . , & John-Sowah, J. (2014). Management of sickle cell disease: Summary of the 2014 evidence-based report by expert panel members. *JAMA*, *312*, 1033–1048. doi:10.1001/jama.2014.10517

Zempsky, W. T., Palermo, T. M., Corsi, J. M., Lewandowski, A. S., Zhou, C., & Casella, J. F. (2013). Daily changes in pain, mood and physical function in children hospitalized for sickle cell disease pain. *Pain Research and Management*, *18*, 33–38.

Cognitive Functioning and Academic Achievement in Children Aged 6–8 Years, Born at Term After Intrauterine Growth Restriction and Fetal Cerebral Redistribution

Mercedes Bellido-González,[1] PhD, PsyD, Miguel Ángel Díaz-López,[2] PhD, MD, Setefilla López-Criado,[2] PhD, MD, and José Maldonado-Lozano,[3] PhD, MD

[1]Department of Developmental Psychology and Education, University of Granada, [2]Department of Gynaecology and [3]Department of Paediatrics, Virgen de las Nieves University Hospital

All correspondence concerning this article should be addressed to Mercedes Bellido-González, PhD, PsyD, Facultad Ciencias Educación, Campus Cartuja s/n., Granada 18071, Spain. E-mail: mmbellid@ugr.es

Received February 19, 2016; revisions received June 3, 2016; accepted June 3, 2016

Abstract

Objective To determine whether cerebroplacental ratio, an indicator of fetal cerebral redistribution (FCR), predicts adverse results for neurodevelopment in intrauterine growth restriction (IUGR) infants. **Methods** In a cohort of 5,702 infants, 64 were IUGR born at term with FCR. Five were excluded. Of the remainder, 32 presented an abnormal cerebroplacental ratio (IUGR-A) and 27 a normal one (IUGR-B). The controls were 61 appropriate-for-gestational-age children. Cognitive and academic outcomes and the odds ratio of lower academic scores were assessed by multivariate analysis of covariance and logistic regression. Results IUGR-A children presented deficits in cognitive functioning and academic achievement in all domains. IUGR-B children presented slight deficits. Suboptimal cognitive functioning in IUGR-A was more marked in working memory. Abnormal cerebroplacental ratio predicted low academic scores in IUGR-A. **Conclusions** FCR is a risk factor for IUGR infants, and cerebroplacental ratio identifies those most severely affected. Intervention programs may produce benefits in early-middle childhood.

Key words: academic achievement; cerebral redistribution; cerebroplacental ratio; cognitive functioning; intrauterine growth restriction.

Introduction

Intrauterine growth restriction (IUGR) infants born at term are known to present increased morbidity and mortality during the neonatal period, in comparison with appropriate-for-gestational-age infants (Murata, Nakata, Sumie, & Sugino, 2011). Fetal Doppler velocimetry is a reliable means of predicting adverse outcomes of restricted fetal growth (Meher, Hernandez-Andrade, Basheer, & Lees, 2015). However, the association between IUGR, documented by Doppler ultrasound, and neurodevelopment during childhood has received little research attention (Murray et al., 2015).

Growth restriction, with respect to the potential development of IUGR infants, is most commonly associated with chronic hypoxia and malnutrition owing to placental insufficiency (Figueras & Gardosi, 2011). The fetus hemodynamically adapts to this pathology (detected by an increase in the umbilical artery pulsatility index—UAPI) through the vasodilation of cerebral circulation (detected by a decrease in the middle cerebral artery pulsatility index—MCAPI) (Berkley,

Chauhan, Abuhamad, & Society for Maternal-Fetal Medicine Publications Committee, 2012). Hemodynamic adaptation with cerebral redistribution takes place to preserve the preferential supply of oxygen and nutrients to the brain (the "brain-sparing effect") (Cohen, Baerts, & van Bel, 2015).

However, MCAPI and UAPI by themselves are less sensitive in predicting adverse perinatal outcomes than either their ratio (MCAPI/UAPI) or the cerebroplacental ratio (Murata et al., 2011). Various approaches have been taken to interpreting the cutoff for abnormal cerebroplacental ratio, including a fixed value of <1.08 or one of "below the 5th percentile for gestational age." Odibo, Riddick, Pare, Stamilio, & Macones (2005) show that both parameters achieve similar levels of efficiency. In the present study, the "below the 5th percentile for gestational age" cutoff is used, among other reasons, because it presents a higher degree of sensitivity. This has been demonstrated in a cross-sectional study (Baschat & Gembruch, 2003) and a longitudinal one (Ebbing, Rasmussen, & Kiserud, 2007). Moreover, we wish to minimize the number of nondetected infants so that an early intervention can be made when necessary.

Cerebroplacental ratio below the 5th percentile for gestational age is an important predictor of adverse outcome (OR = 5.2; Odibo et al., 2005) and an indicator of fetal cerebral redistribution (FCR) (Morales-Roselló et al., 2014), which has implications for assessment of the development of full-term IUGR infants with FCR, and for the well-being of their families (DeVore, 2015).

It is well established that the neurological development of growth-restricted babies with FCR is related to a higher risk of problems during infancy and toddlerhood (Eixarch et al., 2008; Meher et al., 2015). By contrast, the possible impact of cerebral redistribution on long-term development (assessed at school age) has received little research attention, and the results that have been obtained are less conclusive, especially for IUGR infants at term (Arcangeli, Thilaganathan, Hooper, Khan, & Bhide, 2012).

Thus, a study comparing at term IUGR versus control infants found that, by the age of 6–7 years, those with IUGR obtained Intelligence Quotient (IQ) scores normal for their age but significantly lower than those achieved by the controls, with the greatest differences being observed in performance IQ (Leitner et al., 2000). Other studies, however, have reported that IUGR infants present lower levels of performance and verbal IQ than controls (Yanney & Marlow, 2004).

Some studies have examined the consequences in adulthood of being born small-for-gestational-age and IUGR at term, showing that this population suffers cognitive deficits (Tideman, Marsál, & Ley, 2007; Løhaugen et al., 2013), especially with respect to attention, executive functions, auditory memory, performance speed and fine motor function (Østgård et al., 2014), and also has learning difficulties, which may be aggravated when the child lives in poverty (Nomura et al., 2009). Other authors have performed long-term studies of full-term small-for-gestational-age infants (from age 5, 10, 16 years to adulthood), and have concluded that the academic and professional achievement of these infants is adversely affected (Strauss, 2000). A recent study showed that the impairment is more severe when growth restriction is accompanied by cerebral redistribution (Murray et al., 2015). Therefore, every effort should be made in early and middle childhood, as children in this age-group have "good plasticity," capacity and their real-world opportunities can be aligned (Schaffer & Geva, 2016), thus contributing to minimizing the long-term negative effects of IUGR. To take such remedial action, indicators must be identified, to provide early warning signs. In this respect, recent studies have concluded that cerebroplacental ratio provides the most sensitive and specific Doppler index of cerebral redistribution (DeVore, 2015; Morales-Roselló et al., 2014).

In the present study, we hypothesize that IUGR infants with abnormal cerebroplacental ratio will have cognitive and academic deficits during middle childhood and that this ratio is a predictor of these deficits. To determine these questions, we first examine possible differences between IUGR infants with FCR born at term and abnormal cerebroplacental ratio (<5th percentile) or a normal ratio (>5th percentile) versus control infants, as regards cognitive functioning and academic achievement at age 6–8 years. We then examine the association between abnormal cerebroplacental ratio and the academic results obtained by IUGR infants, to predict the likelihood of underachievement, and establish alerts for early intervention as necessary.

Methods

Study Population

A retrospective cohort study of cases and controls was performed. The participants were identified from a cohort of 5,702 single infants born alive between September 2005 and December 2006 at the Virgen de las Nieves University Hospital (a level III perinatal center in Granada, Spain) and then recruited for the follow-up study at 6–8 years. This study was approved by the hospital's Medical Ethics Committee.

The case group was constituted of consecutive infants with the following inclusion criteria: singleton pregnancy, gestation at term (>37 weeks), birth weight <10th percentile according to local standards (Carrascosa et al., 2008) and abnormal MCAPI (<5th percentile). The infants included in this group all had late-onset (third trimester) fetal growth retardation, verified by Doppler ultrasound.

According to recent research findings, Doppler measurements are related to the neurodevelopmental outcomes of growth restriction infants, although certain discrepancies are apparent. Thus, one study reported that small-for-gestational-age infants with normal UAPI have a low degree of development (Savchev et al., 2013), while another noted that an abnormal UAPI is not associated with low scores in development (Llurba, Baschat, Turan, Harding, & McCowan, 2013). On the other hand, Murata et al. (2011) showed that cerebroplacental ratio is more sensitive and specific than MCAPI and UAPI in predicting adverse perinatal outcomes. Taking this background into account, in the present study, the cases were classified according to cerebroplacental ratio into two groups: IUGR-A infants at term with abnormal cerebroplacental ratio (<5th percentile), abnormal MCAPI, and abnormal UAPI (>95th percentile); and IUGR-B infants at term with normal cerebroplacental ratio (>5th percentile), abnormal MCAPI, and normal UAPI (<95th percentile).

The control group of infants with full-term gestation (>37 weeks) and appropriate-for-gestational-age (birth weight between 10th and 90th percentiles according to local standards) was formed by selecting a child of the same gender and maternal educational level (primary school, high school, and college/university education) within ±1 week of each infant with IUGR.

Exclusion criteria for both cases and controls were parental drug consumption, congenital malformation (including chromosomopathies and infections), low Apgar score (<7 at 5 min), signs of fetal acidosis (pH < 7), vision/hearing impairment, cerebral palsy and nonnative speaker of Spanish.

In total, 128 children aged 6–8 years were selected for the study groups. Of these, 64 were IUGR born at term with cerebral redistribution (see flowchart in Figure 1). Five of these infants were then excluded: one had pH < 7, one presented a 5-min Apgar score < 7, one was diagnosed with hearing impairment, one was excluded because parental consent was refused, and one because the mother tongue was not Spanish. The remaining 59 IUGR infants were available for evaluation and follow-up at age 6–8 years. Of these infants, 32 were IUGR-A (with abnormal cerebroplacental ratio) and 27 were IUGR-B (with normal cerebroplacental ratio). Of 64 children identified as potential controls, informed consent was refused for 3, leaving 61 controls aged 6–8 years.

Measures and Procedures

Doppler ultrasound examinations were conducted at the prenatal stage by experienced gynecologists using a General Electric Voluson E8 (GE Medical Systems, Zipf, Austria). The cerebroplacental ratio was calculated as the quotient of MCAPI and UAPI. Values below the 5th percentile at the last examination within 1 week of delivery were considered abnormal and a sign of FCR (Morales-Roselló et al., 2014; Odibo et al., 2005).

Neurological status at birth was determined by clinical assessment performed by a pediatrician, examining posture, behavior, spontaneous movements, muscle tone, crying, and reflexes (Moro, rooting, sucking, grasping, stepping/walking) (Queensland Clinical Guidelines, 2009). Growth status was assessed by reference to height, weight, and head circumference (Carrascosa et al., 2008), and the 5-minute Apgar score. No obvious neurological abnormalities were apparent in any of the case subjects, who were followed up in a periodic review by the pediatrician, following hospital guidelines and in accordance with those of the American Academy of Pediatrics (Hagan, Shaw, & Duncan, 2008).

At age 6–8 years, the neurological status of the cases and controls was reviewed and a pediatric examination conducted to confirm the absence of neuropediatric disorders, including visual/auditory deficiencies, slight alterations in muscle tone and "soft" neurological signs. The following aspects were evaluated: praxis (ability to execute motor actions by imitation or in response to a verbal order), gnosis (the perception, recognition, and naming of stimuli), and synkinesis (the presence of unnecessary, non-proactive movements, together with purposeful movement) (Campistol, 2011).

Cognitive functioning and academic achievement were assessed at age 6–8 years by a psychologist expert in child neurodevelopment (blinded to the Doppler data), using the following tests.

Wechsler Intelligence Scale for Children, Fourth Edition (WISC-IV, 2003), Spanish version (2005). This updated version of the WISC provides five composite scores: the index of overall intellectual capacity (Full Scale IQ) and four specific indices: Verbal Comprehension Index, Perceptual Reasoning Index, Working Memory Index, and Processing Speed Index (mean = 100, SD = 15).

Batería III Woodcock-Muñoz Test of Achievement (Muñoz-Sandoval, Woodcock, McGrew, & Mather, 2005) is the parallel Spanish version of the Woodcock-Johnson III test (Woodcock, McGrew, & Mather, 2001). It includes 22 tests, which are grouped into broad reading, broad written language, and broad mathematics (mean = 100, SD = 15).

The Home Observation for Measurement of the Environment (HOME) method (Bradley & Caldwell, 1984; Palacios, Lera, & Moreno, 1994) consists of a structured interview with the family, from which a

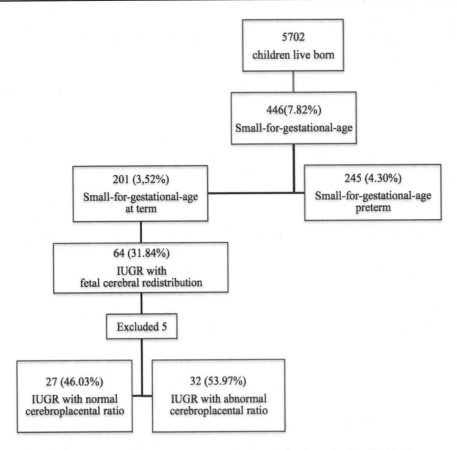

Figure 1. Flowchart of intrauterine growth restriction (IUGR) infants with fetal cerebral redistribution.

scale is derived to measure the quality of stimulation and support received by a child in the family home. The administration of this instrument was systematized and carried out in the participants' homes, giving all of them the same instructions and reading out the items one by one. Raw scores were used for data analysis.

In the first interview, the parents of the cases and controls signed the informed consent, and the HOME method was applied.

The psychological tests were given to the children by a psychologist in a room at the Virgen de las Nieves University Hospital designated for this purpose.

Data Analyses

Quantitative and qualitative data were compared by Student's t-test and the Mann–Whitney U test and Pearson's chi-square test, respectively. Differences were considered significant at $p < .05$. The values of the variables with a normal distribution are expressed as the mean ($\pm$ SD), and those of the variables with a nonnormal distribution, as the median (interquartile range).

Neurodevelopmental outcomes of IUGR-A and IUGR-B infants versus controls at 6–8 years old were analyzed by multivariate analysis of covariance (MANCOVA), with the group factor and the following dependent variables: cognitive functioning (full scale IQ, verbal comprehension index, perceptual reasoning index, working memory index, processing speed index) and academic functioning (broad reading, written language, and mathematics). The covariates were chosen taking into account the differences between the groups and their possible association with the dependent variables. HOME revealed group differences that may influence cognitive and academic results (Downer & Pianta, 2006). Gestational age at delivery presents variability, because the subjects were born "at term," a parameter which covers a 6-week interval from 37 to 42 weeks. According to some authors, even within the "normal term" range, gestational age is a predictor of academic achievement (Noble, Fifer, Rauh, Nomura, & Andrews, 2012). Therefore, the covariates included were HOME and gestational age at delivery.

For the MANCOVA models, multivariate significance of the F-value was assessed using Wilk's lambda p-value.

To determine whether cerebroplacental ratio is a predictor of low academic scores in IUGR infants, a logistic regression model was created, adjusted by the same group of covariates. This model evaluates the probability of IUGR infants presenting lower

Table I. Antenatal Characteristics and Perinatal Outcomes of the Study Groups

	IUGR fetuses at term with fetal cerebral redistribution (n = 59)		Control appropriate-for-gestational-age (n = 61)	p*	p**
	IUGR-A abnormal cerebroplacental ratio (n = 32)	IUGR-B normal cerebroplacental ratio (n = 27)			
Antenatal characteristics					
Maternal age (years)	29.05 ± 4.71	29.24 ± 5.94	31.65 ± 5.46	.064	.122
Primiparous	16 (50.0)	13 (48.1)	27 (44.3)	.456	.200
Body mass index (kg/m^2)	26.34 ± 4.21	24.81 ± 3.63	24.64 ± 2.63	.125	.875
Smoked in pregnancy	3 (9.4)	2 (7.4)	5 (8.2)	.382	.446
Maternal risk factors	4 (12.5)	2 (7.4)	2 (3.3)	.041	.407
Maternal educational level				.981	.847
Primary school	4 (12.5)	4 (14.8)	8 (13.1)		
High school	12 (37.5)	10 (37.0)	22 (36.1)		
College/university education	16 (50.0)	13 (48.1)	31 (50.8)		
Perinatal outcomes					
Gestational age at delivery (weeks)	37.29 ± 1.45	37.48 ± 0.81	38.89 ± 1.34	.000	.000
Caesarean at delivery	7 (21.9)	3 (11.1)	3 (4.9)	.004	.302
Birth weight (g)	2175 ± 457	2391 ± 419	3153 ± 416	.000	.000
Height (cm)	45.26 ± 1.73	43.90 ± 1.84	50.76 ± 2.29	.000	.000
Head circumference (cm)	31.76 ± 1.35	31.80 ± 0.91	34.28 ± 1.12	.000	.000
5-min Apgar score < 7	0 (0)	0 (0)	0 (0)	—	—
Umbilical artery pH	7.21 ± 0.07	7.21 ± 0.03	7.22 ± 0.05	.608	.198
NICU admission	7 (21.9)	3 (11.1)	0 (0)	.000	.000
Gender				.987	.729
Male	16 (50.0)	14 (51.8)	29 (47.5)		
Female	16 (50.0)	13 (48.1)	32 (52.5)		
At 6–8 years					
Age at evaluation (median, IQR)	7 (6–8)	7 (6–8)	7 (6–8)	.930	.811
Weight (g)	26,070 ± 3,125	26,800 ± 3,538	27,545 ± 3,481	.288	.738
Height (cm)	123.8 ± 5.4	124.6 ± 5.9	125.3 ± 5.3	.418	.776
Head circumference (cm)	50.3 ± 1.1	51 ± 1.8	52.1 ± 1.9	.048	.315
HOME	44.52 ± 3.91	48.05 ± 4.62	46.59 ± 3.72	.042	.040

Note. Data are given as n (%), mean ± SD, median (interquartile range, IQR). p-values were calculated using Student's t-test, Pearson's chi-square test, or Mann–Whitney U-test.
  IUGR = intrauterine growth restriction; NICU = neonatal intensive care unit.
  *IUGR with abnormal cerebroplacental ratio versus controls.
  **IUGR with normal cerebroplacental ratio versus controls.

academic scores (<1 SD) than appropriate-for-gestational-age infants. Variables with $p < .05$ and an odds ratio with 95% CI not inclusive of unity in the multivariate analysis were considered to be statistically significant independent variables (predictors) in the model.

The Statistical Package for the Social Sciences (SPSS 20.0; SPSS Inc., Chicago, IL, USA) was used for the statistical analysis.

Results

The characteristics of the sample are described in Table I, with demographic characteristics such as maternal age, parity, and education; measures related to maternal health, such as body mass index, smoking, and other risk factors (hypertension, diabetes); perinatal outcomes such as growth data (weight, height, head circumference); data relating to health and fetal well-being such as Apgar score, pH, neonatal intensive care unit (NICU) admission; and gestational age at birth and type of delivery. Data are also included on the children's growth at age 6–8 years and on the family environment (HOME).

With respect to the maternal characteristics, significant differences in risk factors were observed between both of the IUGR groups and the control group, but there were no differences regarding maternal age, primiparous, body mass index, or smoking. As expected, there were no significant differences regarding maternal educational level, as this was a matching criterion.

With respect to perinatal outcomes, the IUGR groups had significantly lower anthropometric scores (birth weight, height, and head circumference) versus the controls (Table I). Follow-up anthropometric measurements at age 6–8 years revealed no differences, except in head circumference for the IUGR-A infants versus the controls ($t = 2.144, p = .048$).

There were more admissions to the NICU in both IUGR groups. Gestational age was lower in the

Table II. Cognitive and Academic Scores for IUGR With Abnormal Cerebroplacental Ratio Versus Control, and IUGR With Normal Cerebroplacental Ratio Versus Control, at 6–8 Years

Cognitive functioning at 6–8 years	IUGR fetuses at term with fetal cerebral redistribution ($n = 59$)		Control appropriate-for-gestational-age ($n = 61$)	p^*	p^{**}
	IUGR-A abnormal cerebroplacental ratio ($n = 32$)	IUGR-B Normal cerebroplacental ratio ($n = 27$)			
Verbal comprehension index	91.19 ± 13.75	95.52 ± 10.85	103.28 ± 14.38	.008	.038
Perceptual reasoning index	89.48 ± 14.40	104.19 ± 11.80	102.06 ± 11.87	.001	.318
Working memory index	87.71 ± 15.60	94.78 ± 18.63	103.57 ± 16.06	.000	.021
Processing speed index	89.57 ± 15.66	101.90 ± 9.14	98.85 ± 11.97	.022	.387
Full scale IQ	89.34 ± 13.13	101.57 ± 14.16	103.26 ± 13.22	.001	.593
Academic achievement at 6–8 years					
Broad reading	89.87 ± 15.44	101.34 ± 11.34	101.23 ± 14.48	.013	.606
Broad written language	89.38 ± 14.38	96.52 ± 11.93	102.99 ± 14.10	.003	.065
Broad mathematics	87.44 ± 14.86	95.44 ± 12.32	102.51 ± 17.31	.000	.015

Note. Data are given as mean ± SD. MANCOVA adjusted for gestational age at delivery and HOME. IUGR = intrauterine growth restriction.
*IUGR with abnormal CPR versus controls.
**IUGR with normal CPR versus controls.

IUGR-A group. Cesarean delivery owing to suspected fetal distress was more frequent in the IUGR-A group. There were no differences in acidosis at birth (umbilical artery pH). None of the infants had a 5-min Apgar score < 7. There were no differences in gender, which was expected, as this too was a matching criterion.

Cognitive Outcomes

The results for cognitive functioning at age 6–8 years, according to the five composite scores measured by WISC-IV, show that the IUGR-A children presented lower scores than the appropriate-for-gestational-age children for all measures of cognitive functioning: verbal comprehension, perceptual reasoning, working memory, processing speed and full scale IQ (Table II), and effect sizes ranging from 0.68 to 0.98 (Cohen's d). Larger differences were observed in working memory. In contrast, the IUGR-B infants presented lower scores than the appropriate-for-gestational-age children only for verbal comprehension with effect size 0.57 and working memory with effect size 0.51 after adjusting for potential confounders (gestational age at delivery and HOME).

Academic Achievement

Analysis of the differences in academic achievement between the cases and the controls showed that the IUGR-A infants presented significantly lower scores than the controls in the broad academic domains: reading, written language, and mathematics (Table II), and effect sizes ranging from 0.75 to 0.94 (Cohen's d). The differences were larger in mathematics. On the other hand, the IUGR-B infants only presented low scores in broad mathematics (Table II), effect size 0.45. This difference persisted after adjustment for the same group of potential confounders.

Relation Between Cerebroplacental Ratio (as an Indicator of Fetal Cerebral Redistribution) and Academic Achievement

Multiple logistic regression analysis was performed to test the contribution of abnormal cerebroplacental ratio to the prediction of poor academic outcomes (reading, writing, and mathematics <1 SD) at 6–8 years, adjusting for the same potential confounders as in MANCOVA.

The IUGR-A infants had a higher frequency of low scores in every domain: in broad reading, these were 2.38 times greater (95% CI: 1.15–4.91; $p = .019$), in broad written language, 6.07 times greater (95% CI: 1.83–20.05; $p = .003$), and in broad mathematics, 9.79 times greater (95% CI: 2.03–47.15; $p = .004$) than in the controls (Table III).

Discussion

The main aim of this study was to determine whether cerebroplacental ratio, as an indicator of FCR, is a predictor of adverse long-term neurodevelopment in IUGR infants. In doing so, we found that IUGR-A infants with abnormal cerebroplacental ratio, born at term, have cognitive functioning deficit in all domains assessed, compared with control peers, at age 6–8 years, while IUGR-B infants with normal cerebroplacental ratio present deficit only in verbal comprehension and working memory. Moreover, IUGR-A infants differ in all academic domains—reading, writing, and mathematics—from the controls, while IUGR-B differ only in mathematics. In addition, the probability of achieving scores <1 SD in broad reading, writing, and mathematics is significantly higher among IUGR-A infants with abnormal cerebroplacental ratio. These results suggest that FCR is a risk factor

Table III. Logistic Regression Analysis: Abnormal Cerebroplacental Ratio Predictor of Low Academic Scores in IUGR-A Group at 6–8 Years

Academic score < 85	Predictor	B	p	Exp (B)	95% CI
Broad reading	Abnormal Cerebroplacental ratio	0.868	.019	2.382	1.15–4.91
	Gestational age at delivery	1.093	.106	2.982	0.79–11.24
	HOME	0.085	.349	1.088	0.91–1.30
Broad written language	Abnormal cerebroplacental ratio	1.804	.003	6.071	1.83–20.05
	Gestational age at delivery	0.011	.965	1.011	0.61–1.66
	HOME	0.021	.784	1.021	0.88–1.18
Broad mathematics	Abnormal cerebroplacental ratio	2.282	.004	9.797	2.03–47.15
	Gestational age at delivery	0.287	.392	0.750	0.38–1.44
	HOME	0.059	.559	1.061	0.87–1.29

Note. Cerebroplacental ratio was tested for his contribution to the prediction of poor academic achievement. Adjusted for gestational age at delivery and HOME.

for IUGR infants and that cerebroplacental ratio identifies those experiencing greatest weakness. These findings are consistent with previous research, which has reported associations between cerebral redistribution and neurodevelopmental outcome.

Earlier studies have found that small-for-gestational-age full-term fetuses with cerebral redistribution have a higher risk of subtle neurodevelopmental deficits at 2 years of age (Eixarch et al., 2008). A recent review of neurodevelopment outcomes for IUGR children in childhood, documented in utero, reported evidence that FCR is associated with an additional 0.50 SD impairment among IUGR infants born ≥35 weeks' gestation during childhood (Murray et al., 2015). Furthermore, DeVore (2015) considers cerebroplacental ratio to be a useful tool for assessing fetal well-being, and identifies three types of abnormal ratio, depending on whether the MCA and UA Doppler indices are normal or abnormal, which would seem to indicate differing consequences for neurodevelopment. In the present study, two IUGR groups were differentiated, according to the type of cerebroplacental ratio. Thus, IUGR-A infants with an abnormal ratio at 6–8 years present delays in all areas of cognitive function, while IUGR-B infants with a normal ratio only present delays in working memory and verbal comprehension. This consistency among studies regarding the deficit suffered by these children suggests that IUGR-FCR-related deficits appear in the early years of life and persist into childhood, albeit differentially across domains.

Our results show that suboptimal cognitive functioning in IUGR-A infants is strongly apparent in working memory. More broadly, we also observe an impact in domains addressing higher-order cortical association areas, including verbal skills, visuomotor organization, abstract thinking, attention, learning, and short-term memory, which depend mainly on frontal brain activity (Friederici, 2012; Geva, Eshel, Leitner, Fattal-Valevski, & Harel, 2006; Nyhus & Badre, 2015). IUGR is associated with a reduction in frontal volume, identifiable through magnetic resonance imaging (Tolsa et al., 2004) and sonographic biometric estimation (Makhoul et al., 2004). Moreover, the redistribution assessed by cerebroplacental ratio <5th percentile seems to coincide with a decline in the relative perfusion to the frontal lobe in relation to other regions such as the basal ganglia (Eixarch et al., 2008).

The question then arises: what is the magnitude of the differences observed? Previous studies have shown that IUGR children are at risk of deficit in the academic domains (Geva, 2012; Nomura et al., 2009; Strauss, 2000), with mean effect sizes ranging from magnitude 0.31 to 0.53 (Nomura et al., 2009). In the current study, differences were found with a moderate to large effect size in all the areas of cognitive functioning of the IUGR-A children, and a moderate effect in the verbal comprehension and working memory of IUGR-B children. These findings show that the magnitude of the effect is greater in the IGUR-A group, thus confirming that infants in this group are at risk of presenting a deficit in cognitive functioning.

As in cognitive functioning, the IUGR-A children suffered an additional deficit in all the areas of academic achievement, and a large effect size was observed. This outcome is to be expected given the close relationship between these domains throughout middle school (Soares, Lemos, Primi, & Almeida, 2015). Specifically, the differences that were most acute and which produced the largest effect size were observed in mathematics (Tables II and III). These results are consistent with those of other studies, which have highlighted the relationship between working memory and mathematics in typically developing children (Friso-van den Bos, van der Ven, Sanne, Kroesbergen, & van Luit, 2013).

In general, the conclusions drawn by studies of IUGR infants are consistent; on the one hand, that the cognitive decline observed persists into adulthood; and on the other, that this weakness has differing levels of severity, increasing if the infant also presents FCR. Currently, the cerebroplacental ratio provides the most sensitive and specific indicator of cerebral redistribution. Our contribution in the present study is to show that IUGR infants with an abnormal ratio present deficits in all areas related to cognitive functioning, which is reflected in low scores for academic achievement, and therefore such an abnormal ratio predicts these poorer academic results (<1 SD).

This is an interesting finding, as no such predictor of learning difficulties in IUGR children has been reported previously, although it has been observed that these difficulties are more prevalent when anthropometric catch-up is incomplete (Geva et al., 2006). Our results are consistent with those of the latter authors, as the IUGR-A group, at 6 years of age, had not yet achieved head circumference catch-up. Another study has demonstrated the existence of a relation between fetal cerebral blood flow redistribution and a high ratio of head circumference to abdominal circumference (Hershkovitz, Kingdom, Geary, & Rodeck, 2000). Therefore, cerebroplacental ratio as an indicator of redistribution and the probable cause of decreased head circumference might represent a valuable predictor of poor long-term academic results.

We are confident of the solidity of these findings, given the strengths of the research design, including the use of a cohort with different types of IUGR, according to the presence of normal or abnormal cerebroplacental ratio. Moreover, growth restriction was documented using Doppler indices, thus identifying this ratio as a predictor of academic deficits in children with IUGR. In addition, a detailed evaluation was made of the study variables and the tests were applied individually to each of the subjects. The study also benefited from the collaboration of the children's parents, who enabled observation of the family environment, which was assessed by the HOME method.

Despite these strengths, we acknowledge certain limitations to the conclusions we can draw from the current investigation. Our sample size was relatively small, although it was selected taking into account strict inclusion/exclusion criteria for cases and controls, and with matching criteria for both groups. In addition, the effect size measured on cognitive and academic achievement is strong, and so the associations recorded are consistent and do not appear to be greatly affected by sample size. Moreover, the covariates were taken into account in the different levels of analysis, which lends our results greater consistency and coherence.

In summary, the present study provides new knowledge regarding the neurodevelopment of IUGR children aged 6–8 years, by analyzing the relation between redistribution, as measured by cerebroplacental ratio, cognitive function, and academic performance. Our findings suggest that IUGR infants with an abnormal ratio are at increased risk. Therefore, FCR is a risk factor for these infants and the cerebroplacental ratio identifies those experiencing greatest difficulty in middle childhood. Early-intervention programs should be developed to alleviate these weaknesses.

The strongest IUGR-FCR-related deficits are those affecting working memory and mathematics. In consequence, we believe that middle childhood should be considered the target period for the application of specific intervention programs to address the learning disabilities suffered by these children.

Acknowledgments

The authors thank the families and teachers involved for their participation in the study. They also thank the Obstetrics and Gynecology department at the Virgen de las Nieves University Hospital for allowing us the use of their outpatient clinics during the psychological assessment of the participants. This study was supported by University of Granada, Spain; Biosanitary Research Institute, Granada, Spain, and by the Andalusian Plan for Research Development and Innovation: CTS535-Monitoring of Child with Chronic Pathology (MCCP), and CTS340-Department of Obstetrics and Gynecology.

Funding

Institute of Biomedical Research of Granada, Spain Andalusian Plan for Research Development and Innovation: CTS535-Monitoring of Child with Chronic Pathology (MCCP), and CTS340-Department of Obstetrics and Gynecology

Conflicts of interest: None declared.

References

Arcangeli, T., Thilaganathan, B., Hooper, R., Khan, K. S., & Bhide, A. (2012). Neurodevelopmental delay in small babies at term: A systematic review. *Ultrasound in Obstetrics and Gynecology, 40*, 267–275. doi: 10.1002/uog.11112

Baschat, A. A., & Gembruch, U. (2003). The cerebroplacental Doppler ratio revisited. *Ultrasound in Obstetrics and Gynecology, 21*, 124–127.

Berkley, E., Chauhan, S. P., & Abuhamad, A.; Society for Maternal-Fetal Medicine Publications Committee (2012). Doppler assessment of the fetus with intrauterine growth restriction. *American Journal of Obstetrics and Gynecology, 206*, 300–308. (doi: http://dx.doi.org/10.1016/j.ajog.2012.01.022

Bradley, R. H., & Caldwell, B. M. (1984). The HOME inventory and family demographics. *Developmental Psychology, 20*, 315–320. http://dx.doi.org/10.1037/0012-1649.20.2.315

Campistol, J. (2011). Neurología fetal y neonatal. In J. Campistol, H. A. Arroyo, P. Póo, and V. Rugieri (Eds.), *Neurología para pediatras. Enfoque y manejo práctico* (pp. 45–71). Madrid: Ed. Médica Panamericana.

Carrascosa, A., Ferrández, A., Yeste, D., García-Dihinx, J., Romo, A., Copil, A. … Baguer, L. (2008). Estudio transversal español de crecimiento 2008. Parte I: Valores de peso y longitud en recién nacidos de 26-42 semanas de edad gestacional. *Anales De Pediatría, 68*, 544–551.

Cohen, E., Baerts, W., & van Bel, F. (2015). Brain-sparing in intrauterine growth restriction: Considerations for the neonatologist. *Neonatology, 108*, 269–276. doi: 10.1159/000438451

DeVore, G. R. (2015). The importance of the cerebroplacental ratio in the evaluation of fetal well-being in SGA and AGA fetuses. *American Journal of Obstetrics and Gynecology, 213*, 5–15. doi: 10.1016/j.ajog.2015.05.024

Downer, J. T., & Pianta, R. C. (2006). Academic and cognitive functioning in first grade: Associations with earlier home and child care predictors and with concurrent home and classroom experiences. *School Psychology Review, 35*, 11.

Ebbing, C., Rasmussen, S., & Kiserud, T. (2007). Middle cerebral artery blood flow velocities and pulsa- tility index and the cerebroplacental pulsatility ratio: Longitudinal reference ranges and terms for serial measurements. *Ultrasound in Obstetrics and Gynecology, 30*, 287–296.

Eixarch, E., Meler, E., Iraola, A., Illa, M., Crispi, F., Hernandez-Andrade, E., ... Figueras, F. (2008). Neurodevelopmental outcome in 2-year-old infants who were small-for-gestational age term fetuses with cerebral blood flow redistribution. *Ultrasound in Obstetrics and Gynecology, 32*, 894–899. doi: 10.1002/uog.6249

Figueras, F., & Gardosi, J. (2011). Intrauterine growth restriction: New concepts in antenatal surveillance, diagnosis, and management. *American Journal of Obstetrics and Gynecology, 204*, 288–300. doi: 10.1016/j.ajog.2010.08.055

Friederici, A. D. (2012). The cortical language circuit: From auditory perception to sentence comprehension. *Trends in Cognitive Sciences, 16*, 262–268. doi: 10.1016/j.tics.2012.04.001

Friso-van den Bos, I., van der, V., Sanne, H. G., Kroesbergen, E. H., & van Luit, J. E. (2013). Working memory and mathematics in primary school children: A meta-analysis. *Educational Research Review, 10*, 29–44. doi: 10.1016/j.edurev.2013.05.003

Geva, R. (2012). Children born with intrauterine growth restriction: Neuropsychological outcome. *Handbook of growth and growth monitoring in health and disease* (pp. 177–192). New York, NY: Springer.

Geva, R., Eshel, R., Leitner, Y., Fattal-Valevski, A., & Harel, S. (2006). Memory functions of children born with asymmetric intrauterine growth restriction. *Brain Research, 1117*, 186–194. doi: 10.1016/j.brainres.2006.08.004

Hagan, J. F., Shaw, J. S., & Duncan, P. M. (2008). *Bright futures: Guidelines for health supervision of infants, children, and adolescents*, 3rd edn. Pocket Guide. Elk Grove Village, IL: American Academy of Pediatrics.

Hershkovitz, R., Kingdom, J., Geary, M., & Rodeck, C. (2000). Fetal cerebral blood flow redistribution in late gestation: Identification of compromise in small fetuses with normal umbilical artery Doppler. *Ultrasound in Obstetrics and Gynecology, 15*, 209–212.

Leitner, Y., Fattal-Valevski, A., Geva, R., Bassan, H., Posner, E., Kutai, M. ... Harel, S. (2000). Six-year follow-up of children with intrauterine growth retardation: Long-term, prospective study. *Journal of Child Neurology, 15*, 781–786. doi: 10.1177/088307380001501202

Llurba, E., Baschat, A. A., Turan, O. M., Harding, J., & McCowan, L. M. (2013). Childhood cognitive development after fetal growth restriction. *Ultrasound in Obstetrics and Gynecology, 41*, 383–389. doi: 10.1002/uog.12388

Løhaugen, G., Østgärd, H. F., Andreassen, S., Jacobsen, G. W., Vik, T., Brubakk, A. M. ... Martinussen, M. (2013). Small for gestational age and intrauterine growth restriction decreases cognitive function in young adults. *The Journal of Pediatrics, 163*, 447–453. doi: 10.1016/j.jpeds.2013.01.060

Makhoul, I. R., Soudack, M., Goldstein, I., Smolkin, T., Tamir, A., & Sujov, P. (2004). Sonographic biometry of the frontal lobe in normal and growth-restricted neonates. *Pediatric Research, 55*, 877–883. doi: 10.1203/01.PDR.0000119369.21770.7A

Meher, S., Hernandez-Andrade, E., Basheer, S., & Lees, C. (2015). Impact of cerebral redistribution on neurodevelopmental outcome in small-for-gestational-age or growth-restricted babies: A systematic review. *Ultrasound in Obstetrics and Gynecology, 46*, 398–404. doi: 10.1002/uog.14818

Morales-Roselló, J., Khalil, A., Morlando, M., Papageorghiou, A., Bhide, A., & Thilaganathan, B. (2014). Changes in fetal Doppler indices as a marker of failure to reach growth potential at term. *Ultrasound in Obstetrics and Gynecology, 43*, 303–310. doi: 10.1002/uog.13319

Muñoz-Sandoval, A. F., Woodcock, R. W., McGrew, K. S., & Mather, N. (2005). *Batería III Woodcock-Muñoz: Pruebas de aprovechamiento*. Rolling Meadows, IL: Riverside.

Murata, S., Nakata, M., Sumie, M., & Sugino, N. (2011). The Doppler cerebroplacental ratio predicts non-reassuring fetal status in intrauterine growth restricted fetuses at term. *Journal of Obstetrics and Gynaecology Research, 37*, 1433–1437. doi: 10.1111/j.1447-0756.2011.01563.x

Murray, E., Fernandes, M., Fazel, M., Kennedy, S., Villar, J., & Stein, A. (2015). Differential effect of intrauterine growth restriction on childhood neurodevelopment: A systematic review. *BJOG: An International Journal of Obstetrics and Gynaecology, 122*, 1062–1072. doi: 10.1111/1471-0528.13435

Noble, K. G., Fifer, W. P., Rauh, V. A., Nomura, Y., & Andrews, H. F. (2012). Academic achievement varies with gestational age among children born at term. *Pediatrics, 130*, e257–e264. doi: 10.1542/peds.2011-2157 [doi]

Nomura, Y., Halperin, J. M., Newcorn, J. H., Davey, C., Fifer, W. P., Savitz, D. A., & Brooks-Gunn, J. (2009). The risk for impaired learning-related abilities in childhood and educational attainment among adults born near-term. *The Journal of Pediatric Psychology, 34*, 406–418. doi: 10.1093/jpepsy/jsn092

Nyhus, E., & Badre, D. (2015). Memory retrieval and the functional organization of frontal cortex. In D. R. Addis, M. Barense, A. Duarte (Eds.), *The Wiley handbook on the cognitive neuroscience of memory* (pp. 131–149). West Sussex, UK: John Wiley & Sons, Ltd.

Odibo, A. O., Riddick, C., Pare, E., Stamilio, D. M., & Macones, G. A. (2005). Cerebroplacental Doppler ratio and adverse perinatal outcomes in intrauterine growth restriction: Evaluating the impact of using gestational age-specific reference values. *Journal of Ultrasound in Medicine: Official Journal of the American Institute of Ultrasound in Medicine, 24*, 1223–1228. doi: 24/9/1223 [pii]

Østgård, H. F., Skranes, J., Martinussen, M., Jacobsen, G. W., Brubakk, A. M., Vik, T. … Løhaugen, G. C. C. (2014). Neuropsychological deficits in young adults born small-for-gestational age (SGA) at term. *Journal of the International Neuropsychological Society, 20*, 313–323. doi: http://dx.doi.org/10.1017/S1355617714000034

Palacios, J., Lera, M. J., & Moreno, M. C. (1994). Evaluación de los contextos familiares y extrafamiliares en los años preescolares: Escalas HOME y ECERS. *Infancia Y Aprendizaje, 56*, 72–88. doi: 10.1174/021037094 60578945

Queensland Clinical Guidelines. (2009). Routine newborn assessment (previously Examination of the newborn baby). Retrieved from https://www.health.qld.gov.au/qcg/documents/g-newexam.pdf. Accessed July 4, 2015.

Savchev, S., Sanz-Cortes, M., Cruz-Martinez, R., Arranz, A., Botet, F., Gratacos, E., & Figueras, F. (2013). Neurodevelopmental outcome of full-term small-for-gestational-age infants with normal placental function. *Ultrasound in Obstetrics and Gynecology, 42*, 201–206.

Schaffer, Y., & Geva, R. (2016). Memory outcomes following cognitive interventions in children with neurological deficits: A review with a focus on under-studied populations. *Neuropsychological Rehabilitation, 26*, 286–317. doi: 10.1080/09602011.2015.1016537

Soares, D. L., Lemos, G. C., Primi, R., & Almeida, L. S. (2015). The relationship between intelligence and academic achievement throughout middle school: The role of students' prior academic performance. *Learning and Individual Differences, 41*, 73–78.

Strauss, R. S. (2000). Adult functional outcome of those born small for gestational age: Twenty-six–year follow-up of the 1970 British birth cohort. *Jama, 283*, 625–632. doi: 10.1001/jama.283.5.625.

Tideman, E., Marsal, K., & Ley, D. (2007). Cognitive function in young adults following intrauterine growth restriction with abnormal fetal aortic blood flow. *Ultrasound in Obstetrics and Gynecology, 29*, 614–618. doi: 10.1002/uog.4042

Tolsa, C. B., Zimine, S., Warfield, S. K., Freschi, M., Rossignol, A. S., Lazeyras F., … & Hüppi, P. S. (2004). Early alteration of structural and functional brain development in premature infants born with intrauterine growth restriction. *Pediatric Research, 56*, 132–138. doi: 10.1203/01.PDR.0000128983.54614.7E

Wechsler, D. (2005). *Wechsler Intelligence Scale for Children—Fourth Edition—Spanish*. San Antonio, TX: Harcourt Assessment.

Woodcock, R. W., Mathe, N., & McGrew, K. S. (2001). Woodcock-johnson III tests of cognitive abilities examiner's manual. *Itasca: Riverside*.

Yanney, M., & Marlow, N. (2004). Paediatric consequences of fetal growth restriction. *Seminars in Fetal and Neonatal Medicine, 9*, 411–418. doi: 10.1016/j.siny.2004.03.005

Society of Pediatric Psychology
Division 54, American Psychological Association

Please visit our website https://www.societyofpediatricpsychology.org/ for complete membership information and to join.

Our membership benefits include:

- Subscription to the *Journal of Pediatric Psychology*
- Representation and advocacy for pediatric psychology
- Option to join the SPP member listserv, with postings about job openings, discussions of clinical issues, referral requests, etc.
- Option to join the SPP student listserv addressing training and early career issues
- Programming specific to pediatric psychology at the annual APA meeting
- Subscription to the SPP newsletter, *Progress Notes*
- Opportunities to be involved and volunteer in SPP
- Various awards and grants for students and psychologists at all career stages
- Ability to earn free continuing education (CE) credits by reading selected articles in our journal
- Participation in the SPP mentoring program---as mentee or mentor
- Access to online member directory and option to be listed in the directory

---

Society of Clinical Child and Adolescent Psychology
Division 53, American Psychological Association

Come join us! Visit our website https://www.clinicalchildpsychology.org/ for complete membership information. Here are just a few of the reasons to join Division 53.

Our Journal
The *Journal of Clinical Child and Adolescent Psychology* is a leading child psychopathology and treatment journal.

Quest BehavioralPro
Division 53 members are provided behavioral health information for clinical practice, teaching, and research purposes from Quest Health Systems, Inc.

Our Newsletter
InBalance is published 3 times a year offering topical features, news of interest, and important policy-related information.

Our Listservs
A members-only listserv provides a forum for scientific and professional topics. The announce-only listserv alerts you to Division developments. Students may join either of these listservs as well as a Student Only listserv.

Convention Activities
We sponsor several APA Convention activities: symposia, workshops, poster sessions, and a social hour that allow you to network, learn, exchange information, and stay abreast of current clinical and research topics in our field.

Continuing Education
CE credits that can be obtained at the APA annual convention and at sponsored regional conferences designed to advance evidence-based assessment and treatment of children and adolescents.

Task Forces
SCCAP task forces investigate issues pertinent to child mental health policy, treatment, and diagnostics.

The sea of learning has no end

Encourage your library to subscribe to this journal by completing a library recommendation form at:
www.oxfordjournals.org/en/library-recommendation-form.html

Oxford Journals Collection

The Oxford Journals Collection includes highly cited, quality journals in the fields of Medicine, Life Sciences, Humanities, Law, Mathematics, Physical Sciences, and Social Sciences offering access to content dating back to 1996.

Individual libraries and consortia can subscribe to the entire package, a subject subset, or a bespoke selection tailored to meet the needs of the library user.

Benefits for Libraries:

- Perpetual access to paid-for content
- Access available via IP address or remotely
- Mobile-optimized service

Pass this information on to your librarian and encourage them to visit
www.oxfordjournals.org/en/librarians/index.html

www.oxfordjournals.org